TRENDS IN BIPOLAR DISORDER RESEARCH

TRENDS IN BIPOLAR DISORDER RESEARCH

MALCOMB R. BROWN
EDITOR

Nova Biomedical Books
New York

Production Coordinator: Tatiana Shohov
Senior Editors: Susan Boriotti and Donna Dennis
Coordinating Editor: Tatiana Shohov
Office Manager: Annette Hellinger
Graphics: Magdalena Nuñez
Editorial Production: Marius Andronie, Robert Brower, Maya Columbus,
Vladimir Klestov, Matthew Kozlowski and Lorna Loperfido
Circulation: Luis Aviles, Raymond Davis, Melissa Diaz, Marlene Nuñez,
Ave Maria Gonzalez, Jeannie Pappas, Vera Popovic and Frankie Punger
Communications and Acquisitions: Serge P. Shohov
Marketing: Cathy DeGregory

Library of Congress Cataloging-in-Publication Data
Available Upon Request

ISBN: 1-59454-060-8.

Nova Science Publishers, Inc.
400 Oser Ave, Suite 1600
Hauppauge, New York 11788-3619
Tele. 631-231-7269 Fax 631-231-8175
e-mail: Novascience@earthlink.net
Web Site: http://www.novapublishers.com

Printed in the United States of America

CONTENTS

Preface		**vii**
Chapter 1	Demographic and Clinical Features of Mood Disorders *Alessandro Serretti and Laura Mandelli*	**1**
Chapter 2	Bipolar Disorder: Self-interested Networks, Obsessions, and Cycling *James Brody*	**33**
Chapter3	Bipolar Disorder, Migraine and 5-HT *Traiq Mahmood and Trevor Silverstone*	**65**
Chapter 4	Glucose Metabolism in Bipolar Disorder *William T. Regenold and Christopher Marano*	**81**
Chapter 5	Albumin Levels in Bipolar Disorder and Major Depression: Acute Phase Reaction and Inflammation/Immunity *T. L. Huang*	**97**
Chapter 6	Topiramate in the Treatment of Bipolar Disorders *Vasilis P. Bozikas, Christina Andreou and Athanasios Karavatos*	**117**
Chapter 7	Further Research with the Manic-Depressiveness Scale *Michael A. Thalbourne and James Houran*	**139**
Chapter 8	High Dose Fluoxetine-Induced Mania: Bibliographic Review and Clinical Case Report *María Carolina Vairo, Martín Ruiz, Daniel Matusevich and Carlos Finkelsztein*	**153**
Chapter 9	Quality of Life and Economics of Bipolar Disorder *Lizheng Shi and Mauricio Tohen*	**161**
Index		**195**

PREFACE

This new volume gathers important research developments dealing with bipolar disorders. In a world permeated with stress, bipolar disorders have become an all too common occurrence. There are millions of people throughout the world suffering from this disorder. Bipolar disorder, also known as manic-depressive illness, is a brain disorder that causes unusual shifts in a person's mood, energy, and ability to function. Different from the normal ups and downs, the symptoms of bipolar disorder are severe. They can result in damaged relationships, poor job or school performance, and even suicide. The primary psychological factor implicated in the manifestation of bipolar disorder is stressful life events. These can range from a death in the family to the loss of a job, from the birth of a child to a move. Once the disorder is triggered and progresses, "it seems to develop a life of its own." The two poles of bipolar disorder are mania and depression.

The pathogenic bases of Mood disorders are still largely unknown. Several causal factors have been proposed as involved in the etiology of Mood disorders, both biological, genetic and psychosocial. The aim of chapter one is to investigate the "phenotype" of Mood disorders, through the identification of homogeneous samples of patients. The authors used different strategies, which included evaluation of demographic and clinical features, identification of symptomatology structures and the differential response to the pharmacological treatment.

Bipolar disorder (BPD) devastates its carriers and their families while puzzling employers and resisting the best efforts of clinicians and law enforcement officials. There, however, has been little progress in treating it since the introduction of lithium. Statistical physics now offers dynamic models for the behavior of emergent networks, oscillators, and phase transitions that parallel the mood changes and obsessions that we observe in BPD. These ideas are discussed in chapter two in non-technical language with special reference to BPD but could apply to obsessive compulsive disorder, panic, eating disorders, hypochondria, depression, drug dependency, personality disorders, and even hypnotic states, love, religious ecstasy, or scientific insights. There are implications from network theory for both medicinal and cognitive-behavior interventions.

Ancient Greeks believed that migraine was caused by psychological dysfunction, and in more recent times Freud and Breuer considered headache to be a manifestation of neurotic conflict. An association between migraine and affective disorders was increasingly recognised. Although migraine is primarily a neurological condition, it waS estimated that 10% of migraine patients who consulted a doctor complained of mood changes related to the migraine attack. The premonitory symptoms of migraine, which are reported the night before by 25% of those affected with migraine, often include mood changes in the form of transient depression. Furthermore, headache is often a symptom of mood disorders particularly depression. These ideas are discussed in chapter three.

Bipolar mood disorder is ultimately a disorder of the brain. The brain relies almost exclusively on glucose as its substrate for energy metabolism, consuming glucose at a rate far exceeding that of any other bodily organ. It follows, therefore, that information about perturbations of glucose metabolism in bipolar disorder could contribute to our knowledge of the pathophysiology and treatment of the disorder. The aim of chapter four is to promote progress in the understanding and treatment of bipolar disorder by critically reviewing the literature, presenting data, and discussing theoretical and clinical issues regarding glucose metabolism in bipolar disorder.

Albumin plays an important role in physical functions, including serving as a transport and binding protein. At the same time, it is also a negative acute phase protein and related to the immune/inflammatory response in many diseases. Serum albumin levels had be a prognostic marker for mortality in elderly hospitalized patients, human immunodeficiency virus-infected women and prognosis of disease in patients with injury or inflammation. Perhaps, the level of serum albumin might also apply to be a predictive marker for the discussion of the prognosis of drug responses and clinical courses in patients with mood disorders. In chapter five, the relationships between serum albumin levels and mania, major depression, schizophrenia, physical violence and suicide attempts will be discussed. Second, the relationships between the albumin (negative acute phase protein) and cytokines in bipolar disorder will be mentioned. Finally, the importance of the combined data between clinical phenotypes and molecular levels in mood disorders is emphasized.

Bipolar disorder is a mental illness that often requires lifetime treatment. Lithium has revolutionized the treatment of the disorder; however, it is associated with a 20-40% rate of treatment failures, and its use is limited by some of its adverse effects as well as by its narrow therapeutic index, requiring constant monitoring of plasma levels. First-generation anticonvulsants, such as carbamazepine and valproate, have proved themselves quite efficient and, generally, well tolerated alternatives to lithium therapy. However, they too are associated with severe adverse events, especially idiosyncratic ones, while their pharmacokinetic characteristics complicate their use. The newer antiepileptic agents (lamotrigine, gabapentin and topiramate) have recently received increasing attention as candidate mood-stabilizing agents, since they combine more favorable pharmacokinetic properties with fewer side effects. In chapter six, the authors' focus on the role of topiramate in the acute and maintenance treatment of bipolar disorder. Data on general characteristics of the drug (mechanisms of action, pharmacokinetic properties, and drug interactions) are provided. Studies assessing the efficacy of topiramate in bipolar disorder are reviewed. The authors' discuss the efficacy of topiramate in mania, depression, rapid-cycling, and maintenance treatment of bipolar disorder, along with optimal dosages and titration schedules. Finally, safety and tolerability data from clinical experience with topiramate in bipolar patients are summarized, and evidence regarding the weight-reducing properties of topiramate is separately mentioned.

The 18-item Manic-Depressiveness Scale (MDS) has been Rasch-scaled as a result of top-down purification procedures, and now consists of 12 items (8, history of depression; 4, history of mania). In chapter seven this new scoring scheme (the R-MDS) was applied to the data of 250 undergraduates, and it was found that the correlations were mostly very close to the original scoring, but with only two-thirds of the MDS items and with no age or gender bias. Persons scoring high on the R-MDS tended also to subscribe to paranormal belief and experience, score high on magical ideation, high on schizotypal personality (and its three subscales), on mystical experience and on neuroticism, but were low on the lie scale. Not significantly correlated were extraversion, creative personality and Eysenckian psychoticism. Finally, there is some evidence that the R-MDS does not discriminate between bipolar disorder and schizophrenia, and may therefore be a general measure of psychoticism.

In chapter eight the authors' report the case of a 53 year old woman who attempted suicide taking one high-dose of fluoxetine, developing a manic episode 19 days later. Also presented is a review about antidepressant-induced mania. In patients with mood disorders, the frequency of antidepressant-induced mania has been estimated to be 3.7 to 33%, varying across studies that included different diagnoses and different antidepressant treatments. Among the used data basis (Medline) there are papers reporting fluoxetine-induced mania. All of them include patients receiving adequate dose and time fluoxetine treatment. We found no reports of switch occurring after one high-dose of fluoxetine. As the impact on the clinical management of antidepressant-induced manic switches is quite high, several studies have focused on the possible clinical predictors of this phenomenon. By the time, is not possible to determine whether a manic episode is due to the natural course of bipolar disorder or to the medication.

Bipolar disorder, also referred to as manic-depressive illness, may be one of the most complex psychiatric disorders. It can negatively affect patients' quality of life (QoL) and is associated with substantial costs in health care systems. Bipolar disorder is characterized by distinct episodes (manic, depressive, and mixed) and a varied course and clinical features (eg, rapid cycling course and psychotic feature). Patients with bipolar disorder exhibit a periodic exacerbation of discrete symptomatic episodes, ranging from the characteristic manic mood to the dysphoric mood. Chapter nine reviews QoL and economics research in bipolar disorder with a focus on the following areas:

1. Psychometric evaluation of QoL instruments in patients with bipolar disorder
2. QoL and its correlates among patients with bipolar disorder at different stages of the disease
3. Comparisons of QoL among patients with bipolar disorder with that among other patient populations
4. Medication treatment effects on QoL among patients with bipolar disorder
5. Economic consequences associated with bipolar disorder
6. Medication treatment effects on economic outcomes among patients with bipolar disorder.

In: Trends in Bipolar Disorder Research
Editor: Malcomb R. Brown, pp. 1-31
ISBN: 1-59454-060-8

Chapter 1

DEMOGRAPHIC AND CLINICAL FEATURES OF MOOD DISORDERS

Alessandro Serretti and Laura Mandelli
Department of Psychiatry, Vita-Salute University, San Raffaele Institute, Milan, Italy

INTRODUCTION: THE PROBLEM OF DEFINING THE "PHENOTYPE" FOR BIOLOGICAL STUDIES IN MOOD DISORDERS

The pathogenic bases of Mood disorders are still largely unknown. Several causal factors have been proposed as involved in the etiology of Mood disorders, both biological, genetic and psychosocial. Biological explanations have been alternatively related to abnormalities of the noradrenergic [1], serotoninergic [2] and dopaminergic systems [3], to thyroid abnormalities [4], to irregular circadian rhythms [5], immunologic malfunctions [6] and neuroanatomic defects [7]. Genetic investigations, based on families, twins and adoptees, evidenced a significant heritability of Mood disorders, particularly in Bipolar disorder [8-12]. However, despite decades of investigations, no unequivocal evidence has been reported for a definite alteration of some biological system or for a causative role of single gene variants or chromosome regions [13-15].

On the other hand, psychosocial explanations of Mood disorders postulated alternatively the role of stressors and adverse life events [16-18], the role of peculiar familiar patterns [17,19-23], the predisposing effect of some personality disorders or traits [24-31], and the participation of psychodinamic (see [32]) and cognitive features [33-35]. Similarly to biologic studies, no unequivocal factor has been reported to date, and converging evidence point toward an interaction between psychosocial and biological factors, to be identified yet, on the development of Mood disorders.

One of the major difficulties relates to the substantial "phenotipic" heterogeneity that characterizes this mental disturbance. A crucial research challenge would be a more valid definition of the "phenotype" of Mood disorders [36-39]. In fact, though current nosography classifies Mood disorders under few intra-diagnostic groups, they become concrete to the observer into many and different clinical configurations. A great effort has been done to distinguish diagnostic categories. Diagnosis have been based on those symptoms which tend to co-occur, defining syndrome clusters. However, patients included in the same diagnostic category may differ regarding a number of clinical features, such as their symptomathologic presentation, their response to the pharmacological treatment and their overall outcome. Because their substantial heterogeneity, Mood disorders have been proposed either as a junction of similar but etiologically different conditions (categorical conceptualization) or as a continuum of conditions in which etiological factors intervene in dissimilar degrees (continuos conceptualization) [36,40-42].

The intra-class variability, observed within the same psychiatric syndrome, has been hypothesized as one of the major bias for detecting underlying causal factors [39,43-45]. Thus, different etiological factors, either biological and psychosocial, may be involved in conditions which are only apparently similar. Alternatively, the same etiological factors may be involved in different degrees in these partially similar conditions.

A more valid phenotype definition that is closer to the underlying biological structures is strongly needed. As no valid biologic marker is available, the focus should shift toward the appearance of mood disorders.

For these reasons, the investigation of the "phenotype" of Mood disorders, through the identification of homogeneous samples of patients, has been one of the aim of our researches. We used different strategies, which included evaluation of demographic and clinical features, identification of symptomatology structures and the differential response to the pharmacological treatment.

SYMPTOMATOLOGICAL STRUCTURES

Symptomatologic Patterns: Definition

The most straightforward strategy to define a disease is to list its features. In the case of psychiatric disturbances those are psychopathologic symptoms. They were regularly used since the first classifications and current nosography still largely relies on symptoms. However the symptomatologic appearance in clinical practice is much more heterogeneous than what the current nosography allows to characterize. Therefore a strong effort was directed toward the definition of homogeneous symptomatology structures.

Symptomatologic Patterns of Major Psychosis

Symptomatological structures of heterogeneous psychiatric populations have been scarcely studied. For schizophrenia a number of reports proposed and tested models of one to five underlying symptomatologic latent roots [46-52]. A three-factors model, composed by "negative", "positive" and "disorganized" symptoms was proposed by the majority of researchers [49,52-54].

In a first study [38], we aimed to identify symptomatologic structures underlying major psychosis, independently from diagnosis. Symptomatologic structures were extracted by factor-analytic techniques (see [38] for details), on a mixed sample of 1004 patients affected by Mood disorders (Major depression and Bipolar disorder), Delusional disorder or

Schizophrenia spectrum, and evaluated by the Operational criteria checklist for psychotic illness (OPCRIT) [43]. OPCRIT is a 90-item checklist which comprises signs and symptoms that cover major psychosis symptomathology. The OPCRIT checklist includes lifetime evaluations of psychotic and affective symptoms, other than demographic informations, indicators of severity and of illness course.

Factor scores were first obtained, then a confirmatory factor analysis was conducted to evaluate the fitness of the model. We identified four symptomatologic structures accounting for 54.6% of the total variance. Those factors were “excitement”, “depression”, “disorganization” and “delusion” and they were confirmed on a larger sample of 2241 psychiatric patients, including an independent sample of German population [55].

Afterwards, on a sample of 1294 subjects affected by Schizophrenia, Bipolar and Delusional disorder [56], partially overlapping with the previous sample [38], we tested a five-factors model, that comprised as a fifth factor the “negative” one, composed by ‘negative thought disorder’ and ‘blunted affect’. The five-factor model, illustrated in table 1, displayed the best fit compared to other models (from one to four factors).

“Excitement” factor represented a latent structure very specific to Bipolar disorder; in fact bipolar subjects scored very high on it, whereas all other groups scored very low. The “depression” factor scored very high among depressives, but Psychotic disorder NOS and Schizophreniform disorder also had some subjects scoring high. The “disorganization” factor was similar to that found by other researchers for schizophrenia [49,53,54]. The “delusion” factor was not specific to any diagnosis and, finally, the "negative" factor was quite limited to schizophrenia.

Table 1. The five-factors model of Major psychosis. Best fit result of exploratory factor analysis for 29 items of the OPCRIT checklist over 1294 subjects affected by Bipolar disorder, Delusional disorder or Schizophrenia. Modified from[56]

Factors	Excitement	Depression	Disorganization	Negative	Delusion
Symptoms	-Distractibility -Agitated activity -Irritable mood -Dysphoria -Increased sociability -Increased self esteem -Grandiose delusions	-Loss of energy -Loss of pleasure -Poor concentration -Slowed activity -Self reproach -Suicidal ideation -Poor appetite -Diminished libido -Diurnal variation	-Bizarre behaviour -Positive thought disorder	-Negative thought disorder -Blunted affect	-Persecutory delusions -Organized delusions -Delusions of influence -Bizarre delusions -Widespread delusions -Abusive accusatory voices -Del. & hall. last for 1 week -Jealous delusions -Delusional perception

Note: For each item of each factor, the factor loading value was higher than 0.4.

Our confirmatory factor analyses evidenced that major psychosis symptomatology is composed by five factors: “excitement” (mania), “depression”, "delusion", “disorganization” (positive symptoms) and “negative”. These symptomathologic clusters were evidenced on mixed samples, composed by mood disorder subjects, delusionals, subjects affected by disorders of the schizophrenic spectrum and other psychotics NOS. Thus, those factors should be considered only regarding this kind of patients. However, symptomathologic clusters could represent a helpful instrument to categorize patients independently from the specific diagnosis, but only considering their symptomathologic presentation.

Delusional Symptomatology

Despite its clinical relevance, delusional disorder symptomatology has been poorly studied. Delusional disorder presentation is polymorphic: hallucinations are at times reported, the wideness of delusions varies considerably and mood disturbances may occur.

In a previous investigation [57], we performed a factor analysis on signs and symptoms of Delusional disorder. Symptomatologic structures were extracted by factor-analytic techniques, on a mixed sample of 180 patients affected by Delusional disorder, evaluated by the OPCRIT checklist. Factor scores were first obtained, then a confirmatory factor analysis was performed to evaluate the fitness of the model. We identified a four-factors structure, that gave the best fit and explained 62% of the total variance. The four factors were: “depression”, “hallucinations”, “delusion” and “irritability” (see table 2).

The factor “depression” explained 20.7% of the total variance but only a minority of subjects presented depressive symptoms. The second factor “hallucination” was primarily composed of hallucination items. The third factor “delusion” was composed of well organized delusions and, together with the “hallucination” factor, it may be considered an indicator of overall severity. “Hallucination” and “delusion” factors resulted widely represented among these subjects. Finally, the fourth factor, labeled “irritability” included irritable mood and agitation. Only a small proportion of subjects presented irritability symptoms.

Table 2. The Four-factors Model of Delusional disorder. Best Fit Result of Exploratory Factor Analysis for 11 Items of the OPCRIT Checklist over 180 Subjects Affected by Delusional Disorder. Modified From[57]

factors	depression	hallucination	delusion	irritability
symptoms	-loss of pleasure -poor concentration -slowed activity	-non-affective hallucinations in any modality -delusions and hallucinations for 1 weeks -other psrimary delusions -widespread delusions	-weel-organized delusions -persecutory delusions	-irritable mood -agitated activity
total variance explained (%)	20.7	16.9	13.8	10.6

For each item of each factor, the factor loading value was higher than 0.4.

Depressive Symptomatology

Fewer reports have been produced regarding symptomathologic structures in Mood disorders. For Major depression, models composed of three distinct factors have been proposed. Those, mainly subdivided depressive and anxiety symptomatology, with a third minor factor regarding behavior [40].

Depressive disorder is a polymorphic syndrome with a wide range of clinical manifestations. Many factorial analyses were aimed at validation of scales for depression. However, most analyses of depressive symptomatology were performed ignoring psychotic symptoms, despite a substantial proportion of depressives presents psychotic features.

The Hamilton Rating Scale for Depression [58] was the most studied scale and it covers a wide range of cognitive and somatic items. Factorial analyses generally yielded a main severity factor and two secondary anxiety and sleep factors (for a review see [59]). Previous attempts at factor analyses of the Montgomery Asberg Depression Rating Scale (MADRS) [60] resulted inconsistent [61,62]. These discrepancies should mainly due to the high inter-item correlation which characterizes MADRS items. Other factorial analyses were performed with composite instruments and revealed separate factors of anxiety [63,64], retardation [65] and endogenous-neurotic symptoms [66-68].

In a previous work [69], we performed an analysis of depressive symptomatology, including psychotic symptoms, on a large sample of mood disorder subjects (n=669), evaluated by the OPCRIT checklist. We performed a factor analysis on 25 OPCRIT items, related to depressive symptomathology and including delusions and hallucinations.

Table 3. The Three-factors Model of Depressive Disorders. Best Fit Result of Exploratory Factor Analysis for 25 Items of the OPCRIT Checklist over 669 Subjects Affected by Mood Disorders. Modified From[69]

Factors	Core	Psychotic	Atypical
Symptoms	-Loss of pleasure -Loss of energy/Tiredness -Excessive self reproach -Diminished libido -Poor appetite -Slowed activity -Poor concentration -Early morning waking -Weight Loss -Diurnal variation -Suicidal ideation -Initial insomnia -Middle insomnia	-Persecutory Delusions -Delusions & hallucinations last for one week -Persecutory/jealous delusions & hallucinations -Well organised delusions -Delusions of influence -Delusions of guilt	-Increased appetite -Weight gain -Excessive sleep -Dysphoria
Total variance explained (%)	23.6	11.6	0.8

For each item of each factor, the factor loading value was higher than 0.4.

A three factor structure gave the best fit and explained 43.2% of the total variance (see table 3). The first factor, labeled "core" symptoms, explained 23.6% of the total variance and was a general depression factor in which classical depressive symptoms clustered. The second factor was composed of items describing "psychotic" symptoms (delusions and hallucinations). The third factor was only composed of "atypical" symptoms. However, only a small proportion of subjects presented symptoms of "psychotic" and "atypical" factors.

Factor analysis focuses on variables correlation and it groups symptoms, but it does not describe subjects. Therefore, we performed also a cluster analysis in order to identify homogeneous subgroups of patients. The best fit was a four-clusters solution (Table 4). The first cluster was composed mainly of patients exhibiting atypical features. The second cluster showed low scores of the "core" depression factor and intermediate scores of psychosis. This latter was composed mainly of bipolar subjects presenting mild depressive phases. The third cluster was the largest and was composed of major depressive episodes without psychotic features. The last cluster was composed mainly of psychotic depressives.

In conclusion, depressive symptomatology proved to be composed of three factors, namely 'core', 'psychotic' and 'atypical' symptoms.

Table 4. Clusters for the Three Factors of Depression. Modified From [69]

	Cluster 1 (n=87)	Cluster 2 (n=155)	Cluster 3 (n=272)	Cluster 4 (n=155)
Factor Scores	Meanst.dev	Meanst.dev	Meanst.dev	Meanst.dev
Core	0.2±0.8	-1.5±0.4	**0.5±0.5**	**0.5±0.6**
Delusion	-0.1±0.8	**0.01±0.8**	-0.7±0.4	**1.3±0.7**
Atypical	**2.2±0.8**	-0.1±0.5	-0.4±0.4	-0.3±0.6

The four clusters clearly differentiate subpopulations of depressed patients. See text for details.

Manic Symptomatology

Manic episodes, which are mandatory for the diagnosis of bipolar disorder, are traditionally (DSM, ICD, RDC) viewed as 'mood episodes'. However several studies, proposed that variables related to activation level, and not to mood state, constitute the core characteristics of the manic syndrome [70].

Fewer reports have been produced regarding symptomatological structures in Mood disorders. For Bipolar disorder, three-factors models, similar to that found for schizophrenia [52] were detected. Cassidy et al. Proposed manic states as composed by 'dysphoria', 'psychomotor acceleration', 'psychosis', 'increased hedonic function' and 'irritable aggression' [71].

We performed an analysis of manic symptomatology [72] in a large sample of mood disorder subjects (n=509), evaluated by the OPCRIT checklist. A three factors solution was obtained and it explained 52.4% of the total variance (table 5).

The first factor explained the largest part of the variance and it was composed by psychic and motor "excitement". "Psychosis" items composed the second factor and "irritability" items the third.

As expected, the large majority of subjects presented at least some excitement symptoms. Moreover, a large portion of subjects presented at least some psychotic symptoms, disconfirming the reported clinical observation that only a minority of subjects present psychotic features during affective episodes [73]. The "irritability" factor was the only one with a normal distribution, suggesting that irritability is a common feature among manic episodes.

Table 5. The Three-factors Model of Mania. Best Fit Result of Exploratory Factor Analysis for 15 Items of the OPCRIT Checklist over 509 Subjects Affected by Bipolar Disorder. Modified From [72]

Factors	Excitement	Psychosis	Irritability
Symptoms	-Excessive activity -Reduced need of sleep -Elevated mood -Distractibility -Increased sociability -Thoughts racing -Increased self esteem -Agitated activity	-Delusions & hallucinations last for one week -Persecutory/jealous delusions & hallucinations -Persecutory Delusions -Grandiose Delusions	-Dysphoria -Irritable mood -Reckless activity
Total variance explained (%)	28.0	13.8	10.6

For each item of each factor, the factor loading value was higher than 0.4.

Dysthymic Symptomatology

Dysthymia is a common disorder, with a 3–5% lifetime prevalence in the general population, and it is associated with considerable psychosocial impairment [74-77]. Based on the work of Akiskal et al. [78], current official nosography classifies dysthymia among Mood disorders. The primary distinction between dysthymia and major depressive disorder is that dysthymia is chronic, but symptomatically less severe [79]. In DSM-IV [79], among symptoms considered typical of major depression, only psychomotor disturbance and suicidality are excluded from the dysthymia criteria list.

An unresolved question is how dysthymia should be defined symptomatologically within the spectrum of Mood disorders. Since the first contributions of Akiskal et al. [78], emotional-cognitive symptoms have been delineated as being much more characteristic of dysthymia than vegetative and psychomotor symptoms [80,81]. We confirmed that observation from analyses of depressive and anxiety symptomatology in a large sample of dysthymic patients (n=512) [82]. In that study we used the Montgomery Asberg Depression Rating Scale (MADRS) [60] and the Hamilton Anxiety Rating Scale (HAM-A) [83] to assess depressive and anxiety symptoms.

Symptoms most frequently observed, besides depressed mood (100% by definition), were 'low energy or fatigue' (96%) and 'poor concentration or indecisiveness' (88%), followed by 'low self-esteem' (80%), 'insomnia or hypersomnia' (77%), 'poor appetite or overeating' (69%) and 'feeling of hopelessness' (42%).

Interestingly, in the subjects with fewer than five symptoms, the most frequent were 'low energy' or 'fatigue' (93%), 'poor concentration' or 'indecisiveness' (79%) and 'low self-esteem' (77%), the other symptoms being present in no more than half the sample.

MADRS factor analysis identified two main factors: the first consisting of 'apparent sadness' and 'reported sadness', and the second 'concentration difficulties' and 'lassitude' (see table 6). The two factors were not correlated, so 'sadness' and 'lassitude' may belong to distinct psychopathologic clusters. 'Inability to feel', 'pessimistic thoughts' and neurovegetative items (appetite and sleep) loaded on neither factors. 'Suicidal thoughts' were uncommon in this sample, as suicide risk or recent suicide attempts were exclusion criteria.

HAM-A factor analysis identified two factors clearly differentiating somatic and psychic symptoms (table 7). Three items loaded on neither factors: 'intellectual functioning', 'depressed mood' and 'insomnia'. The two factors were positively correlated.

Table 6. The Two-factors Model of Dysthymia.
Best Fit Result of Exploratory Factor Analysis for MADRS Items over 512 Subjects Affected by Mood Disorders. Modified From [82]

Factors	Sadness	Lassitude
Symptoms	-Apparent sadness -Reported sadness	-Concentration difficulties -Lassitude
Total variance explained (%)	11.7	6.7

For each item of each factor, the factor loading value was higher than 0.4.

Table 7. The Two-factors Model of Anxiety in Dysthymia.
Best Fit Result of Exploratory Factor Analysis for HAM-A Items over 512 Subjects Affected by Mood Disorders. Modified From [82]

Factors	Somatic anxiety	Psychic anxiety
Symptoms	-Somatic-sensory -Cardivascular -Respiratory -Somatic-muscular -Gastrointestinal -Genitourinary -Autonomic	-Anxious mood -Tension -Behaviour
Total variance explained (%)	16.4	10.4

For each item of each factor, the factor loading value was higher than 0.4.

That study involved the largest sample of pure dysthymics ever studied. Our results indicate that dysthymic disorder appears to primarily involve emotional-cognitive symptoms over neurovegetative ones, particularly in the less severe forms of the illness. The psychological symptoms themselves seem to cluster into sadness versus mental fatigue. As for anxiety symptoms, they appear divisible into somatic and psychic clusters, with the latter prevailing in dysthymia.

Conclusions

The above-mentioned studies showed that few main symptomatology structures may be observed in mood disorders (depression, mania, delusion) and that other may emerge in specific subgroups of subjects. This approach was useful for genetic studies and it allowed to identify some liability factors for specific symptomatology structures [84-88].

Mood Disorder Subtypes

Symptoms are not the only information we have on mood disorders. Subjects may be defined by a range of further features, the same symptomatology may appear in dramatically different conditions considering other clinical and demographical factors. Therefore some of our investigations focused on those factors.

Long after the pioneering work of Kraepelin [89], manic-depressive illness was adequately investigated only during the most recent decades. In the late '60s it has been divided into Bipolar and Major depressive disorders. Then, Bipolar disorder was subtyped in type I and type II disorders, and Major depressive disorder was divided into recurrent and single episode. DSM-IV includes other diagnostic subgroups, such as the Dysthymic disorder, the Cyclotimic disorder and minor depression. These forms were not considered in our studies (for a description of these forms see [79]).

Most common Mood disorders are characterized by recurrent major depressives episodes, separated by normotimic phases (Major depressive disorder, recurrent) or by both major depressive and manic episodes interchanged by normotimic periods (Bipolar disorder, type I). In Bipolar disorder, type I, also mixed episodes, defined by concurrent depressives and manic symptoms, can occur.

Bipolar disorder, type II, is characterized by the occurrence of depressive episodes and hypomanic phases, i.e. at least three manic symptoms for less than one week, or for a longer time but without a significant interference with the ordinary individual's functioning. In both Major depressive and Bipolar disorders, psychotic features can also occur, but they appear only during affective episodes and they should recover before or concurrently the recovery from manic or depressive symptoms. The prevalence of psychotic depression is estimated to be about 20% of depressive episodes and around 0.6% in the general population [73,90].

"Rapid cycling" criteria is an illness course specifyer, included in DSM-IV [79] for Bipolar disorder, that refers to a high recurrence of affective episodes (at least four episodes per year). Rapid-Cyclers range from 13 to 20% of all bipolars [91-93]. "Seasonality" is an other important illness course specifier and it identifies those forms of Mood disorders characterized by a higher recurrence during particular seasons, such as spring or autumn.

Several differences have been reported not only between major depressives and bipolar subjects, but also among Bipolar disorder sub-types. In the attempt to resolve some of the discrepancies in the literature, in a number of reports, we investigated patients affected by Mood disorders, comparing subjects for demographic, clinical, symptomathological and outcome features [94-98].

To assess differences among Mood disorder subtypes, we collected data from a large sample of 1832 patients, affected by Major depression, single episode (n=120), Major depression, recurrent (n=708), Bipolar disorder, type I (n=863) and Bipolar disorder, type II (n=141) [96].

On a sample of 652 patients, that was a part of the previous one, we analyzed the patterns of manic symptoms in bipolars, type I (n=158), bipolars, type II (n=122) and major depressives (n=372) to test the hypothesis that mania and hypomania have different features and ascertain which of those manifestations can occur also in unipolar depression [98].

Delusional depression was investigated on a sample of 288 patients regarding their clinical and demographic features [94] and their symptomathologic presentation [95]. Finally, rapid cycling bipolar disorder was investigated on a sample of 275 rapid cyclers, compared to 320 patients affected by non-rapid cycling bipolar disorder [97].

Patients ware assessed using the Schedule for Affective Disorder and Schizophrenia (SADS) SADS [99], Structured Clinical Interview for DSM-III-R, Version 1.0 SCID[100] and the Operational Criteria for psychotic illness checklist OPCRIT [43] with a lifetime perspective [44]. Depressed patients were administered the Hamilton Rating Scale for Depression HAMD-21 [58], at the in index episode, prior to treatment.

Major Depressive Disorder

In our studies, the most important demographic specifier of the Major depressive disorder was the female sex. In fact, according to a wide literature [91,101-104], compared to bipolars, major depressives, recurrent (MDR) were characterized by a higher ratio of females. This ratio decreased from MDR, bipolars, type II (BP-II), bipolars, type I (BP-I) to major depressives, single episode (MDSE).

In Major depressive disorder the most important symptomathologic specifier was the appearance of melancholic features. MDR subjects showed more depressive symptoms and more melancholic features than BP-I, while atypical symptoms were more frequent among bipolars [105-109] and decreased from BP-I to MDSE through BP-II and MDR subjects.

The occurrence of a single lifetime major depressive episode was more likely linked to stressful life events. In fact, MDSE subjects showed a higher incidence of precipitant events at the onset compared to other patients. Moreover, they were markedly less characterized by a symptomatology of retardation [107,110-112]. Finally, one or two manic symptoms were observed in more than 30% of major depressive patients. Psychomotor agitation was the most frequent manifestations, present in 18% of depressives [98].

Delusional Depression

In our subjects, demographic and clinical specifiers of psychotic depression were a low educational level and a high rate of cluster A personality disorders (mainly paranoid). The low level of education among delusional subjects was not explained by an early onset of the illness and we hypothesized a premorbid alteration of the functioning [113]. Regarding other clinical and demographic features, a substantial similarity between non-delusional and delusional patients was observed.

According to previous reports [114-116,117, Parker, 1995 #425,118], in our sample we found a more severe depressive symptomathology among delusionals, even after the exclusion of items directly involved with delusional symptoms. Delusional subjects showed more severe "core" symptoms ('depressed mood', 'guilt', 'inability to work/loss of interest', 'retardation', 'psychic anxiety', 'fatigue' and 'suicidal ideation'). Moreover, we found reduced or absent diurnal variations of depressive symptoms in delusional forms.

Bipolar Disorder, Type I

Demographic specifiers of Bipolar disorder, type I, were a high educational level and the single or divorced marital status. In fact, in our sample, BP-I subjects had a higher mean education level than MDR and, marginally, than BP-II; we observed a trend toward BP-I subjects to be not married compared to MDR subjects [102].

Clinical specifiers of the Bipolar disorder, type I, were an early age of onset, an early age at first lifetime treatment, a high number of lifetime episodes and high number of hospitalizations. In fact, in accordance to previous findings, BP-I were characterized by a earlier age of onset and a lower age at first lifetime psychiatric treatment, compared to MDR [91,102,119-122]. BP-I also showed a higher number of episodes and hospitalizations compared to MDR [91,120,122].

As previously mentioned, atypical symptoms were more frequent among BP-I patients [105-109,123,124]. Another important symptomathologic feature of Bipolar disorder, type I was the appearance of delusions. In accordance to previous findings [125,126], BP-I patients showed a much higher lifetime incidence of psychotic symptoms, both delusions and hallucinations. BP-I subjects also showed a higher lifetime incidence of disorganized symptoms and a lower illness perception than others patients.

When compared with BP-II, BP-I subjects had a higher prevalence of reckless activity, distractibility, psychomotor agitation, irritable mood and increased self esteem [98].

Bipolar Disorder, Type II

Bipolar disorder, type II, was not characterized by distinctive demographic specifiers. Age of onset in BP-II was intermediate between MDR and BP-I [119], but we could not confirm a reported difference between BP II and MDR regarding this feature [91,105,127,128].

Compared to MDR, BP-II showed a higher number of episodes. However, in disagreement with a previous report [127], the number of hospitalization of BP-II was similar to the MDR one. Suicide risk was a quite distinctive feature of Bipolar disorder, type II. As it was previously reported [91,129-131], BP-II showed more suicide attempts than BP-I and, as a trend, than MDR [112,127,129,130].

Bipolar Disorder, Rapid Cycling

Demographic specifiers of rapid cycling Bipolar disorder were female sex, a late onset and a late age at first lifetime treatment. Our findings were in agreement with previous observations that reported rapid cycling bipolars (RC) to be predominantly females [91-93,132-138] and with a late onset [91].

Clinical specifiers of rapid cycling Bipolar disorder were less severe depressive and excitement symptoms and less symptoms of psychosis and disorganization. In our sample, RC disease course was associated with a lower risk for any psychotic features, in particular among BP-II. RC showed a less severe symptomatology of delusion, disorganization, excitement and depression. Moreover, though the risk of suicide attempt was not associated with the non-rapid cycling or rapid cycling illness course, RC subjects had a lower risk for violent suicide attempt, particularly among BP I subjects.

Table 8. Demographic and Clinical Specifiers of Mood Disorder Sub-types Identified in our Studies

	Mood disorder sub-types*					
	MDSE	**MDR**	**MD, delusional**	**BP-I**	**BP-II**	**BP, rapid cycling**
Specifiers						
Sex		female				female
Educational level				high		
Marital status		married		single/divorced		
Personality			cluster A			
Onset		late		early	intermediate	late
First lifet. treatm.		late		early		late
life-events	at the onset					
No. episodes				high	high	
No. hospitaliz.				high		
Depressive symptomatology	less retardation than MDR	mainly melancholic	more severe; reduced mood diurnal variations	more atypical symptoms; lower illness perception than MDR	similar to MDR	less severe
suicide risk					high	low for violent type
manic symptomathology					compared to BP-I, less irritability, increased self-esteem, reckless activity, distractibility, psychomotor agitation	less severe than BP, non-recurrent
Disorganization				present		low
Psychosis				high		low

MDSE=Major depression, single episode; MDR=Major depression, recurrent; MD, delusional= delusional Major depression; BP-I=Bipolar disorder, type I; BP-II=Bipolar disorder, type II; BP, rapid cycling=Bipolar diosrder, rapid cycling.

Overall, the above mentioned findings identified specific demographic and clinical features of Mood disorder sub-types. The view that Bipolar disorder, type I is quite different from the remaining subtypes emerged, while Bipolar disorder, type II appeared to lack specificity. Delusional depression appeared as a more severe depressive form. On the contrary, rapid cycling bipolar disorder emerged as an overall less severe disease, at least from a symptomatologic point of view, when compared to non-rapid cycling bipolar disorder, and this was particularly true in Bipolar disorder, type I.

Long Term Outcome, Social Adjustment and Self-esteem during Remission

Long Term Outcome

Beyond symptomatology and demographic features, other factors are of interest, specifically those related to the natural history of the disorder and to the impact on other dimensions such as self esteem and social adjustment.

The lifetime course of mood disorders ranges in fact from a single episode of illness to a recurrent pattern with few or no intervals [91,139]. Despite many efforts over recent decades, at present only few factors have been shown to be associated with a given time course of the affective illness. The main prognostic factor seems to be linked with the number of illness episodes itself. Mounting evidence indicates that, on average, cycle length appears to get progressively shorter and, after three to five episodes, the extent of shortening slows down and approaches a level that is probably the individual maximum frequency of episodes [91,140].

Amongst early predictors, polarity has probably been investigated the most: bipolar subjects show a less favorable prognosis compared to major depressives [140-142]. Among bipolars, an onset with manic or mixed symptomatology is generally considered an indicator of even poorer prognosis [143]. The presence of psychotic features have also been associated with a higher rate of relapse [141,144]. The relationship between course of illness and age of onset remains unclear [145-149].

Female gender in major depressive disorder [150], family history of severe psychiatric illness [151], personality disorders [25], comorbidity with substance abuse or dependence [152] have also been associated with a worse illness course, and the possible role of psychosocial factors is still a debated issue [142,148].

On a large sample of subjects (n=426) affected by Mood disorders we investigated retrospectively the time course of the illness, in order to identify factors associated with outcome [153]. We observed a marked deteriorating course, with an increasing number of episodes, corresponding to an increasingly shorter interval between episodes, up to a plateau frequency of one episode per year on average. A diagnosis of bipolar disorder, a manic onset among bipolars and a higher number of episodes were all associated with a shorter duration of intervals between episodes.

Polarity proved to be the strongest time course predicting factor. On average, bipolars presented shorter intervals between episodes (Figure 1), but differences between bipolars and major depressives decreased with increasing episode number.

A favorable course indicator that has been proposed was, in women, an onset of illness during the post partum period [154-156]. Post Manic and depressive episodes are relatively common in the postpartum period and a series of follow up studies after a postpartum index episode demonstrated a more favorable course in women who had no previous history of psychiatric illness or who had experienced previous puerperal illness only [155].

To investigate whether postpartum mood disorders had a different prognosis than non puerperal forms, we analyzed the effect of postpartum onset on the number of relapses in a sample of bipolar (n=109) and major depressive women (n=145) (Serretti & Olgiati;

unpublished data). Patients with postpartum onset disorders were compared to disease-matched non postpartum controls.

Bipolar patients who experienced their first episode in the postpartum, showed significantly lower manic episodes. Among major depressives, postpartum onset leads to fewer relapses.

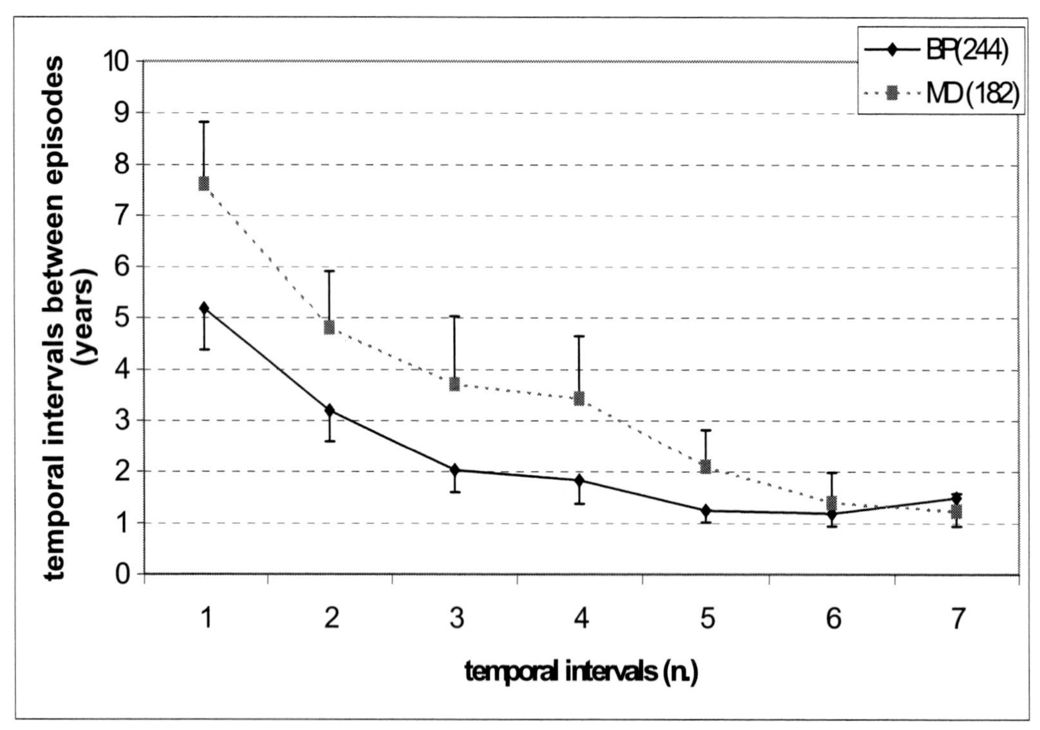

Figure 1. Temporal intervals between episodes (years) in Major depressive disorder (n=182) and Bipolar disorder (n=244).[153]

Those results indicate that female bipolars and major depressives, which experience their first episode during the postpartum period, have fewer relapses than non puerperal counterparts. However, further research is warranted to replicate these findings in larger samples and ascertain whether different pathophysiological mechanisms cause relapses in postpartum and non postpartum affective diseases.

Overall these studies indicated that Mood disorders are mental illnesses characterized by a relatively marked deteriorating course, with an increasing number of episodes and an increasingly shorter interval between episodes. This deteriorating course was more evident among bipolars, among those having a manic episode at the onset and a higher number of previous episodes. On the other hand, in women, a post partum onset appeared to be a protective factor against recurrent relapses. The analysis of the time course of mood disorders allowed us to identify some genetic factors linked to the periodicity [Benedetti, 2003 #5330; Cusin, 2001 #2070; Smeraldi, 2002 #2867].

Social Adjustment and Self-esteem during Remission of Symptomatology

Many authors have described significantly poorer social adjustment, even in fully remitted patients (for a review see[157]). Further, impairment in social functioning has been hypothesized to increase the liability of developing major depression; thus social adjustment has been proposed by some as predictive of outcome [158-160].

Depressive syndromes may follow environmental stressors; on the other hand, mood disorders per se are a cause of social malfunction during episodes, and job or social consequences may endure long after episode remission. Further, social problems may be related with residual depressive symptoms, even of minimal severity [161-163]. Poor social adjustment may be also associated with mood disorders because of the high comorbidity with personality disorders and their maladaptive consequences.

In major depressives, Shapira et al. [161] evidenced a poorer social adjustment, but not in bipolars. Bawens et al. [164] found a worse functioning in the area of work and global social dysfunctions among all mood disorder patients. Further, they found impaired working adjustment related with recurrent episodes [159]. In the work of Bawens et al. [164], depressives differed from bipolars mostly with regard to a worse adjustment in the "marital role", an area in which bipolars reported scores closer to controls.

At the opposite, in a previous study [165], we found only bipolars having a significant worse adjustment in the "marital role", and not major depressives. In a following paper [165], we compared 185 patients affected by Mood disorders with a group of 100 control subjects. Individual degree of social adjustment was assessed by the Social Adjustment Scale (SAS) [166], a self-administered scale [164] composed by 54 multiple-choice items. Scores can be grouped into the following seven sub-areas: 1) Work, 2) Spare time (social and leisure activities), 3) Extended Family, 4) Marital role, 5) Parental role, 6) Family unit, 7) Finance. The SAS is routinely used for research purposes and validated in multiple samples.

All mood disorder patients exhibited a worse global social adjustment and, in particular, in the areas of "spare time", "extended family" and "finance". Bipolars showed a trend for a more impaired global social adjustment, and they had a worse adjustment also in all familiar areas and in "finance" [167-169].

Compared to controls, mood disorder patients also exhibited a lower self-esteem, as evaluated by the Self Esteem Scale (SES) [170]. Thus, according to Pardoen et al. [171] a low self-esteem level may characterize mood disorders patients, even during remission.

The outcome for delusional depressives is generally considered to be poor when compared to non-delusional subjects [115,168,172]. Follow-up studies report a more severe outcome for psychotic subjects with shorter symptom free intervals, longer episodes of illness and poorer social and occupational functioning [116,173-175]. In our studies [153,176] we did not observed a worse outcome of delusionals in terms of number of episodes. However, remitted delusional patients showed a marginally worse social adjustment than non-delusionals. The difference was significant within the 'Family' sub-area of the SAS [177]. These results furnished evidence of poor inter-episode function in patients with delusional mood disorder.

Differential Response to Pharmacological Treatment

A similarity between mechanisms linked to the pathophysiology of Mood disorders and mechanisms controlling drug response (e.g. the serotonin transporter genes) have been proposed [178,179]. Thus, responsiveness to a particular drug may be used as a tool for selecting a more homogeneous group of patients [180,181].

Response to Antidepressants

The outcome after a treatment with antidepressant therapies is a possible tool for selecting homogenous samples. In a study we observed that a positive response to fluvoxamine is a familial trait and selects families with a higher genetic loading [182]. Following, on a sample of 68 Italian families of bipolar probands, who were responsive to fluvoxamine, we performed a complex segregation analysis and a Mendelian dominant model of transmission best fitted [183]. Those results strongly suggested the utility of using pharmacological criteria as a tool to identify true genetic disorders and they opened the way for a series of pharmacogenetic studies which allowed identifying a number of genes related to drug response [184].

Predictors of Lithium Treatment Response

Lithium is used as a first line for the treatment of acute manic phases and as prophylaxis for recurrent manic and depressive episodes [91,185-189]. However, its effectiveness varies widely, to the point that the importance of its impact on the course of the illness, especially on the long-term, has been questioned [190-192]. Clinical predictors have been studied, but the lack of consensus and the low predicting value make them not a definite guideline for the clinician [193,194]. Reported clinical predictors of favorable long term response to lithium are summarized in box 1.

Conversely, a late initiation of lithium administration was associated with a poor response [213]. A sequence of depression-mania-normal interval, and continuous cycling with no normal intervals, were both associated with poor outcomes [91,208].

Among the various issues that have to be considered before initiating lithium prophylaxis, clinical presentation plays an important role. In major depressives, the presence of psychomotor retardation and malancholia during depressive episode was associated with a favourable response to lithium responders [199]. Others, however, have found patients with retarded depression to be poor lithium responders [201].

Box 1. Clinical Predictors of Favorable Long-term Response to Lithium

- atypical symptomatology of mood disorders [79] and the absence of comorbidity with other DSM-IV axis I disturbances (such as substance abuses or mental retardation) [91,195-198],
- presence of retarded-endogenous symptomatology profile, i.e. characterized by psychomotor inhibition, diurnal variation, neurovegetative symptomatology [193,194,199,200], though this is not an univocal finding [201,202],
- presence of psychotic features such as auditory or (less frequently) visual hallucinations that for their content may be considered mood-congruent (e.g. guilt) [203],
- an initial response during the first 6–12 months of lithium [204], even if this evaluation should not be considered a predictor because is not available at the beginning of treatment,
- female sex [205],
- absence of personality disorder [206],
- good social adjustment [207], even if social adjustment could influence directly the disease time course therefore producing a spurious association [91],
- a peculiar sequence of episode characterized by the mania-depression-normal interval [198,208,209]
- early start of treatment [210-213], this is relatively consistent finding across studies suggesting a possible pathoplastic activity of lithium.

Previously, we aimed to investigate the influence of melancholic features on lithium prophylactic effect, on a sample of 61 inpatients [200]. All enrolled patients were receiving lithium as maintenance therapy, with doses adjusted to obtain 12 hr plasma levels within standard therapeutic range. Subjects were evaluate using the Schedule for Affective Disorders and Schizophrenia (SADS) [99], the Operational Criteria for Psychotic Illness checklist (OPCRIT) [43] and medical records, according to DSM-IV criteria [79]. The efficacy of prophylactic treatment with lithium was evaluated by the difference between the recurrence rates before and during lithium treatment. Recurrence rates were evaluated by taking into account the occurring episodes of illness over the months, from the onset to the beginning of lithium prophylaxis (pre-lithium recurrence index) and from the beginning of prophylaxis to the time of assessment (on-lithium recurrence index) [213,214]. Melancholia was defined using OPCRIT items: “slowed activity”, “diurnal variations”, “excessive self-reproach” and “early morning weaking”. Analyses confirmed the previously reported correlation between early lithium administration and a better lithium outcome [213]. However, present sample was partially overlapped with those of Franchini et al. [213], thus that finding did not represent an independent confirmation. A significant correlation between high melancholia scores and good lithium outcome was observed. The two variables, early lithium administration and many melancholic features, provided an independent contribution and together explained 31% of the total variance in lithium outcomes.

Antidepressant Associated Manic and Hypo-manic Switches in Bipolar Disorder

A major drawback to the use of antidepressants for acute bipolar depression is the risk of induction of mania. In fact, several clinicians observed that antidepressants can precipitate mania or rapid cycling. Thus, manic switches represent a crucial problem for the treatment of bipolar depressed patients [215].

The relationship between manic switches and pharmacological therapy is not easy to investigate, mainly because the mechanisms of "switching" from depression to mania are not completely clear. The likelihood features and clinical predictors of switch also remain poorly understood [91].

In a previous work we investigated possible clinical differences between bipolar subjects with at least one manic or hypo-manic episode, according to DSM-IV criteria, immediately following depression ("switched") during antidepressant therapy, and bipolar subjects who never had one ("not switched"). Analyses were conducted on a sample of 169 'switched' patients affected by Bipolar disorder (type I and type II). Those subjects were compared to a sex, age (± 5 years), and ethnicity matched group of 247 bipolars randomly selected from our pool of bipolar subjects [88].

In our sample, switched subjects were marginally older than not-switched. Switched subjects more frequently had experienced a depressive polarity at the first episode than not switched ones, they showed less manic episodes but they had a higher number of previous depressive episodes than not-switched. Moreover, switched subjects were significantly less delusional but more likely bipolars type II and rapid cyclers.

That study evidenced some clinical features which were likely to play a role in conferring susceptibility to manic switches during antidepressant treatment. However, further studies are required to investigate other possible related factors influencing the timing of manic–depressive cycle.

Conclusion

All the above-mentioned studies were performed with the aim of identifying sub-populations of subjects, defined by homogeneous symptomatologies, common clinical features, comparable outcome and similar response to pharmacological treatments. The identification of homogeneous samples of patients may be of particular importance both for the clinician, to appropriately diagnose, target therapies and make prognosis, and for the researcher, applied to biological-genetic or pharmacological issues, where homogeneity is crucial.

Present data were derived from a large global sample of Italian subjects affected by Major psychosis and Mood disorders. These subjects were collected since early '90, among patients admitted to the Mood disorder center, San Raffaele Hospital of Milan, Department of Psychiatry.

A considerable effort was addressed to the identification of common symptomathologic structures underling major psychoses. In part 2 we described a general factor model composed by five symptomathologic clusters ("disorganization", "depression", "excitement", "delusion" and "negative"), derived on symptoms observed on a mixed sample of patients affected by Major depression, Bipolar disorder, subjects affected by the Schizophrenic spectrum and other NOS psychotics. Following, we analyzed specific diagnostic groups, obtaining symptomatologic clusters for each of those considered (Delusional disorder, Depression, Dysthymia and Mania).

In part 3, we described our studies focused on the investigation of demographic and clinical features which may characterize distinctively the various forms of Mood disorders. We found out specifiers for Major depressive disorder (such as melancholic symptoms), for delusional depression (low educational level, cluster A Personality disorder, severe depression episodes, absent mood diurnal variations), for Bipolar disorder, type I (high education, single and divorced status, early age of onset, numerous affective episodes and hospitalizations, appearance of atypical depressive symptoms and delusions, lower illness perception), for Bipolar disorder, type II (high number of affective episodes, high risk of suicide attempts) and for Bipolar disorder, rapid cycling (female sex, late onset, less severe depressive and manic forms, less occurring psychotic and disorganization symptoms).

In part 4, we described our studies focused on the long term outcome of Mood disorders. In our sample of patients, we found out a marked deteriorating course, with an increasing number of episodes and an increasingly shorter interval between episodes. It has to be noted that our data were derived from a population of severe patients. In fact, our Center is a tertiary care setting and therefore we cannot exclude a potential bias associated with severity of illness. However, we observed a more marked deteriorating course among bipolars compared to major depressives, among those having a manic episode at the onset and a higher number of previous episodes. On the contrary, a post partum onset appeared to be a protective factor against recurrent relapses.

Outcome of Mood disorders was analyzed not only in term of lifetime relapse, but also in terms of social functioning during well being phases. We evidenced a worse global social adjustment for mood disorder patients, even during normotimia. Social functioning was more markedly impaired among bipolars compared to major depressives.

Since responsiveness to a particular drug has been proposed as a potential tool for selecting homogeneous group of patients [180,181,183], in part 5 we investigated clinical features associated with the response to the pharmacological treatment of Bipolar disorder (lithium salts) and with the "switching" effect of antidepressant drugs. Significant effects of an early administration of lithium and melancholic depressive features during depression on the response to lithium treatment were evidenced, being both associated with a favorable outcome. Finally, some clinical features associated with the "switching" to mania/hypomania after a treatment with antidepressant drugs for depression, were evidenced (depressive polarity at the onset, many previous depressive episodes but few manic ones).

Our results represented both positive and negative confirmations of previous investigations, but also some unreported data have been observed. While some results seem well established, others remain uncertain or provisional, thus requiring further confirmation.

REFERENCES

[1] Brunello N, Blier P, Judd LL, Mendlewicz J, Nelson CJ, Souery D, Zohar J, Racagni G. Noradrenaline in mood and anxiety disorders: basic and clinical studies. *Int Clin Psychopharmacol* 2003; 18: 191-202.

[2] Meltzer HY, Lowy MT. The serotonin hypothesis of depression. In: Melzer HY, ed: *Psychopharmacology: the third generation of progress*. New York: Raven Press, 1987.

[3] Diehl D, Gershon S. The role of Dopamine in mood disorders. *Comprehensive Psychiatry* 1992; 2: 115-120.
[4] Musselman DL, Nemeroff CB. Depression and endocrine disorders: focus on the thyroid and adrenal system. *Br J Psychiatry Suppl* 1996: 123-8.
[5] Duncan WC, Jr. Circadian rhythms and the pharmacology of affective illness. *Pharmacol Ther* 1996; 71: 253-312.
[6] Leonard BE. The immune system, depression and the action of antidepressants. *Prog Neuropsychopharmacol Biol Psychiatry* 2001; 25: 767-80.
[7] Soares JC, Mann JJ. The functional neuroanatomy of mood disorders. *J Psychiatr Res* 1997; 31: 393-432.
[8] Allen MG. Twin studies of affective illness. *Arch Gen Psychiatry* 1976; 33: 1476-8.
[9] Bertelsen A, Harvald B, Hauge M. A Danish twin study of manic-depressive disorders. *Br J Psychiatry* 1977; 130: 330-51.
[10] Johnson GF, Leeman MM. Analysis of familial factors in bipolar affective illness. *Arch Gen Psychiatry* 1977; 34: 1074-83.
[11] Cadoret RJ. Evidence for genetic inheritance of primary affective disorder in adoptees. *Am J Psychiatry* 1978; 135: 463-6.
[12] Kendler KS, Neale MC, Kessler RC, Heath AC, Eaves LJ. Familial influences on the clinical characteristics of major depression: a twin study. *Acta Psychiatr Scand* 1992; 86: 371-8.
[13] Risch N, Botstein D. A manic depressive history. *Nature Genetics* 1996; 12: 351-353.
[14] Badner JA, Gershon ES. Meta-analysis of whole-genome linkage scans of bipolar disorder and schizophrenia. *Mol Psychiatry* 2002; 7: 405-11.
[15] Segurado R, Detera-Wadleigh SD, Levinson DF, Lewis CM, Gill M, Nurnberger JI, Jr., Craddock N, DePaulo JR, Baron M, Gershon ES, Ekholm J, Cichon S, Turecki G, Claes S, Kelsoe JR, Schofield PR, Badenhop RF, Morissette J, Coon H, Blackwood D, McInnes LA, Foroud T, Edenberg HJ, Reich T, Rice JP, Goate A, McInnis MG, McMahon FJ, Badner JA, Goldin LR, Bennett P, Willour VL, Zandi PP, Liu J, Gilliam C, Juo SH, Berrettini WH, Yoshikawa T, Peltonen L, Lonnqvist J, Nothen MM, Schumacher J, Windemuth C, Rietschel M, Propping P, Maier W, Alda M, Grof P, Rouleau GA, et al. Genome Scan Meta-Analysis of Schizophrenia and Bipolar Disorder, Part III: Bipolar Disorder. *Am J Hum Genet* 2003; 73: 34-48.
[16] Kendler KS, Kessler RC, Neale MC, Heath AC, Eaves LJ. The prediction of major depression in women: toward an integrated etiologic model. *Am J Psychiatry* 1993; 150: 1139-48.
[17] Pardoen D, Bauwens F, Dramaix M, Tracy A, Genevrois C, Staner L, Mendlewicz J. Life events and primary affective disorders. A one year prospective study. *Br J Psychiatry* 1996; 169: 160-6.
[18] Paykel ES. Life events and affective disorders. *Acta Psychiatr Scand Suppl* 2003: 61-6.
[19] Miller IW, Keitner GI, Whisman MA, Ryan CE, Epstein NB, Bishop DS. Depressed Patients With Dysfunctional Families: Description and Course of Illness. *Journal of Abnormal Psychology* 1992; 101: 637-646.

[20] Miller IW, McDermut W, Gordon K, Keitner GI, Ryan CE, Norman W. Personality and Family Functioning in Families of Depressed Patients. *Journal of Abnormal Psychology* 2000; 109: 539-545.

[21] Gilman SE, Kawachi I, Fitzmaurice GM, Buka SL. Family Disruption in Childhood and Risk of Adult Depression. *American Journal of Psychiatry* 2003; 160: 939-946.

[22] Reinherz HZ, Paradis AD, Giaconia RM, Stashwick CK, Fitzmaurice GM. Childhood and Adolescent Predictors of Major Depression in the Transition to Adulthood. *American Journal of Psychiatry* 2003; 160: 2141-2147.

[23] Ingram RE. Origins of Cognitive Vulnerability to Depression. *Cognitive Therapy & Research* 2003; 27: 77-88.

[24] Pilkonis PA, Frank E. Personality pathology in recurrent depression: nature, prevalence, and relationship to treatment response. *Am J Psychiatry* 1988; 145: 435-41.

[25] Black DW, Bell S, Hulbert J, Nasrallah A. The importance of Axis II in patients with major depression. A controlled study. *Journal of Affective Disorders* 1988; 14: 115-22.

[26] Alnaes R, Torgersen S. Personality and personality disorders predict development and relapses of major depression. *Acta Psychiatrica Scandinavica* 1997; 95: 336-42.

[27] Hansenne M, Reggers J, Pinto E, Kjiri K, Ajamier A, Ansseau M. Temperament and character inventory (TCI) and depression. *J Psychiatr Res* 1999; 33: 31-6.

[28] Richter J, Eisemann M, Richter G. Temperament and character during the course of unipolar depression among inpatients. *Eur Arch Psychiatry Clin Neurosci* 2000; 250: 40-7.

[29] O'Leary D, Costello F. Personality and outcome in depression: an 18-month prospective follow-up study. *J Affect Disord* 2001; 63: 67-78.

[30] Brieger P, Ehrt U, Marneros A. Frequency of comorbid personality disorders in bipolar and unipolar affective disorders. *Compr Psychiatry* 2003; 44: 28-34.

[31] Grucza RA, Przybeck TR, Spitznagel EL, Cloninger CR. Personality and depressive symptoms: a multi-dimensional analysis. *J Affect Disord* 2003; 74: 123-30.

[32] Gabbard GO. Psychodynamic psychiatry in Clinical practice. The DSM-IV edition., 1994.

[33] Beck AT, Rush AJ, Shaw BF, Emery G. Cognitive therapy of depression: Guilford Press, 1987.

[34] Seligman MEP. Helplessness: on depression, development, and. New York: Freeman, 1992.

[35] Gotlib IH, Kurtzman HS, Blehar MC. The cognitive psychology of depression. Hove: Psychology Press, 1997.

[36] Winokur G. Classification of chronic psychoses including delusional disorders and schizophrenias. *Psychopathology* 1986; 19: 30-4.

[37] Keefe RS, Silverman JM, Siever LJ, Cornblatt BA. Refining phenotype characterization in genetic linkage studies of schizophrenia. *Soc Biol* 1991; 38: 197-218.

[38] Serretti A, Macciardi F, Smeraldi E. Identification of symptomatologic patterns common to major psychoses: proposal for a phenotype definition. *American Journal of Medical Genetics* 1996; 67: 393-400.

[39] Berrettini W. Progress and pitfalls: bipolar molecular linkage studies. *Journal of Affective Disorders* 1998; 50: 287-97.

[40] Kendler K, Heat A, Martin N, Eaves L. Symptoms of anxiety and symptoms of depression. *Archives of General Psychiatry* 1987; 44: 451-457.

[41] Kendler KS, Neale MC, Kessler RC, Heath AC, Eaves LJ. Major depression and generalized anxiety disorder. Same genes, (partly) different environments? *Arch Gen Psychiatry* 1992; 49: 716-22.

[42] Akiskal HS. The bipolar spectrum: research and clinical perspectives. *Encephale* 1995; 21 Spec No 6: 3-11.

[43] McGuffin P, Farmer A, Harvey I. A polydiagnostic application of operational criteria in studies of psychotic illness. Development and reliability of the OPCRIT system. *Archives of General Psychiatry* 1991; 48: 764-770.

[44] Farmer AE, Williams J, Jones I. Phenotypic definitions of psychotic illness for molecular genetic research. *American Journal of Medical Genetics* 1994; 54: 365-371.

[45] Berrettini WH. On the future of genetic research in bipolar and schizophrenic syndromes. *Neuropsychopharmacology* 1999; 21: 1-2.

[46] Crow TJ. Molecular pathology of schizophrenia: more than one disease process? *British Medical Journal* 1980; 280: 66-68.

[47] Andreasen NC, Grove WM. The classification of depression: traditional versus mathematical approaches. *American Journal of Psychiatry* 1982; 139: 45-52.

[48] Mortimer AM, Lund CE, Mc Kenna PJ. The positive-negative dichotomy in schizophrenia. *British Journal of Psychiatry* 1990; 157: 41-49.

[49] Liddle PF, Barnes TRE. Syndromes of chronic schizophrenia. *British Journal of Psychiatry* 1990; 157: 558-561.

[50] Peralta V, Cuesta M, De Leon J. An empirical analysis of latent structures underlying schizophrenic symptoms: a four-syndrome model. *Biological Psychiatry* 1994; 36: 726-736.

[51] Von Knorring L, Lindstrom E. Principal components and further possibilities with the PANSS. *Acta Psychiatrica Scandinavica* 1995; 91(suppl 388): 5-10.

[52] Maziade M, Roy MA, Martinez M, Cliche D, Fournier JP, Garneau Y, Nicole L, Montgrain N, Dion C, Ponton AM. Negative, psychoticism, and disorganized dimensions in patients with familial schizophrenia or bipolar disorder: continuity and discontinuity between the major psychoses. *American Journal of Psychiatry* 1995; 152: 1458-63.

[53] Bilder RM, Mukergee S, Rieder RO, Pandurangi AK. Symptomatic and neuropsychological components of defect state. *Schizophrenia Bulletin* 1985; 11: 409-419.

[54] Andreasen NC, Arndt S, Alliger R, Miller D, Flaum M. Symptoms of schizophrenia. Methods, meanings, and mechanisms. *Archives of General Psychiatry* 1995; 52: 341-51.

[55] Serretti A, Rietschel M, Lattuada E, Krauss H, Schulze T, Müller D, Maier W, Smeraldi E. Major psychoses symptomatology: factor analysis of 2241 psychotic subjects. *European Archives of Psychiatry & Clinical Neuroscience* 2001; 251: 193-8.

[56] Serretti A, Olgiati P. Dimensions of major psychoses: a confirmatory factor analysis of six competing models. *Psychiatry research* in press.

[57] Serretti A, Lattuada E, Cusin C, Smeraldi E. Factor analysis of delusional disorder symptomatology. *Comprehensive Psychiatry* 1999; 40: 143-147.

[58] Hamilton M. Development of a rating scale for primary depressive illness. *British Journal of Social & Clinical Psychology* 1967; 6: 278-296.

[59] Bech P, Malt U, Dencker S, Ahlfors U, Elgen K, Lewander T, Lundell A, Simpson G, Lingjaerde O. Scales for assessment of diagnosis and severity of mental disorders. *Acta Psychiatrica Scandinavica* 1993; 87 Suppl 372: 37-40.

[60] Montgomery S, Asberg M. A new depression scale designed to be sensitive to change. *British Journal of Psychiatry* 1979; 134: 382-9.

[61] Craighead W, Evans D. Factor analysis of the Montgomery-Asberg Depression Rating Scale. *Depression* 1996; 4: 31-3.

[62] Galinowski A, Lehert P. Structural validity of MADRS during antidepressant treatment. *International Clinical Psychopharmacology* 1995; 10: 157-61.

[63] Clark D, Beck A, Beck J. Symptom differences in major depression, dysthymia, panic disorder, and generalized anxiety disorder. *American Journal of Psychiatry* 1994; 151: 205-9.

[64] Maes M, Meltzer H, Cosyns P, Schotte C. Evidence for the existence of major depression with and without anxiety features. *Psychopathology* 1994; 27: 1-13.

[65] Parker G, Hadzi Pavlovic D, Brodaty H, Boyce P, Mitchell P, Wilhelm K, Hickie I, Eyers K. Psychomotor disturbance in depression: defining the constructs. *J Affect Disord* 1993; 27: 255-65.

[66] Carney M, Roth M, Garside R. The diagnosis of depressive syndromes and the prediction of ECT response. *British Journal of Psychiatry* 1965; 111: 659-674.

[67] Rassaby E, Paykel E. Factor patterns in depression. A replication study. *Journal of Affective Disorders* 1979; 1: 187-94.

[68] Basoglu M. Symptomatology of depressive disorder in Turkey. A factor-analytic study of 100 depressed patients. *J Affect Disord* 1984; 6: 317-330.

[69] Serretti A, Lattuada E, Cusin C, Macciardi F, Smeraldi E. Analysis of depressive symptomatology in mood disorders. *Depression and Anxiety* 1998; 8: 80-85.

[70] Bauer MS, Crits-Christoph P, Ball WA, Dewees E, McAllister T, Alahi P, Cacciola J, Whybrow PC. Independent assessment of manic and depressive symptoms by self-rating. Scale characteristics and implications for the study of mania. *Archives of General Psychiatry* 1991; 48: 807-12.

[71] Cassidy F, Forest K, Murry E, Carroll B. A Factor Analysis of the Signs and Symptoms of Mania. *Archives of General Psychiatry* 1998; 55: 27-32.

[72] Serretti A, Rietschel M, Lattuada E, Krauss H, Held T, Nothen M, Smeraldi E. Factor analysis of Mania. *Archives of General Psychiatry* 1999; 56: 671-672.

[73] Johnson J, Horwath E, Weissman MM. The validity of major depression with psychotic features based on a community study. *Archives of General Psychiatry* 1991; 48: 1075-1081.

[74] Howland RH. General health, health care utilization, and medical comorbidity in dysthymia. *Int J Psychiatry Med* 1993; 23: 211-38.

[75] Keller MB. Dysthymia in clinical practice:course, outcome and impact on the community. *Acta Psychiatr Scand Suppl* 1994; 383: 24-34.

[76] Kessler R, McGonagle K, Zhao S, Nelson C, Hughes M, Eshleman S, Wittchen H, Kendler K. Lifetime and 12-month prevalence of DSM-III-R psychiatric disorders in the United States. Results from the National Comorbidity Survey. *Archives of General Psychiatry* 1994; 51: 8-19.

[77] Leader J, Klein D. Social adjustment in dysthymia, double depression and episodic major depression. *Journal of Affective Disorders* 1996; 37: 91-101.

[78] Akiskal HS. External validating criteria for psychiatric diagnosis: their application in affective disorders. *J Clin Psychiatry* 1980; 41: 6-15.

[79] American Psychiatric Association. Diagnostic and Statistical Manual of Mental Disorders, 4th Edition. Washington DC: American Psychiatric Association, 1994.

[80] Keller M, Klein D, Hirschfeld R, Kocsis J, McCullough J, Miller I, First M, Holzer Cr, Keitner G, Marin D, Shea T. Results of the DSM-IV mood disorders field trial. *American Journal of Psychiatry* 1995; 152: 843-9.

[81] Klein DN, Kocsis JH, McCullough JP, Holzer CE, 3rd, Hirschfeld RM, Keller MB. Symptomatology in dysthymic and major depressive disorder. *Psychiatric Clinics of North America* 1996; 19: 41-53.

[82] Serretti A, Jori MC, Casadei G, Ravizza L, Smeraldi E, Akiskal H. Delineating psychopathologic clusters within dysthymia: a study of 512 out-patients without major depression. *Journal of Affective Disorders* 1999; 56: 17-25.

[83] Hamilton M. The assessment of anxiety states by rating. *Brit J Med Psychol* 1959; 32: 50-55.

[84] Serretti A, Macciardi F, Smeraldi E. Dopamine Receptor D2 Ser Cys311 Variant Associated With Disorganized Symptomatology of Schizophrenia. *Schizophrenia Research* 1998; 34: 207-210.

[85] Serretti A, Macciardi F, Catalano M, Bellodi L, Smeraldi E. Genetic variants of dopamine receptor D4 and psychopathology. *Schizophrenia Bulletin* 1999; 25: 609-618.

[86] Serretti A, Lilli R, Lorenzi C, Smeraldi E. Further evidence supporting the association between the Dopamine receptor D2 Ser/Cys311 variant and disorganized symptomatology of schizophrenia. *Schizophrenia Research* 2000; 43: 161-162.

[87] Serretti A, Lattuada E, Lorenzi C, Lilli R, Smeraldi E. Dopamine receptor D2 ser/cys 311 variant is associated with delusion and disorganization symptomatology in major psychoses. *Molecular Psychiatry* 2000; 5: 270-274.

[88] Serretti A, Lilli R, Lorenzi C, Lattuada E, Smeraldi E. DRD4 exon 3 variants associated with delusional symptomatology in major psychoses: A study on 2,011 affected subjects. *Am J Med Genet* 2001; 105: 283-90.

[89] Kraepelin E. Psychiatrie (8° ed). Leipzig: Johann Ambrosius Barth, 1909-1915.

[90] Roose S, Glassman A. Delusional depression. In: Georgotas A, Cancro R, eds: *Depression and Mania*. New York: Elsevier Science Publishing Co Inc, 1988, pp 76-85.

[91] Goodwin F, Jamison K. Manic-depressive illness. New York: Oxford University Press, 1990.

[92] Bierkowska B, Rybakowski J. Rapid cycling bipolar affective illness. *Psychiatr Pol* 1994; 28: 443-54.

[93] Tondo L, Baldessarini RJ. Rapid cycling in women and men with bipolar manic-depressive disorders. *Am J Psychiatry* 1998; 155: 1434-6.

[94] Serretti A, Lattuada E, Cusin C, Gasperini M, Smeraldi E. Clinical and demographical features of psychotic and nonpsychotic depression. *Comprehensive Psychiatry* 1999; 40: 358-362.

[95] Lattuada E, Serretti A, Cusin C, Gasperini M, Macciardi F, Smeraldi E. Symptomatologic analysis of psychotic and non-psychotic depression. *Journal of Affective Disorders* 1999; 54: 183-187.

[96] Serretti A, Mandelli L, Lattuada L, Cusin C, Smeraldi E. Clinical and demographic features of mood disorder subtypes. *Psychiatry Research* 2002; 112: 195-210.

[97] Serretti A, Mandelli L, Lattuada E, Smeraldi E. Rapid cycling mood disorder: Clinical and demographic features. *Compr Psychiatry* 2002; 43: 336-43.

[98] Serretti A, Olgiati P. Patterns of manic symptoms in bipolar I, bipolar II and major depressive disorders. *Journal of affective disorders* in press.

[99] Endicott J, Spitzer R. A diagnostic interview: the schedule for affective disorders and schizophrenia. *Archives of General Psychiatry* 1978; 35: 837-844.

[100] Spitzer RL, Williams JBW, Gibbon M, First MB. Structured Clinical Interview for DSM-III-R, Version 1.0 (SCID). Washington, DC: American Psychiatric Press, 1990.

[101] Winokur G, Crowe RR. Bipolar illness. The sex-polarity effect in affectively ill family members. *Arch Gen Psychiatry* 1983; 40: 57-8.

[102] Rouillon F. Epidemiology of bipolar disorders. Current studies. *Encephale* 1997; 23 Spec No 1: 7-11.

[103] Cvjetkovic-Bosnjak M. [Clinical characteristics of unipolar and bipolar depression]. *Med Pregl* 1998; 51: 329-32.

[104] Hendrick V, Altshuler LL, Gitlin MJ, Delrahim S, Hammen C. Gender and bipolar illness. *J Clin Psychiatry* 2000; 61: 393-6; quiz 397.

[105] Benazzi F. Prevalence of bipolar II disorder in outpatient depression: a 203-case study in private practice. *J Affect Disord* 1997; 43: 163-6.

[106] Benazzi F. Prevalence of bipolar II disorder in atypical depression. *Eur Arch Psychiatry Clin Neurosci* 1999; 249: 62-5.

[107] Bourgeois M, Martinez R, Degeilh B, Peyre F. Predictive factors in the bipolarization of depressive disorders. *Encephale* 1988; 14: 353-7.

[108] Benazzi F. Depression with DSM-IV atypical features: a marker for bipolar II disorder. *Eur Arch Psychiatry Clin Neurosci* 2000; 250: 53-5.

[109] Perugi G, Akiskal HS, Lattanzi L, Cecconi D, Mastrocinque C, Patronelli A, Vignoli S, Bemi E. The high prevalence of "soft" bipolar (II) features in atypical depression. *Compr Psychiatry* 1998; 39: 63-71.

[110] Dunner DL. Sub-types of bipolar affective disorder with particular regard to bipolar II. *Psychiatr Dev* 1983; 1: 75-85.

[111] Andreasen NC, Grove WM, Coryell WH, Endicott J, Clayton PJ. Bipolar versus unipolar and primary versus secondary affective disorder: which diagnosis takes precedence? *J Affect Disord* 1988; 15: 69-80.

[112] Kupfer DJ, Carpenter LL, Frank E. Is bipolar II a unique disorder? *Compr Psychiatry* 1988; 29: 228-36.

[113] Sands JR, Harrow M. Vulnerability to psychosis in unipolar major depression: is premorbid functioning involved? *American Journal of Psychiatry* 1995; 152: 1009-1015.

[114] Coryell W, Winokur G, Shea T, Maser J, Endicott J, Akiskal H. The long-term stability of depressive subtypes. *American Journal of Psychiatry* 1994; 151: 199-204.

[115] Coryell W. Psychotic Depression. *Journal of Clinical Psychiatry* 1996; 57 Sup.3: 27-31.

[116] Coryell W, Leon A, Winokur G, Endicott J, Keller M, Akiskal HS, Solomon D. Importance of psychotic features to long-term course in major depressive disorder. *American Journal of Psychiatry* 1996; 153: 483-489.

[117] Parker G, Hadzi-Pavlovic D, Hickie I, Mitchell P, Wilhelm K, Brodaty H, Boyce P, Eyers K, Pedic F. Psychotic depression: a review and clinical experience. *Australian & New Zeland Journal of Psychiatry* 1991; 25: 169-180.

[118] Bellini L, Gatti F, Gasperini M, Smeraldi E. A comparison between delusional and non-delusional depressives. *Journal of Affective Disorders* 1992; 25: 129-138.

[119] Peselow ED, Dunner DL, Fieve RR, Deutsch SI, Rubinstein ME. Age of onset of affective illness. *Psychiatr Clin (Basel)* 1982; 15: 124-32.

[120] Winokur G, Coryell W, Endicott J, Akiskal H. Further distinctions between manic-depressive illness (bipolar disorder) and primary depressive disorder (unipolar depression). *American Journal of Psychiatry* 1993; 150: 1176-81.

[121] McMahon FJ, Stine OC, Chase GA, Meyers DA, Simpson SG, DePaulo JR, Jr. Influence of clinical subtype, sex, and lineality on age at onset of major affective disorder in a family sample. *Am J Psychiatry* 1994; 151: 210-5.

[122] Angst J, Preisig M. Course of a clinical cohort of unipolar, bipolar and schizoaffective patients. Results of a prospective study from 1959 to 1985. *Schweiz Arch Neurol Psychiatr* 1995; 146: 5-16.

[123] Benazzi F. Atypical depression in private practice depressed outpatients: a 203-case study. *Compr Psychiatry* 1999; 40: 80-3.

[124] Benazzi F. Prevalence and clinical features of atypical depression in depressed outpatients: a 467-case study. *Psychiatry Res* 1999; 86: 259-65.

[125] Akiskal HS, Walker P, Puzantian VR, King D, Rosenthal TL, Dranon M. Bipolar outcome in the course of depressive illness. Phenomenologic, familial, and pharmacologic predictors. *J Affect Disord* 1983; 5: 115-28.

[126] Weissman MM, Prusoff BA, Merikangas KR. Is delusional depression related to bipolar disorder? *American Journal of Psychiatry* 1984; 141: 892-893.

[127] Allilaire JF, Hantouche EG, Sechter D, Bourgeois ML, Azorin JM, Lancrenon S, Chatenet-Duchene L, Akiskal HS. Frequency and clinical aspects of bipolar II disorder in a French multicenter study: EPIDEP. *Encephale* 2001; 27: 149-58.

[128] Benazzi F. Major depressive episodes with hypomanic symptoms are common among depressed outpatients. *Compr Psychiatry* 2001; 42: 139-43.

[129] Dunner DL, Gershon ES, Goodwin FK. Heritable factors in the severity of affective illness. *Biol Psychiatry* 1976; 11: 31-42.

[130] Goldring N, Fieve RR. Attempted suicide in manic-depressive disorder. *Am J Psychother* 1984; 38: 373-83.

[131] Rihmer Z, Pestality P. Bipolar II disorder and suicidal behavior. *Psychiatr Clin North Am* 1999; 22: 667-73, ix-x.

[132] Coryell W, Endicott J, Keller M. Rapidly cycling affective disorder. Demographics, diagnosis, family history, and course. *Archives of General Psychiatry* 1992; 49: 126-31.

[133] Lish JD, Gyulai L, Resnick SM, Kirtland A, Amsterdam JD, Whybrow PC, Price RA. A family history study of rapid-cycling bipolar disorder. *Psychiatry Res* 1993; 48: 37-46.

[134] Persad E, Oluboka OJ, Sharma V, Mazmanian D, Kueneman K. The phenomenon of rapid cycling in bipolar mood disorders: a review. *Can J Psychiatry* 1996; 41: 23-7.

[135] Robb JC, Young LT, Cooke RG, Joffe RT. Gender differences in patients with bipolar disorder influence outcome in the medical outcomes survey (SF-20) subscale scores. *J Affect Disord* 1998; 49: 189-93.

[136] Kilzieh N, Akiskal HS. Rapid-cycling bipolar disorder. An overview of research and clinical experience. *Psychiatr Clin North Am* 1999; 22: 585-607.

[137] Shelton MD, Calabrese JR. Current Concepts in Rapid Cycling Bipolar Disorder. *Curr Psychiatry Rep* 2000; 2: 310-315.

[138] Akiskal HS, Bourgeois ML, Angst J, Post R, Moller H, Hirschfeld R. Re-evaluating the prevalence of and diagnostic composition within the broad clinical spectrum of bipolar disorders. *J Affect Disord* 2000; 59 Suppl 1: S5-S30.

[139] APA. Guidelines for assessing the decision-making capacities of potential research subjects with cognitive impairment. American Psychiatric Association. *Am J Psychiatry* 1998; 155: 1649-50.

[140] Kessing LV, Andersen PK, Mortensen PB, Bolwig TG. Recurrence in affective disorder. I. Case register study. *British Journal of Psychiatry* 1998; 172: 23-8.

[141] Angst J. The course of affective disorders. *Psychopathology* 1986; 19: 47-52.

[142] Kessing LV. Recurrence in affective disorder. II. Effect of age and gender. *British Journal of Psychiatry* 1998; 172: 29-34.

[143] Keller MB. The course of manic-depressive illness. *Journal of Clinical Psychiatry* 1988; 49: 4-7.

[144] Tohen M, Waternaux CM, Tsuang MT. Outcome in Mania. A 4-year prospective follow-up of 75 patients utilizing survival analysis. *Archives of General Psychiatry* 1990; 47: 1106-11.

[145] Giles DE, Jarrett RB, Biggs MM, Guzick DS, Rush AJ. Clinical predictors of recurrence in depression. *American Journal of Psychiatry* 1989; 146: 764-7.

[146] Hughes DC, DeMallie D, Blazer DG. Does age make a difference in the effects of physical health and social support on the outcome of a major depressive episode? *American Journal of Psychiatry* 1993; 150: 728-33.

[147] Hughes SR, Khorkova O, Goyal S, Knaeblein J, Heroux J, Riedel NG, Sahasrabudhe S. Alpha2-macroglobulin associates with beta-amyloid peptide and prevents fibril formation. *Proc Natl Acad Sci U S A* 1998; 95: 3275-80.

[148] Keitner GI, Ryan CE, Miller IW, Zlotnick C. Psychosocial factors and the long-term course of major depression. *Journal of Affective Disorders* 1997; 44: 57-67.

[149] Winokur G, Kadrmas A. A polyepisodic course in bipolar illness: possible clinical relationships. *Comprehensive Psychiatry* 1989; 30: 121-7.

[150] Winokur G, Coryell W, Keller M, Endicott J, Akiskal H. A prospective follow-up of patients with bipolar and primary unipolar affective disorder. *Archives of General Psychiatry* 1993; 50: 457-65.

[151] Neuman RJ, Geller B, Rice JP, Todd RD. Increased prevalence and earlier onset of mood disorders among relatives of prepubertal versus adult probands. *Journal of the American Academy of Child & Adolescent Psychiatry* 1997; 36: 466-73.

[152] Mueller TI, Lavori PW, Keller MB, Swartz A, Warshaw M, Hasin D, Coryell W, Endicott J, Rice J, Akiskal H. Prognostic effect of the variable course of alcoholism on the 10-year course of depression. *American Journal of Psychiatry* 1994; 151: 701-6.

[153] Cusin C, Serretti A, Lattuada E, Mandelli L, Smeraldi E. Impact of clinical variables on illness time course in mood disorders. *Psychiatry Research* 2000; 97: 217-227.

[154] Platz C, Kendell RE. A matched-control follow-up and family study of 'puerperal psychoses'. *Br J Psychiatry* 1988; 153: 90-4.

[155] Bell AJ, Land NM, Milne S, Hassanyeh F. Long-term outcome of post-partum psychiatric illness requiring admission. *J Affect Disord* 1994; 31: 67-70.

[156] Robling SA, Paykel ES, Dunn VJ, Abbott R, Katona C. Long-term outcome of severe puerperal psychiatric illness: a 23 year follow-up study. *Psychol Med* 2000; 30: 1263-71.

[157] MacQueen GM, Young LT, Joffe RT. A review of psychosocial outcome in patients with bipolar disorder. *Acta Psychiatr Scand* 2001; 103: 163-70.

[158] Stefos G, Bauwens F, Staner L, Pardoen D, Mendlewicz J. Psychosocial predictors of major affective recurrences in bipolar disorder: a 4-year longitudinal study of patients on prophylactic treatment. *Acta Psychiatrica Scandinavica* 1996; 93: 420-6.

[159] Bauwens F, Pardoen D, Staner L, Dramaix M, Mendlewicz J. Social adjustment and the course of affective illness: a one-year controlled longitudinal study involving bipolar and unipolar outpatients. *Depress Anxiety* 1998; 8: 50-7.

[160] Reimherr FW, Strong RE, Marchant BK, Hedges DW, Wender PH. Factors affecting return of symptoms 1 year after treatment in a 62-week controlled study of fluoxetine in major depression. *J Clin Psychiatry* 2001; 62 Suppl 22: 16-23.

[161] Shapira B, Zislin J, Gelfin Y, Osher Y, Gorfine M, Souery D, Mendlewicz J, Lerer B. Social adjustment and self-esteem in remitted patients with unipolar and bipolar affective disorder: a case-control study. *Compr Psychiatry* 1999; 40: 24-30.

[162] Judd LL, Akiskal HS, Zeller PJ, Paulus M, Leon AC, Maser JD, Endicott J, Coryell W, Kunovac JL, Mueller TI, Rice JP, Keller MB. Psychosocial disability during the long-term course of unipolar major depressive disorder. *Arch Gen Psychiatry* 2000; 57: 375-80.

[163] Altshuler LL, Gitlin MJ, Mintz J, Leight KL, Frye MA. Subsyndromal depression is associated with functional impairment in patients with bipolar disorder. *J Clin Psychiatry* 2002; 63: 807-11.

[164] Bauwens F, Tracj A, Pardoen D, Vander Elst M, Mendlewicz J. Social adjustment of remitted Bipolar and Unipolar out-patients. A comparison with age-and sex-matched controls. *Brit J Psychiatry* 1991; 159: 239-244.

[165] Serretti A, Macciardi F, Di Bella D, Catalano M, Smeraldi E. Self-Esteem in Remitted Patients With Mood Disorders Is Not Associated With the Dopamine Receptor D4 and the Serotonin Transporter Genes. *Psychiatry Research* 1998; 80: 137-144.

[166] Weissman M, Paykel E, Siegel R, Klerman G. The social role performance of depressed women: comparison with a normal group. *Am J Orthopsychiatry* 1971; 41: 390-415.

[167] Harrow M, Goldberg JF, Grossman LS, Meltzer HY. Outcome in manic disorders. A naturalistic follow-up study. *Archives of General Psychiatry* 1990; 47: 665-71.

[168] Coryell W, Scheftner W, Keller M, Endicott J, Maser J, Klerman G. The enduring psychosocial consequences of mania and depression. *American Journal of Psychiatry* 1993; 150: 720-7.

[169] Serretti A, Cavallini MC, Macciardi F, Namia C, Franchini L, Souery D, Lipp O, Bauwens F, Smeraldi E, Mendlewicz J. Social adjustment and self-esteem in remitted patients with mood disorders. *European Psychiatry* 1999; 14: 137-42.

[170] Rosenberg M. The measurement of self-esteem: *Society and the Adolescent Self-Image*: Princeton University Press, 1965, pp 16-36.

[171] Pardoen D, Bauwens F, Tracy A, Martin F, Mendlewicz J. Self esteem in recovered Bipolar and Unipolar outpatients. *Br J Psychiatry* 1993; 163: 755-62.

[172] Brown RP, Frances A, Kocsis JH, Mann JJ. Psychotic vs. nonpsychotic depression: comparison of treatment response. *Journal of Nervous & Mental Disease* 1982; 170: 635-7.

[173] Rothschild AJ, Samson JA, Bond TC, Luciana MM, Schildkraut JJ, Schatzberg AF. Hypothalamic-pituitary-adrenal axis activity and 1-year outcome in depression. *Biological Psychiatry* 1993; 34: 392-400.

[174] Coryell W, Keller M, Lavori P, Endicott J. Affective syndromes, psychotic features, and prognosis. I. Depression. *Archives of General Psychiatry* 1990; 47: 651-7.

[175] Strakowski SM, Keck PE, McElroy SL, West SA, Sax KW, Hawkins JM, Kmetz GF, Upadhyaya VH, Tugrul KC, Bourne ML. Twelve-Month Outcome After a First Hospitalization For Affective Psychosis. *Archives of General Psychiatry* 1998; 55: 49-55.

[176] Serretti A, Lattuada E, Smeraldi E. Outcome of affective psychosis. *Depression and Anxiety* 1999; 10: 50-54.

[177] Weissman MM, Bothwell S. Assessment of social adjustment by patient self-report. *Archives of General Psychiatry* 1976; 33: 1111-5.

[178] Maes M, Meltzer HY. The serotonin hypothesis of major depression. In: Bloom FE, Kupfer DJ, eds: *Psychopharmacology: The fourth generation of progress.* New York: Raven Press, 1995, pp 933-944.

[179] Collier D, Stöber G, Li T, Heils A, Catalano M, Di Bella D, Arranz M, Murray R, Vallada H, Bengel D, Müller-Reible C, Roberts G, Smeraldi E, Kirov G, Sham P, Lesh P. A novel functional polymorphism within the promoter of the serotonin transporter gene: possible role in susceptibility to affective disorders. *Molecular Psychiatry* 1996; 1: 453-460.

[180] Orsini A. Antidepressant responses and segregation analyses in affective families. In: Racagni G, Smeraldi E, eds: *Anxious Depression: assessment and treatment.* New York: Raven Press, 1987.

[181] Smeraldi E, Petroccione A, Gasperini M, Macciardi F, Orsini A, Kidd KK. Outcomes on lithium treatment as a tool for genetic studies in affective disorders. *Journal of Affective Disorders* 1984; 6: 139-51.

[182] Franchini L, Serretti A, Gasperini M, Smeraldi E. Familial concordance of fluvoxamine response as a tool for differentiating mood disorder pedigrees. *Journal of Psychiatric Research* 1998; 32: 255-259.

[183] Serretti A, Franchini L, Gasperini M, Rampoldi R, Smeraldi E. Mode of inheritance in mood disorders families according to fluvoxamine response. *Acta Psychiatrica Scandinavica* 1998; 98: 443-450.

[184] Serretti A, Lilli R, Smerladi E. Pharmacogenetics in affective disorders. *European Jourmal of Pharmacology* 2002; 438: 117-128.
[185] Shou M. Forty years of lithium treatment. *Archives of General Psychiatry* 1997; 54: 9-13.
[186] Baldessarini RJ, Tondo L, Hennen J. Effects of lithium treatment and its discontinuation in bipolar manic-depressive disorders. *Journal of Clinical Psychiatry* 1999; 60: 77-84.
[187] Coppen A. Lithium in unipolar depression and the prevention of suicide. *Journal of Clinical Psychiatry* 2000; 61: 52-56.
[188] Maj M. The impact of lithium prophylaxis on the course of bipolar disorder: a review of the research evidence. *Bipolar Disorders* 2000; 2: 93-101.
[189] Baldessarini RJ, Tondo L. Does lithium treatment still work? Evidence of stable responses over three decades. *Arch Gen Psychiatry* 2000; 57: 187-90.
[190] Silverstone T, Romans S. Long term treatment of bipolar disorder. *Drugs* 1996; 51: 367-82.
[191] Goldberg JF, Harrow M, Leon AC. Lithium treatment of bipolar affective disorders under naturalistic followup conditions. *Psychopharmacology Bulletin* 1996; 32: 47-54.
[192] Coryell W, Winokur G, Solomon D, Shea T, Leon A, Keller M. Lithium and recurrence in a long-term follow-up of bipolar affective disorder. *Psychological Medicine* 1997; 27: 281-287.
[193] Abou-Saleh MT, Coppen A. Who responds to prophylactic lithium? *Journal of Affective Disorders* 1986; 10: 115-25.
[194] Abou-Saleh MT. Who responds to prophylactic lithium therapy? *British Journal of Psychiatry* 1993; (suppl 21): 20-6.
[195] Gitlin MJ, Alshuler LL. Unanswered questions, unknown future for one of our oldest medications. *Archives of General Psychiatry* 1997; 54: 21-23.
[196] Gershon S, Soares JC. Current therapeutic profile of lithium. *Archives of General Psychiatry* 1997; 54: 16-20.
[197] Grof P, Alda M, Grof E, Zvolsky P, Walsh M. Lithium response and genetics of affective disorders. *Journal of Affective Disorders* 1994; 32: 85-95.
[198] Yazici O, Kora K, Ucok A, Tunali D, Turan N. Predictors of lithium prophylaxis in bipolar patients. *J Affect Disord* 1999; 55: 133-42.
[199] Maj M, Arena F, Lovero N, Pirozzi R, Kemali D. Factors associated with response to lithium prophylaxis in DSM III major depression and bipolar disorder. *Pharmacopsychiatry* 1985; 18: 309-13.
[200] Serretti A, Lattuada E, Franchini L, Smeraldi E. Melancholic features and response to lithium prophylaxis in mood disorders. *Depression and Anxiety* 2000; 11: 73-79.
[201] Ananth J, Engelsmann F, Kiriakos R, Kolivakis T. Prediction of lithium response. *Acta Psychiatrica Scandinavica* 1979; 60: 279-86.
[202] Angst J, Weis P, Grof P, Baastrup PC, Schou M. Lithium prophylaxis in recurrent affective disorders. *Br J Psychiatry* 1970; 116: 604-14.
[203] Rosenthal NE, Rosenthal LN, Stallone F, Fleiss J, Dunner DL, Fieve RR. Psychosis as a predictor of response to lithium maintenance treatment in bipolar affective disorder. *Journal of Affective Disorders* 1979; 1: 237-45.

[204] Abou-Saleh MT, Coppen AJ. Predictors of long-term outcome of mood disorders on prophylactic lithium. *Lithium* 1990; 1: 27-35.

[205] Viguera AC, Tondo L, Baldessarini RJ. Sex differences in response to lithium treatment. *American Journal of Psychiatry* 2000; 157: 1509-1511.

[206] Grof P, Hux M, Grof E, Arato M. Prediction of response to stabilizing lithium treatment. *Pharmacopsychiatria* 1983; 16: 195-200.

[207] Staner L, Tracy A, Dramaix M, Genevrois C, Vanderelst M, Vilane A, Bauwens F, Pardoen D, Mendlewicz J. Clinical and psychosocial predictors of recurrence in recovered bipolar and unipolar depressives: a one-year controlled prospective study. *Psychiatry Research* 1997; 69: 39-51.

[208] Maj M, Pirozzi R, Starace F. Previous pattern of course of the illness as a predictor of response to lithium prophylaxis in bipolar patients. *Journal of Affective Disorders* 1989; 17: 237-41.

[209] O'Connell RA, Mayo JA, Flatow L, Cuthbertson B, O. Brien BE. Outcome of bipolar disorder on long-term treatment with lithium. *British Journal of Psychiatry* 1991; 159: 123-9.

[210] Maj M, Pirozzi R, Magliano L, Bartoli L. Long-term outcome of lithium prophylaxis in bipolar disorder: a 5-year prospective study of 402 patients at a lithium clinic. *American Journal of Psychiatry* 1998; 155: 30-5.

[211] Tondo L, Baldessarini RJ, Hennen J, Floris G. Lithium maintenance treatment of depression and mania in bipolar I and bipolar II disorder. *American Journal of Psychiatry* 1998; 155: 638-645.

[212] Maj M. Long-term impact of lithium prophylaxis on the course of bipolar disorder. In: Christodoulou G, Lecic-Tosevski D, Kontaxakis VP, eds: *Issues in Preventive Psychiatry*. Basel: Karger, 1999, pp 79-82.

[213] Franchini L, Zanardi R, Smeraldi E, Gasperini M. Early onset of lithium prophylaxis as a predictor of good long-term outcome. *European Archives of Psychiatry & Clinical Neuroscience* 1999; 249: 227-230.

[214] Gasperini M, Scherillo P, Manfredonia MG, Franchini L, Smeraldi E. A study of relapses in subjects with mood disorder on lithium treatment. *European Neuropsychopharmacology* 1993; 3: 103-10.

[215] Wehr TA, Goodwin FK. Can antidepressants cause mania and worsen the course of affective illness? *American Journal of Psychiatry* 1987; 144: 1403-11.

In: Trends in Bipolar Disorder Research
Editor: Malcomb R. Brown, pp. 33-64

ISBN: 1-59454-060-8

Chapter 2

BIPOLAR DISORDER: SELF-INTERESTED NETWORKS, OBSESSIONS, AND CYCLING[1]

James Brody[2]
Editor, Evolutionary Psychology & Clinical Sociobiology, Behavior on Line

INTRODUCTION

Bipolar disorder (BPD) devastates its carriers and their families while puzzling employers and resisting the best efforts of clinicians and law enforcement officials. There, however, has been little progress in treating it since the introduction of lithium. Statistical physics now offers dynamic models for the behavior of emergent networks, oscillators, and phase transitions that parallel the mood changes and obsessions that we observe in BPD.

Emergent networks are found widely in nature, including within living cells and clumps of them. Life evolved in the midst of network phenomena and our minds have been selected to align with them. Neurons in the brain connect not only under genetic guidance but also according to network rules and the structure of those connections bias the network toward certain kinds of behavior. Thus, driven thoughts and cycling moods fit nicely onto an emergent networks platform, one that extends the schema developed by Hebb and Edelman.

We can expect networks to vary in dominance from moment to moment as we dream, play, strive, or procreate. Networked sequences of thought and action that contribute to our survival and reproductive success, however, become liabilities when they take complete charge of us. We then take on expansive goals as we become elated or unload them when we become despondent. In either state, we neglect the small clustered tasks of daily living. It is also likely that any one expression of BPD may arise from infection, genetic variation, trauma, or some mix of the three that simplify the network properties in a particular mind.

Emergent networks, oscillatory phenomena, and phase transitions are closely linked to each other in mathematics, physics, and biology. Pendulums, crickets, and even NASCAR drivers satisfy conditions for the synchronization of independent oscillators: (1) there must be

---

[2] James Brody, Ph.D. 1262 West Bridge St. Spring City, PA, 19475 Jbrody@compuserve.com. www.behavior.net/forums/evolutionary

a fundamental on-off pattern, (2) the oscillators must be weakly linked, and (3) the oscillators must be very similar to each other (Strogatz, 1993). Clumps of neurons also satisfy these conditions. *Bipolar obsessions and cycling, thus, appear to be almost inevitable and the challenge may be to discover not why they occur but why they don't.*

Further, a neural assembly can assume living properties that meet its own needs rather than those of its carrier. Living organizations accomplish work, reproduce, and arrange environments to suit their own interests. Natural selection occurs when neural organizations compete within their carrier for limited attention, time, and wealth: the most active suppresses the less active and gains influence. The conscious impact can be that of an invader that takes over the mind of its host, commandeers resources, and resists suppression or dispersal while it grows and reproduces. We have seen these "selfish" effects with genes; we also find them in mental organizations that live off of us.

These ideas are discussed in non-technical language with special reference to BPD but could apply to obsessive compulsive disorder, panic, eating disorders, hypochondria, depression, drug dependency, personality disorders, and even hypnotic states, love, religious ecstasy, or scientific insights. There are implications from network theory for both medicinal and cognitive-behavior interventions.

THE IMPORTANCE OF A DIFFERENT METAPHOR

Richard Feynman showed us, as much as he told us, a great deal about quantum physics. His father understood mathematics as patterns and drilled "Ritty" with colored tiles in pattern-matching tasks (Gleick, 1992). The younger Feynman responded to the older one's demonstrations, made lots of drawings at physics meetings, and eventually shared a Nobel Prize with Julian Schwinger and Tomonaga Shin'ichiro in 1965 for their unified theory of quantum electrodynamics. Near the end of his life, Feynman dipped an O-ring into ice water on national television to show why *Challenger* exploded during launch.[3] Whether you attribute Feynman's imagery to his father's genes or lessons, Feynman reminds us that models influence the thoughts that we have and share. Although Feynman died in 1988, his lessons are still with us. Recent discoveries about emergent networks now give us the luxury of a different model for the excesses that we find in BPD.

High self esteem, increased goal-directed activity, excessive pleasurable activities, and heightened word flow characterize mania; bipolar disorders compound these features with intense mood changes of varied duration and sometimes a heightened risk for suicide. Deterioration in executive functions (behaviors that manage other behaviors, Brody, 2001) and the growth of deviant beliefs (delusions, grandiosity, ideas of influence, paranoia, and extreme religiosity) are not unusual: indeed, either factor can amplify the others.

There are strong associations between BPD and erratic school careers and employment and marital difficulties. There are overlaps with eating disorders, attention-deficit, hyperactivity disorder, panic, social phobia, and substance abuse (*American Psychiatric Association*, 1994).[4] There are also aspects of BPD that resemble the repetitive habits that we

---

[3] Feynman, often a happy manic, cracked safes at Los Alamos, played the bongos, joked, and drew nudes of women that he picked up in bars! When an adolescent, he paid his little sister four cents per week as his lab assistant, letting her shock herself while his friends watched.

[4] The International Society for Affective Disorders lists 68 conditions of interest to researchers in BPD.

find in obsessive-compulsive disorder, depression, phobias, anxiety reactions, and even some addictions. BPD also occurs in varied intensities: that is, clinic populations differ only in degree from those who avoid hospitalization and are either uncomfortable with themselves or comfortable with themselves but miserable for everyone around them. In regard to preoccupation and overt behavior, manic and bipolar individuals do the things customary to human nature and for which we find equivalents in other species but BPD means that we do them in a more immediate, extreme fashion.

Network theory implies that repetitive behaviors may depend on one foundation. Emergent networks align with our common sense but the research methods, supported by many international teams with advanced calculus and electronic simulations, can be as difficult as analyses of enzyme cofactors and rate constants in pharmacology or, for that matter, epidemiological meta-analyses in psychiatry. This chapter draws material from three disciplines: network physics, psychiatry, and cognitive-behavior therapy but it is written so that specialists from any one of them will not get lost in the other two. The relatively new tool of network theory has features that align with common sense, describe the characteristics of bipolar disorder, and help us to explore new ways to organize our thoughts about this affliction and our tactics for changing its course.

BAMBI LOVED A BASEBALL PLAYER[5]

"I'm sick of being this way. I wanted to die last night. DO something!"

Bambi spent scarce dollars in order to attend major league games where she enjoyed attention from the other fans, players, ticket-takers, parking attendants, and even the hot dog vendor. The home team during warm-up threw the ball to her 12 year old son more than they threw it to the sons of less glamorous mothers. She most sought recognition, however, from a third baseman and she crashed into depression and panic when he ignored her or she imagined that he might be homosexual or living happily with a younger woman. Her irritability soared when her two children made her stay home. She sometimes raged when her husband tried to converse with her.

Theologians might find Bambi "possessed" and she would not argue with them: "Thoughts just take over my mind."[6] Mental health clinicians find her obsessed and manic, diagnoses often made when pleasures and annoyances grow too large and swamp our other tasks. Clergy or counselor would expect her to mute her passions in favor of her children's interests and, by one schedule or another, restrict her opportunities for mischief. We would also risk making her sleepy, pimpled, or fat with mood stabilizers even though she treasured her energy level, perfect complexion, and size 4 figure.

Like most of us, she preferred possession to medicine and wanted our help but on her terms that, ironically, protected her obsession. It was too much fun to give up. Another irony: her quest competed with her ties to other members of her family and her quest became a more immediate cage than was her marriage. A third irony: the metaphor that she was inhabited by

---

[5] All personal names were changed for this chapter.

[6] Archy-the-cockroach said about a moth who incinerated himself on a cigar lighter: "...i would rather have half the happiness and twice the longevity but at the same time i wish there was something i wanted as badly as he wanted to fry himself." (Marquis, 1973, p 108).

a demon may be a useful one. Ideas may be planted by genetic propensities (Plomin, DeFries, McClearn, & Rutter, 1977; Scarr & McCartney, 1983; Plomin, DeFries, McClearn, & McGuffin, 2000; Barkow, Cosmides, & Tooby, 1992; Rowe, 1994) and feed on circumstance to arrange our thoughts and collections in ways that treat us, their carrier, as an environment to be harvested. In extreme cases, paranoid individuals not only look for scrutiny but elicit it, obsessive-compulsives find dirt that is personally objectionable, and manic-depressives discover reasons to be elated or discouraged.

Bambi is important not only as a model for obsessive behavior but also for the many normal souls who, driven by their careers and hobbies, seek matching quests when they ask a prospective mate, "What do you like to do?" And obsessions sometimes pay their rent in surprising ways that lead to innovation, wealth, and greatness. Driven individuals are up late and talk about, with, or to their passions or deities; they also pace laboratory halls at midnight, sometimes with a roll of amino acid data in one pocket and a pint of scotch in another but mumble or shout to their dreams. Whether driven by fun or fear, we each feed our demons and every one of them thrives within the structures and fences of emergent networks.

TINKER TOYS: NETWORKS, EVOLUTION, AND MENTAL ORGANIZATIONS

A Short History of Networks and Reentrant Signaling

Theory and research in emergent networks find similar rules in an extraordinary array of events, rules that rest on statistical payoffs and lead to empirical study by a multitude of independent investigators. Their work is summarized by Gleick (1987), Waldrop (1992), Kauffman (1993, 1995, 2000), Barabási (2002), Buchanan (2002), Strogatz (2003), and Watts (2003, 2004). The implications are substantial for the disciplines of neurology, psychology, psychiatry, sociology, ecology, and evolutionary biology.

Networks consist of nodes and the connections between them, called links (Barabási, 2002). The Hungarian mathematicians Paul Erdös and Alfred Rényi began the systematic study of *random* networks that are static and the connectivity between nodes may be represented by a bell curve with a mean, range, and standard deviation. This chapter, however, is concerned exclusively with *nonrandom, emergent networks*. In contrast to random networks, emergent networks grow (therefore, “emergent”) and incoming nodes are preferentially attached to nodes that already have the most links (therefore, “nonrandom”). In Barabási’s terms, “the rich get richer.” The connectivity of emergent networks is characterized by straight lines on log-log paper: there are a few nodes with many connections but many nodes with only one or two.

Networks often follow patterns similar to those that we once made with *Tinker Toys*. Some spools are more important than others and some of them grow or shrink in importance as they acquire connections to other spools. *Similar functional relationships occur between the members of an emergent network regardless of the nature of those members.* That is, emergent networks are observed in cellular biochemistry, assemblies of genes, scientific citation patterns, electrical power grid connections, and the ties between actors, computer scientists, mathematicians, or physicists: a few key individuals link vast numbers of their peers who are often not directly connected to each other. Granovetter (1973) found these relationships in regard to job discovery: most leads come indirectly from the friend of a friend. Not only humans but also insect societies (Fewell, 2003) and even dolphins form emergent networks (Lusseau, 2003).

These organizations have been observed before. In 1926 Alfred Lotka saw them in scientific achievements (Murray, 2003). The great evolutionary biologist, Sewall Wright, noticed clustered networks in the early 1920s: animal breeders separated their stocks according to a specific trait but used periodic crossbreeding to prevent the expression of harmful recessive genes (Provine, 1986/1989; Sagan & Druyan, 1992). (This model also applies to Mayr's concept of "founder effects" wherein isolated small populations of descendants, each from a slightly different ancestor, lead to distinct species [Mayr, 1976]. Periodically break the isolation by means of crossbreeding and each community deviates less from its neighbors.)

Hebb (1949) suggested that reverberating circuits create learning and memory. Other scientists apply similar concepts in order to understand (1) the fact of seamless integration between different sensory qualities of color, shape, shade, and even words and odors and their contexts and (2) how such integration is achieved by widely scattered locations in the brain (Gazzaniga, 1992). Edelman (1987), for example, introduces the concept of "reentrant signaling" between separate communities of neural clusters. Each local neural community both influences and is influenced by other communities that manage a slightly different aspect of a sensation, action, or memory (Edelman, 1999; Gazzaniga, 1992; Tononi, 1994; Sporns, 1994; Singer, 1994; Sacks, 1987, 1992). Injury sometimes leads to perceptual voids because interconnecting axons are sheared and separate the islands.

Network theory provides heuristic insights into these phenomena but with greater detail than was previously available (Barabási, 2002; Buchanan, 2002; Strogatz, 2003; Watts, 2003, 2004). Network insights apply to normal thought as well as to moods and delusions and to our treatments for them, whether traditional, pharmacological, or cognitive-behavior (CBT).

The next sections of this chapter:

- Describe three stages in emergent networks, stages that apply to normal as well as manic thinking,
- Consider the evolutionary foundations for obsessions,
- Present the controversial idea that mental networks show living properties of their own that sometimes work against the interests of their carrier,
- Introduce the concept of oscillating systems as found in physics and biology, and
- Reinterpret our strategies for medication and cognitive-behavior therapy.

There are three broad categories of emergent networks: clustered, hierarchic, and winner-take-all (Barabási, 2002). (I discuss later the possibility that these categories represent developmental stages rather than static endpoints.)

Stages in Networks: Clusters, Hierarchies, and Black Holes

Clusters

Swarms of fireflies and communities of crickets synchronize their activities in much the same ways as humans: through clustering that involves constant monitoring of your neighbor as each of you adjust your conduct to match one another (Barabási, 2002; Buchanan, 2002; Camazine, Deneubourg, Franks, Sneyd, Theraulaz, & Bonabeau, 2001; Strogatz, 2003). There are also intermittent checks of more distant participants. The effect is that of a myopic neighborhood with a few strategic telescopes that look into the next block. In human terms, most of the friends of one individual are usually close friends with each other but clusters are usually connected to other clusters by one member. Thus, a cluster of five friends may connect to five or more other clusters.[7] Watts and Strogatz (1998; Strogatz, 2003) found that adding a few direct links between remote clusters greatly reduces the number of steps required for access between their members. For example, if a New Yorker develops one contact in Tokyo, he also gains second, third, and fourth degree contact with other people in Tokyo. Such sparse connections to distant clusters not only provide huge gains in speed (Watts & Strogatz, 1998) but also in resistance to jamming (Toroczkai & Bassler, 2004).

Clusters have several advantages: (1) each member interacts closely with other cluster members; and (2) there is periodic access to information available from other clusters. By means of linked clusters, a dispersed group of political advocates, a field of crickets, or a swarm of fireflies chant, chirp, or flash in unison.[8] Since these strategies apply to job leads and to research collaboration, they should also apply to college chums, therapists and clients, and even to terrorist cells.

Multitudes of small specialized circuits of sparse connectivity between cluster arrangements could be the organizational trick that allows a mind to detect and adjust to minute environmental changes and to communicate them rapidly to the entire network.[9] Sparse connections between clusters allow the sense of a small neighborhood to continue but provide powerful shortcuts to distant clusters. *Allow one cluster, however, to set the pace for many others and the clusters form a hierarchic network. Let a cluster dominate the entire organization and delusions and black holes appear wherein the dominant cluster suppresses competing activity.* Amplify the rate of onset and intensity of such dominance and an individual's private rituals become public annoyances. On the other hand, diversify the resources for a network and Glenn Close no longer kills Michael Douglas.

---

[7] Granovetter in 1973 used the concept for a model of social contact and job acquisition (Barabási, 2002; Strogatz, 2003). Many sociologists and some biologists (e.g. 6Fewell, 2003, also see review by Segestrale, 2000) view "gene" explanations as inadequate for understanding social behavior but sociology has taken to network theory which is even more reductionist than genetics. See Barabási (2002).

[8] "Flash mobs" are in the news. For example, a group of individuals, linked by cell phones, will converge with little notice on a park or public square, chant in unison, and scatter before authorities arrive. Such demonstrations have influenced elections and have both constructive and destructive potential (Strogatz, 2003). Cluster arrangements can easily produce these outcomes for entertainment or for political and military purposes such as synchronous attacks by homicide bombers.

[9] Kauffman (2000) argues that species and environments tune each other towards stability. Applying Kauffman's idea to delusions suggests that we often bargain with our quests in order to restrain them while we do other things. After all, large delusions, like large mutations, are apt to be maladaptive. Large mutations don't match external environments and large ideas disrupt established organizations within a mind. Mutual stabilization resembles the behavior of tuned oscillators in which drifts in one partner are corrected by adjustments in the second (Strogatz, 1993). Result: there are many of us who are only a little bit crazy.

Hierarchic Networks: The Rich Get Richer

Large things emerge from small things that connect to each other in orderly patterns that form a *hierarchic* network (Barabási, 2002). First, hierarchic networks contain *nodes.* Nodes can be individual people, a business, a web page, or an amino acid. (Nothing precludes a neuron, idea, or concept from being a node.) Second, *links* connect the nodes and may consist of telephone lines, letters, Internet addresses, axons, or exchanges of substrates and products within a cell. (It is also possible for individuals to serve as links between their peers.) Third, nodes with many connections are known as *hubs.* Hubs allow for the rapid collection and distribution of information between any two nodes even when the network becomes quite large. Finally, recruitment to an emergent network is not random: joining a hub appears to vary with the number of links already connected to that hub: thus, "the rich get richer."

Hierarchic networks often fit a *power law* distribution wherein one to three hubs directly connect to about 80% of the other members: the result is that a few individuals have many connections but most have only one to three. (The economist, Vilfredo Pareto, first noticed this pattern in the distribution of wealth in the 1900s: 20% of the individuals often control 80% of the resources.) Power laws are associated with a great deal of system stability because there are very few large scale events such as major earthquakes, species extinctions, wars, or power failures or, for that matter, *grand mal* seizures within the nervous system (Kauffman, 2000). In an arrangement that resembles the sidewalks and streets in human communities, most connections in the brains of *C elegans*, cats, and rhesus link adjacent neurons, many axons travel further but within a brain area, and others make bundles that go to remote areas, a pattern that fits within a power law of infrequent large events buffered by lots of small ones.

Hierarchic organization allows hubs to connect to massive numbers of nodes with little effect on the number of connections needed to get from any one node to any other in the network. For example, forty-three species were mapped for the average number of links between chemicals in their cells. Regardless of species size, the number was approximately three: a few molecules participate in the majority of the reactions but many participate in only one or two (Albert & Barabási, 2001; Barabási, 2002). Species in large ecosystems are generally connected by two links on food chains. About six links separate any two Americans, four to six connect most scientists, and 19 links will take you from any web page to any one of a billion others.

These effects are also seen in language. Chanco and Solé found, based on the 100 million word collection of *British National Corpus*, that 2.67 steps connect any two words in British English. Clustering of word associations was 4000 times greater than random. (See also Strogatz 2003; Albert & Barabási, 2001.) Yook, Jeong, & Barabási (2001) linked words if they were synonyms according to the Merriam-Webster Dictionary. The average path length was 4.5 for a cluster of 22,311 words; the clustering coefficient was 0.7, compared to a value of 0.0006 for a random network of the same size. (See also Albert & Barabási, 2001.)

Winner-Take-All Networks

Sometimes one hub maintains its percentage of influence in a network regardless of competition from new arrivals: the dominant hub cannot be displaced by newcomers. Barabási (2002) compares these hubs to black holes and applies the metaphor to Microsoft's dominance of operating systems for personal computers.[10] Black holes also occur within human minds but we call them delusions, obsessions, or faiths when they involve aliens, ambitions, or gods. Frank & Cook (1995) describe winner-take-all outcomes in contests, tournaments, entertainment and technology: rapid communication and competition bring disproportionate success to the very top contender. Mackay (1841/1980) tells of infectious beliefs in the mid-19th century and earlier that involved alchemy, mesmerism, and financial schemes that rapidly spread across several continents. There are more violent examples of large-scale dominance by a limited set of beliefs and individuals: Hitler's rhetoric prior to and during WW2 was most strident just before he initiated a series of battles (Ertel, 1981; discussed in Eibl-Eibesfeld, 1989. Ertel also found that Nietzsche's writing style was far more dogmatic during a syphilitic attack, perhaps a microcosm in a single mind of the network phenomena that also underlay National Socialism. Strogatz, 1993, also notes similarities between Nazism and network synchronization. Camazine et al, 1991, discuss synchronization mechanisms for large groups of insects and fish).

Evolutionary Roots for Networks and Delusions

Bambi acted in ways typical of many women in the same circumstances (Buss, 2003). Her husband was out of work three times in five years and took a job that paid much less than he once earned. He was depressed about his job and his relationship with Bambi and preferred to be at home rather than out socializing. She, however, wanted a partner who was more lively, assertive, wealthy, and sophisticated: her careful attention to her appearance and hostility to her mate hinted of changes in her reproductive goals even though she consciously wanted no more children. She exercised and regained her bridal weight, stood very erect, wore make-up with range and striking power, reduced her leg veins, bared her midriff, and fretted over the complex highlights of her thick black hair.

Networks and Modularity in the CNS

> "Rather than being a vast, fixed network whose connection strengths change slowly, the effective cortical connectivity is highly dynamic, changing on fast as well as slow time scales. This allows the cortex to be rapidly reconfigured to meet changing computational and communications needs." (Laughlin & Sejnowski, 2003, p. 1873)

"Modularity," the concept that we have not a single mind but many of them, each specialized for a particular survival task, is a controversial topic in philosophy, neurology, and accounts of human evolution (Rose & Rose, 2001; Pinker, 2001; Fodor, 1983, 2001; Cosmides & Tooby, 1992). Emergent networks have properties consistent with a modular mind but also allow for rapidly changing configurations within it. Good health, maturity, learning, social alliances...all contribute to, and reflect, independent but interacting strategies, each one tracking specific environmental and physiological conditions. (These algorithms are known in evolutionary psychology as psychological adaptations. See Barkow et al, 1992.) Clusters allow for sensitive tracking of very specific kinds of information, whether from

[10] "Black hole" is somewhat confusing, sometimes labeled as "the rich get richer" or as one hub's retaining a constant percentage of new links, regardless of competition (Bianconi & Barabási, 2000). The popular implication is that of an organization that consumes all competitors.

external or internal sources. Clustered relationships should also allow autonomous modules that allow frequent mutual influence between immediate neighbors but less frequent communication to neighboring or distant clusters.

Parallel processing allows simultaneous, incompatible routines. Events that look like "reaction formation" in humans are called "displacement" when a rooster scratches dirt and pecks gravel instead of fighting. And given the comparative autonomy of clustered organizations and their unfolding in parallel developmental cascades (Raff, 1996), indecision is to be expected and sometimes resolved by slight, momentary differences in the relative influence of one cluster in comparison with another. "I dunno why I did that" may be literally true. And instances of disconnected, sometimes incompatible behavior sequences should be more likely after injuries that shear long distance connections between related clusters. (See below, "The Dangers When Clusters Merge.")

Our Psychological Adaptations and the Content of Delusions

Natural selection applies not only to physical traits but also to behaviors known as "psychological adaptations" that include stereotypic, efficient, modular strategies for becoming a parent, winning a battle, catching food, escaping an enemy, finding your way, or changing your environment (Hess, 1962; Buss, 1999; Miller, 2000; Barkow, Tooby & Cosmides, 1992; Pinker, 2002; Kauffman, 2000; Turner, 2000; Odling-Smee, Laland, & Feldman, 2003). Metazoans have shared these strategies and elaborated them, perhaps for the last 500 million years (Raff, 1996; Gerhart and Kirschner, 1997; Gould, 2002).

The tactic of picking up small improvements while retaining core genetic, biochemical, and network relationships eventually produced not only hominids but also allowed our discovery of social contracts and refinement of our adherence to them, manufacture of tools, and our more innovative creation of environments that match our nature. Incremental, cumulative mutations in both genes and customs, thus, allow us to have both ancient goals and innovation in the tools that we use to satisfy them (Gerhart and Kirschner, 1997; Kirschner & Gerhart, 1998). Moths might stare at a candle flame but with even greater persistence, Bambi can stare at a baseball player.

Psychological adaptations are conceived as genetically-based and responsive to a combination of external conditions, past successes, and hormonal status but resilient to disruption by social learning. They are thought to be shared by every normal human and to have structural and behavior analogs in species that are closely related to us. They are often fun to do and easy to learn as well as modular and hierarchic (Tooby & Cosmides, 1992; Buss, 1999; Miller, 1999, 2000). For example, our tools for seeing, orienting, grasping, and throwing work together as a targeting mechanism. And despite the complicated nature of these tasks, no one has to pay us males, whether Eskimo, South African, or Brooklynite, to throw rocks at a rabbit or swat a fly in midair. When we are 6 years old, a pretty girl who sits next to us elicits boredom; when we are 14, we glimpse her once at 100 feet and never again get her out of our mind.[11] Thus, psychological adaptations are the things that we humans do

[11] Barkow, et al. (1992) posit a "universal human nature" composed of psychological adaptations. Even breathing, however, is not a universal trait. As in the case of breathing, those of us lacking in, for example, social perception usually depend on other people to compensate for our particular disabilities. We have few sanctions for excessive political skill but plenty for those who are deficient.

when left to ourselves. They also provide content for many of the excesses that we find in bipolar disorder.[12]

Dominance hierarchies have particular relevance to BPD content. They occur widely in nature but network theory lets us see their extra dimensions: we not only enhance, defend, or restore our social standing and the assets that come with it (Price, 1967; Price & Sloman, 1987; Gardner, 1982, 1995; Stevens & Price, 2000; Sloman & Gilbert, 2000) but also have complex subsidiary relationships even with people and creatures who do not beat us up. Ulysses had aspirations for fame, wealth, and territory, so did Klebold and Harris who shot their classmates at Columbine High School. Even our grooming, our quest for attention, and our tendency to flock according to similarity of belief and custom help us to function in networks where we find not only masters and servants but also allies, food, mates, alarms, and protectors. Because of cross-species and cross-cultural similarities, these relationships are thought to be evolutionary products and, therefore, expressions of genetic interests that also conform to network statistics. These survival and reproductive concerns seed one obsession or another that, watered by our circumstances, germinates in accord with the seasons of our life.

Migration: An Evolutionary Foundation of Suicide?

Bipolar disorder entails a heightened risk for suicide which, however, has an uncertain relationship to depression: most depressed people don't kill themselves but if someone does, then we usually look hard, perhaps too hard, for depression. Preliminary research, however, relates suicide to loss of mating opportunities and financial resources (Buss, 1999). Acquisitions of partners and of resources are the twin drivers of Darwinian theory, usually called sexual and natural selection or more simply, "sex and death" (Sterelny & Griffiths, 1999). Analyses of suicide and investigations of specific ones might:

1) Acknowledge the chaotic nature of human events. That is, we explain weather better than we predict it and similarly for choices that people make to kill themselves.
2) View suicide as migratory behavior. Ration food, warmth, water, and companionship and expect wings and restlessness to unfold in the minds of birds and humans.

This view is consistent of our leaving notes, giving away our favorite things as if to instill a continuing social contract with the recipients, and promising to keep in touch from the other side. There is, after all, no point to being remembered if we are not coming back. It is also consistent with our using our cars to start our trip and even a gunshot promises an escape from our self. Suicide should be more frequent in spring and fall when elders and other species also migrate with us. And the migration hypothesis is entirely consistent with religious themes of warriors' paradises, allies that understand and support us, and lands of milk and honey that will also attract many females. (These promises are so tempting that religion denies migratory benefits to anyone who tries to collect them early!)

[12] Gardner (1982; 1995) compared CEOs with hospitalized manics and concluded the groups were qualitatively identical, differing in the intensity of their behavior but not the content of their beliefs. Many have proposed evolutionary mechanisms for human misery (Price, 1967; Gardner, 1982, 1995; Glantz & Pearce, 1989; Wenegrat, 1990; Gilbert & Sloman, 2000; McGuire and Troisi, 1998; Stevens and Price, 2000; Nesse & Williams, 1994; Brody, 2002; Cory & Gardner, 2002) but a conscious neglect of individual genetic variation has so far crippled therapeutic innovation.

Our Constant Companion: Animism

> A small boy spun between the tables around me at a mall food court. He eventually ran head first into a chair and screamed.
> His father turned around and shouted, "Bad chair! Bad, bad chair!"
> The child still cried so I explained, "You yelled at the wrong chair."
> Dad yelled at the correct chair and the youngster stopped crying.

Popper (1992) remarked that scientists generally think about either clocks or clouds. I strongly prefer the former but am here forced to confront the latter. I enjoy empiricism most intensely when I find linear outcomes between causes and consequences. I like not only to know about strings and levers but also to pull and push them. Thus, the next paragraphs annoy me and will annoy other clinicians and scientists, perhaps giving them reasons to discount what I've said about emergent networks. I surrender, however, to animism every day in my small town where we gossip at noon and attribute willfulness to complex outcomes. After all, linearity occupies but a small part of what I experience but fate can be seen everywhere, deviling me from clouds of probabilities and mutually contingent events. It's simpler to blame fate as if it had will than to discover its tools.

Folk religion attributed living properties to seas, trees, and winds: movement implied life and purpose. We still tend to make the same judgments in our casual moments although Newtonian science substituted mathematics, mechanics, measurement, and reductionism for mythological drama. Thus, animism is an old habit in human explanations and science works to be free of it. If, however, emergent networks can take on living properties, we might as well use, both for serendipity and for communication, the same concepts and notations that we apply to the moving things that have skin. It may be that science is ready to cross again, but in the opposite direction and with greater comfort, the frontiers between the living and non living and to consider organizations that have some of both qualities. Animism returns to our drawing rooms but scientists, instead of playwrights, now tell stories about emergent systems that arrange and adapt to their environments, grow, travel, and reproduce (e. g., (Corning, 2003; Brody, Bloom, & Turner, 2001; Kauffman, 2000; Turner, 2000; Sober & Wilson, 1998; Sigmund, 1993). If my cat can have motives, so might my obsessions.

In contrast to science, the traditional professions of the law, education, and theology never abandoned the idea of invaders for the human mind. Lawyers debate *mens rea* in criminal cases, that is, did their client have the capacity to exert self control? And if not, then therapy (exorcism?) is indicated rather than punishment. Teachers and parents exclaim about a student, "I just don't know what came over him." In a parallel world, many religions accept the theory of evolution but retain the concept of free will: theologians make their followers eligible for punishment for the same reasons that lawyers do.

Our client's instinct is that "I'm OK but something else moved in." *The metaphor can be deceptive but, carefully used, it might pay off in our treatment of obsessions and BPD because (1) we and our clients appear to instinctively use it, and (2) it's a convenient way to think of networks in dynamic terms.* It might not hurt if we agreed with these beliefs, encouraging our clients to distinguish between what they personally want to do and what their visitor wants. Most clinicians reify clusters of symptoms and talk as if a separate living being rides within our client who shares this viewpoint when he talks about "*having* a good week" instead of "making a good week happen." Addicts and their counselors argue the impossibility of "kicking the habit" by free will (perhaps an expression of truth or, perhaps, an attempt to avoid consequences). Considering delusions to have living properties and to express self-interest should lead to ignoring, redirecting, or weakening unwanted companions by strengthening their competitors. (Some of us are more formidable when we take our adversaries personally!)

> Jake was certain that three former friends tracked his cell phone and told anonymous lies about him to each of his *in seriatim* employers. Jake told his new boss to expect suspicious calls about him. He also collected magazine articles about tracking antennas and stared at neighbors to be sure they weren't staring at him. Of course, they stared back. Although Jake may have been harassed years ago by a small group of individuals, his own thoughts transferred the persecution to new people and it grew. Jake could momentarily challenge his thoughts in our sessions as if they were a specimen on a microscope slide but an instant later they reared up, challenged him back and he surrendered again. Jake was a clever husband to his thoughts, not arguing with them and taking a nap whenever he could.

Networks and Ideas as Living Systems that Modify Their Carriers

Living systems can be defined by not by protein, carbon, or skin but by (1) replication and (2) completion of work cycles. Adjunctive tools include the sensors that find variations in the energy levels of surrounding elements and the behavior sequences that extract energy from those differences (Kauffman, 2000). Kauffman's definition might apply to repetitive patterns of CNS activity just as it does to bacteria, flies, mice, or Meg Ryan.

Kauffman's definition is somewhat chilling when we consider that mental organizations may exhibit self interests that override those of their carrier. We are not surprised when organisms with separate skins both work and replicate but it's difficult to accept betrayal from within our own minds. Mental organizations, however, acquire Wilson's "ultimate adaptation" and (1) modify their environments, and (2) such environments, once modified, support the further development of their greedy occupant (Allport, 1955; Scarr and McCartney, 1983; Popper, 1984/1992; Rowe, 1994, 2002; Wilson, 1975/2000; Kauffman, 2000; Lewontin, 1998/2000; Laland, Odling-Smee, & Feldman, 2000; Brody 1999, 2000; Turner, 2000; Brody, Turner, & Bloom, 2002; Odling-Smee et al., 2003). A bacterium moving to a richer glucose concentration changes its world (Kauffman, 2000). So does Meg when she dictates the terms of her next movie. *And so does a delusion that runs its carrier's life.* The conscious impact of these outcomes can be like that of an invader that takes over the mind of its host, commandeers resources, and resists suppression or dispersal while it grows and jumps from one susceptible carrier to a second one.[13]

Delusions Defend Themselves and Sometimes Make More Delusions

> Bambi knew that possessing her baseball player was not an option. Thus, it could be said that her fantasy used her when she begged or borrowed tickets or strolled close to home plate or the bullpen before a game. It also used her son to gain closer access to the team during warm-ups. The fantasy became more persistent, driving out her other interests and she became more

[13] Dawkins (1976) concocted the same model for "memes," units of cultural inheritance. "Memes," however, have concrete equivalents and appear to belong to environments of ideas that each of us manufactures. Dawkins, therefore, reversed selection's arrow but possibly without realizing it. Organisms choose between and modify physical settings, the elements of those settings compete with each other for retention by their living occupants. See also Turner, 2000; Brody, 1999; Brody, Turner, & Bloom, 2001.

irritable with her children when there was no game. She often noticed the player's picture on the front page of the newspaper or during a television program and immediately changed pages or channels. She lectured herself for a foolish ambition but in the next moment angrily challenged her self-doubt: "Why can't I have my dream just like those other women who, although younger, are less attractive and deserving than I am?"

There are indications consistent with the idea that an obsession can defend itself:

3) Whether we call it habituation or down-regulation, clients usually become less sensitive to a medication, not more so. The medicine, however, does not become weaker, mood changes and obsessions become more resilient.
4) Give an antidepressant to a client with prior manic episodes and the client often has more of them and more frequently (Goldberg, Harrow, & Grossman, 1995). A similar effect occurs with lithium (Swann, Bowden, Calabrese, Dilsaver, & Morris, 2000) further, "Over the last 20 years little progress has been made in reducing the length of depressive episodes in those with bipolar illness" (Frankle, Perlis, Deckersbach, Grandin, Gray, Sachs, & Nierenberg, 2002).
5) Clients often quit medications because they worry about having a chronic illness and taking medications that control their moods (Roy-Byrne, 2003). (They may also quit because the medication triggers bait-poisoning, Brody, 1997).
6) There is some evidence that BPD is associated with impaired executive functions, mental skills that manage our behavior and allow consistency when we apply cognitive-behavior interventions. Sustained attention, for example, erodes with repeated bipolar episodes (Clark, Iversen, & Goodwin, 2002; Cavanagh, Van Beck, Muir, & Blackwood, 2002; Ferrier and Thompson, 2002).[14] And cognitive behavior methods gain or lose effect in accord with group support and with the ability of the client to be persistent in their practice.
7) Multiple bipolar episodes are resistant to treatment and occur more frequently as the number of cycles increases (Goldberg, et al., 1995: Gitlin, Swendsen, Heller, & Hammen, 1995; Frankle et al. 2002; Judd, Akiskal, Schettler, Coryell, Endicott, Maser, Leon, & Keller, 2003).
8) The client uses nicotine, amphetamines, cannabis, or alcohol for immediate, short term gains but with delayed, long term effects that interfere with the intended actions of antidepressants and mood stabilizers.

These phenomena are consistent with the existence of an organization that, by whatever mechanisms, defends itself. It can also grow and reproduce.[15]

[14] Network models predict that lapses in sustained attention and executive functions probably amplify the effects of BPD as much as the reverse.

[15] Seeds for these phenomena are easy to find in modern life: An expectant mother, one with a history of bipolar disorder, smokes, passing on her nicotine addiction to her already restless fetus. Einstein was led by his delusions and in one sense, relativity discovered him. John is angered once in the morning by his adoptive son but remains angry for the rest of the day. Jake is paranoid and tells his new boss to expect calls from strangers who want him to fire Jake. Tony erroneously suspects his wife of cheating, he angers, she angers, and he concludes that his suspicions are correct. Wives sometimes resent their husband's interest in football, model airplanes, hunting, or racing automobiles. These interests compete with her and their children for scarce family resources and elicit in her jealousies perhaps as corrosive as those provoked by his infatuation with another woman.

1) A narrow preoccupation can enlarge its scope. Tony's conviction that his wife had sex with his neighbor expanded to include several neighbors, his brother, his physician and even some of the patients and extended from his immediate present across ever greater intervals into his past. Such a preoccupation could also expand from sexual infidelity to taking our money, alienating our children, or poisoning us.
2) Delusions and moods can flare, subside, idle for long periods of time, then kindle to take over our minds once more. These recurrences are associated with increased resistance to medication and may become more frequent (Swann, et al. 2000).
3) Delusions appear to jump from one mind to another. We recruit our friends and lovers on the basis of their similarity to us, not only in values and interests (Buss, 2003) but also psychopathology (Maes, Neale, Kendler, Hewitt, Silberg, Foley, Meyer, Rutter, Simonoff, Pickles, & Eaves, 1998). There are genetic contributions to all of these factors (Eaves, Martin, & Heath, 1990; Martin, Eaves, Heath, Jardine, Feingold, & Eysenck, 1986). Eye contact, laughter, and context signal a shared openness to particular kinds of ideas. Instruction, imitation, and conversation spread a preoccupation and its quests from one receptive mind to a second one. Large public secondary schools make it more likely that partners can be found for whatever quirks may exist in any one student. Internet search engines supply an international list of prospective soul mates. Thus, one person with a superstition finds and infects like-minded others: fads, cults, and religions bloom like summer mold on neighboring pieces of fruit.
4) We may find that delusions, like infections, reproduce best if they imitate a successful bacterium or virus, spreading before the symptoms are obvious (Ewald, 1994). They also travel to our children if the infection is still tiny when we reproduce. After all, too much deviance in a rutting adolescent scares away mates and allies. With time, those same quirks ripen within marriages and parenting as different family members take up the slack. Small wonder that teenagers swear to "never act like my mother," middle-agers in marital spats angrily deny these similarities but admit them in quiet moments with a therapist, but when older, acknowledge the resemblance and sometimes take pride in it.

MECHANISMS FOR GROWTH

Oscillators and Cycling

> "Compared with controls, patients had significantly more variability in mood ratings. However, patients' mood swings were more significantly organized and structured, and therefore potentially more predictable. While mood swings in normal controls were random, the mathematical model demonstrated a measurable and predictable relation between changes in mood at one point in time and subsequent changes in mood" (Dubovsky, 1999).

The foundations for bipolar cycling may lie in the fundamentals of oscillation. Crickets, fireflies, hearts, menses, sleep, pendulums, electrical generators, Bose-Einstein condensates, and Josephson junctions oscillate between on and off but they also synchronize (Strogatz, 2003). Kuramoto derived a proof that synchronization is to be expected between oscillators if:

(1) there is an on-off, repetitive pattern, (2) the oscillators are weakly linked, and (3) the oscillators are nearly identical to each other. Transpose this model to neural systems that take on tasks and we possibly recognize elation. Likewise for neural systems that disengage from tasks. Shut down one task and you may shut down others. The latter possibly corresponds to depression. The surprise is not that synchrony occurs but that it is not more pervasive

Phase Transitions: An On-Off Switch

> "... a *phase boundary* separates networks that exhibit frozen, orderly dynamics from those that exhibit chaotic dynamics. The existence of this boundary leads us to a very general and potentially very important hypothesis: Parallel-processing systems lying in this interface region between order and chaos may be those best able to adapt and evolve. Further, natural selection may be the force which pulls complex adaptive systems into this boundary region" (Kauffman, 1993, p. 218).

The foundations for BPD cycling also rest in statistical physics. Kauffman (1993, 1995) studied electronic decision networks for three decades and found that a very narrow boundary, a "phase transition," lies between rigid organizations and chaotic ones. Phase transitions are thin havens wherein organization emerges but variation continues. They occur widely: we experience a phase transition when we float in water, too heavy to fly and too light to sink. Phase transitions occur in many gases and liquids and in magnetized materials. They also occur in social and mathematical computations that involve participants with conflicting demands: more demands from fewer participants predict an insolvable problem (Hayes, 1997; Anderson, 1999; Ball, 1999, 2002). The overlap between the properties of phase transitions in computation problems and those in liquids and gases is startling (Anderson, 1999).

The earth's orbit, our atmosphere, global temperature range, and climate all have the property of a phase boundary that separates contrasting and almost limitless extremes. The flow of the Gulf Stream may exhibit a phase transition and reverse direction with little notice. There are phase transitions in the number of hours that we sleep and in physiological variables such as heart rate, blood pressure, and in the partial pressures of oxygen and carbon dioxide in our blood. Traffic flow, crowd panic, and even hand clapping in auditoriums move between randomness and coherence. Human life occupies a phase boundary that runs 26,000 miles laterally but only from three miles below to five miles above the surface of the earth, a distribution like that of a water spider. And most important for this chapter, we show phase transitions when we organize ourselves into groups through our logical and social computations (Hayes, 1997; Ball, 1999, 2002). Neural firing patterns sometimes exhibit a narrow range of heightened sensitivity to small changes in input while being generally resistant to stimuli on either side of that range, one side from a failure to reach threshold and the other from satiation.

According to Kauffman's work, change the average number of links from two to three in a random network and amorphous organizations solidify (Kauffman, 1995). His observations are consistent with events in emergent networks: increase connectivity and stereotypic order appears. Reverse the degree of connectivity and autonomous but chaotic arrangements are seen again. *Phase transitions are the logical equivalent of an electric switch: one that stays "on" until taken past a very narrow point at which it flips to "off"* (Brody, 2002). There are no gradations in either direction once you pass out of the phase transition and it is in the properties of ordered and chaotic regimes that you may have great difficulty getting back to the boundary between them. We need to start promptly to detect and dismantle the construction of a highly organized obsession!

The link between phase transitions and emergent networks and BPD is surprising: phase transitions are strongly associated with power laws! That is, large dramatic changes are usually infrequent as conflicting moods within human minds tune each other to prolonged stability; organisms and environments tune each other in a similar manner (Kauffman, 2000). "Maturation" describes the former, "stability" the latter. Whether within minds, genotypes, geological events, or in the constructions of organisms and settings, too big a change by a key participant leads to disruption and sometimes extinction. The adaptive, evolvable, choice is for many small changes to occur in both partners and each aligns with the other in a process of continual adjustment and readjustment. In more colloquial terms, hubs can manage change in stable environments by the acquisition or sacrifice of a few nodes.

If (1) we conceive self-regulation to consist of opposing processes of initiative and withdrawal, (2) a narrow dynamic range of connectivity allows us to select either strategy in small amounts, then (3) disrupt connectivity and switching can be abrupt, extreme, and triggered by small influences, whether internal or external. Given that inhibition refines the complex systems that evolved in phylogeny and in personal ontogeny, disturb that inhibition and we can predict oscillations to occur in our thoughts and moods after infection, trauma, or genetic variations or for that matter, sudden changes in our loves, income, and social standing. *We face, therefore, the strong possibility of not only multiple expressions of bipolar disorder but also multiple foundations for any one expression.*

Raise-the-Stakes

> In Hebb's words: "...neurons that fire together wire together; neurons out of synch fail to link" (Pinker, 2002, p. 92).

There's a reciprocity strategy ("raise-the-stakes," RTS, Roberts & Sherratt, 1998; Camazine et al, 2001) that has the positive feedback characteristics consistent with the growth of delusions from normal thought. RTS simply means "open small and if your opponent matches or exceeds your offer, increase it." RTS overlaps with contiguity models for conditioning and learning and supplies a bonus, not only cementing connections but also amplifying them. Events associated in time, thus, wind up in the same network and make it larger. In computer simulations RTS defeats more traditional, durable reciprocity strategies such as Tit-for-Tat. RTS can apply to conversational gambits: speak to another person and if they answer in an equal or greater number of words, pursue the conversation and topic. If not, disengage. RTS could amplify small, successful gambits within neural networks into larger ones and consequences that are greater than expected could have even more impact on learning and performance.

RTS supports Barabási's idea of "fitness" in networks: the number of links connected to a node. The oldest nodes are part of the environment for those that come later and, therefore, often acquire more links. Thus, phylogenetically or ontogenetically older behaviors may have greater power to direct or to disrupt human lives. There is also a *fitness connectivity product* for nodes: the number of links at a particular time multiplied by the rate at which the node recruits new links (Barabási, 2002). A newcomer with a higher fitness connectivity product may displace an older hub. A fitness connectivity product can describe the marketing success of a new invention or might apply to the potency of a fast-growing attachment. Spooning with Cindy Lou temporarily replaces football with the guys. Within the contexts of attention, love, and territory, we can each experience the fixation that Bambi found in the third baseman.

The Dangers When Clusters Merge

Barabási (2002) and others discuss clustered, hierarchic, and winner-take-all arrangements as three distinct organizations. *There is every possibility that these arrangements represent continuous stages rather than discrete outcomes.* That is, under some conditions, clusters become hierarchies, and hierarchies melt into winner-take-all, and winner-take-all may collapse back into clusters and hierarchies. Kauffman (1995), for example, describes the decentralization undertaken by IBM when its organization no longer responded to local markets. Winner-take-all gave into to local influences and broke into a set of sparsely connected hierarchic arrangements. (Frank & Cook, 1995, review economic conditions under which winner-take-all markets emerge.)

Clusters can represent the modules of CNS functioning but those clusters can link first into hierarchic networks and then into an obsessive black hole after an injury or an epiphany in which a limited set of beliefs come to dominate all aspects of an individual's thought. That is, instinct and learning underlie many subsets of ideas. Subsets of ideas and strategies merge when the host is hungry, frightened, acquiring territory, or in estrus: scattered strategic hierarchies first become orderly, then more rigid and then irresistible either in love or crises in mid May or when a reward is due in the instant.

One possibility is that fixed ideas arise from dominance: some "thing" lets one of them overrun competing beliefs. BPD represents, therefore, too much of whatever is going on. On the other hand, obsessions and quests might reflect a failure of inhibition from alternative ideas and external distractions: our passions are not necessarily tougher in their roots; influence from the competition is weaker. There are four parallel sources of evidence.

1) Bianconi (Bianconi & Barabási, Barabási, 2002, p. 101) converted networked hubs and links into terms from quantum physics. That is, the fitness of nodes corresponds to quantum energy levels in a Bose gas.[16] This creative translation finds that hubs have lower energy levels but isolated nodes, perhaps comparable to an outer electron shell, have higher. *It may be in physics as well as human thought and societies that large organizations are both more probable and cheaper to maintain for each participant but dispersed clusters of ideas are less probable and more expensive and supported by their small but sometimes surprising access to otherwise unexploited resources.*

[16] Bose and Einstein derived predictions that molecules in gases near absolute zero (-273 degrees K) will act as a single molecule. A case can be made that a loss of resources in social systems and in individual participants leads to greater stereotypy: individuals can be treated as identical and interchanged with one another. (See Brody, 2003, for an application of network concepts to social organizations and Brody, under review, to psychological adaptations.)

2) Evolutionary change often accrues from the partial inhibition of existing developmental cascades, gene duplication with modification, redirection to new goals of older developmental processes, and changes in the synchronization of developmental programs that mature in parallel with each other (Raff, 1996). Environmental stress, however, interferes with a restorative protein, *Hsp90*, and releases more primitive features (Queitsch, Sangster, & Lindquist, 2002; Rutherford & Lindquist, 1998). *Hsp90* then maintains the older phenotype and transmits the change to the offspring of the stressed organism.[17]
3) Bipolar and other mood disorders often emerge after even mild head injuries (Holsinger, Steffens, Phillips, Helms, Havlik, Breitner, Guralnik, & Plassman, 2002; Robinson & Jorge, 2002) and reveal not only problems in mood regulation but also in sustained attention and possibly executive functions (Clark, Iversen, & Goodwin, 2002; Cavanagh, Van Beck, Muir, & Blackwood, 2002; Ferrier and Thompson, 2002). We can also expect obsessions, delusions, and stereotyped repetitive thoughts and conduct to follow infections (Torrey, 2002; Ewald, 2000). Such agents might disrupt inhibitory connections between distant neural clusters. These possibilities could apply to any *idée fixe* that levies costs such as OCD, Tourettes, explosive or homicidal behaviors, panic or eating disorders, hypochondria, depression, delusions, personality disorders, false memories, or, less destructively, hypnotic states, love, religious ecstasy, and scientific quests.
4) Pennington (1991) observes that executive functions, behaviors that help us to manage other behaviors, are perhaps the most newly evolved and, therefore, depend most on the integrity of related systems. Disruption should not always be associated with a total loss of skills but with stereotypy and impulsiveness as well as a higher risk for many of the aggravations that sometimes escort BPD. Given the importance of anticipation and reasoning for many cognitive procedures, a lapse of executive functions should predict longer treatment duration and a greater dependency on medicines and coaches (Brody, 2001).

Networks appear to have a dynamic bias toward simplification and dominance by a limited number of players whenever there is an erosion of resources. This bias perhaps underlies immaturity, heightened emotionality, all-or-none judgments, over-generalization, and the selective retention of both rules and experiences. It also makes BPD features more probable! Further, we might expect injury, illness, depression, and mutation to impede interconnectivity by a drying up of network assets and to make both stereotypic conduct and delusions more likely. Our mental experiences of sickness and death are limited and fixed rather than complex and varied. Again, Nietzsche's writing was more absolutist during a syphilitic attack (Ertel, 1981). The effect is also comparable to K-Mart's moving to the edge of a small town: local, varied, but more costly preferences disappear and so do the shopping opportunities that match them. According to Frank and Cook (1995) we might expect that everyone in a poor town to buy the same CD, rather than each of us buying a different one

[17] Raff (1996) notes that disinhibition should be possible for gene sequences up to 5 million years old! In ordinary development, the disinhibition of an older sequence often occurs through the inhibition of the customary inhibitory sequences! (Kirschner & Gerhart, 1998).

and sharing. These outcomes, however, should usually be restrained by the diverse resources provided by the multiple environments that we experience, both inside and out of our skin.

Thus, observations from the study of networks, mutations and stress, psychiatric research, and learning disorders are mutually consistent: behavioral flexibility depends on the inhibition of all-or-none behaviors. No surprise! Lateral inhibition between different hubs and their associated networks may ordinarily help the organism remain sensitive to subtle changes in contexts, a state comparable to that described by Kauffman (2000) when organisms and settings stabilize each other over generations. Interfere with the stability of those clusters and delusions take change in a winner-take-all manner that may parallel shifts in the network conditions within their carrier's mind.

REARRANGING SPOOLS AND DOWELS WITH MEDICATION AND CBT

> I found building things with an *Erector Set* to be faster and more fun that taking them apart and once I finished a tower or airplane, I left it sitting on the living room floor. My mother, however, had her own schema for organization and eventually I put the pieces back in their box. Bipolar disorder and its obsessions need a good mother who takes them apart and puts the components back where they belong.

It is not the case that manic individuals do too much of everything: instrumental behavior and goal-directed thoughts may increase but contemplation, delay, inhibition, and subtle conformity to social environments decrease. A teenage girl shouts with glee when her rock star is to give a concert but balks at earning the ticket money or doing her homework. And depression is characterized not only by despondency but also by excess contemplation, delay, and inhibition although adjustment to changing social contexts is still limited.

Normal inhibition arises both from competition between networks as well as from clustered arrangements within each of them that track small, momentary variations in local environments, arrangements that allow an alert mind to sit under a tree and consider the outcomes from varied choices, delay goal-pursuit until opportune moments, and adjust goals for shifting contexts (Bronowski, 1977; Barkley, 1997). In evolutionary development, the truncation of some developmental sequences while others step in usually results from active inhibition rather than deletion: the former sequences are still present if unexpressed (Raff, 1996; Carroll, Grenier, & Weatherbee, 2001). Likewise for the neural communities that normally mediate rest, circumspection, consultation, and delay. The BPD individual cannot gain access to them but through an unusual failure of inhibition: that is, options that once competed for attention no longer do so.

In network terms, some nodes have too much influence and others too little. And given that emergent networks are pervasive and demonstrate substantial assets including resilience, intimacy, and speed, we can expect to find them a determined adversary when we modify activity, emotionality, executive functions, and beliefs. Bring any one of these factors, however, within normal boundaries and the client should have a better outcome. Kuramoto's rules again come to mind but now as a framework for reconsidering our mainstays for treating BPD: synchrony emerges as a function of similarity and interconnectivity. In other words, decrease the similarity of the participants, reduce interconnectivity, and synchrony should become less likely.

The next section argues that medication changes diffuse systems, whether a range of moods or the relative dominance of extreme beliefs, but erases neither problem; cognitive-behavior therapy (CBT) often targets a belief but that one belief may be reinforced by a network of cognitive allies. Therapists face a dilemma: medication sometimes erodes the skills that CBT requires, CBT takes time that the client may not have.

Being Less Full of Our Self: Medication

We drop a capsule in our mouth and later remain calm while giving our three year old his next time-out. It is absurd to expect these outcomes from juices and powders except that we sometimes get them. And physicians attempt to poison a delusion with chemicals just as if it were a bacterium, a position that agrees with Bambi's sense that she carried an invader. Emergent networks, however, may underlie (1) medicine's ability to demoralize an army of thoughts, quieting the noisiest but silencing none of them, (2) the similar effects that we sometimes get from very different medicines, and (3) the stubbornness with which some thoughts and feelings regain their original vigor despite medicines.

First, in a winner-take-all network, one goal dominates all others and all behavior is organized toward the attainment of that goal. Quests recruit allies and supplies. In networks as in sensory systems, whatever is larger, more intense, more colorful, or more immediate inhibits our awareness of competing sights, sounds, and skin sensations (von Bekesy, 1967). On the other hand, reduce mass action and diversity again appears in human consciousness.

Second, Watts and Strogatz (1998; Barabási, 2002) found that emergent networks are resilient to either generalized or random attacks. There may be 100 or more than a million nodes that participate in a network but only 20% or fewer manage 80% of the transactions. Thus, medicines often allow key ideas to remain but they are less noticeable. It is one thing to believe in aliens, it is another to shout to them in Times Square at noon. We might also examine the possibility that some medicines that were originally developed for very different purposes (e.g., schizophrenia, seizures, anxiety) may have similar outcomes and work for a common reason: they all reduce the coherence in assemblies of neural organizations.

Breaking up plagues in communities, however, depends not on giving a little bit of help to every infected person but on curing or isolating the one in twenty (the hubs) with high frequency social contacts (Watts & Strogatz, 1998; Barabási, 2002). Targeting the key players, however, can be difficult with chemicals. We instead muffle the good guys as well as the bad with medicines, assuring, through a process often sensed as boredom, that no dictators take charge. Our clients, however, often want to turn down the attraction of a few ideas without taking the sparkle from all of them.

Unfortunately, all cells, whether they are neural or simply grow hair, have nearly the same metabolism (Gerhart & Kirschner, 1997). Thus, giving something that works in most individuals entails a substantial risk of incapacitating them! Most psychotherapeutic agents elicit physical discomforts and may erode abilities to think, remember, read, concentrate, and plan. Medicines sometimes impair not just physical stamina, but word flow, alertness, and social skills along with it. These liabilities motivate the client to quit medicines and, indirectly, help a delusion, one that may have been selfish but a lot of fun, to survive. The situation is so difficult that clinicians who inform the patient of all possible side effects risk convincing him to refuse medication, lie about taking it, skip doses, or take it only until the door to the behavior unit is unlocked.[18]

Networks Applied to Cognitive-Behavior Therapy

Seasons, schedules, sleep patterns, and thoughts may influence both the onset and the intensity of a bipolar episode as well as its companions and therapy may attempt to adjust energy level, moods, ideas, or self-management. Move early to bring any one of these four into a normal range and the client could go back into synchrony with other members of his neighborhood. Thus, we need not, indeed, must not, be helpless: we can do more than watch the clock and reach for our medicine when an episode is due.

Cognitive therapy depends on relatively intact abilities to challenge first impressions, pinpoint difficulties, anticipate risks, follow rules, and rearrange consequences. Cognitive-behavior therapy regulates troublesome thoughts in a more selective way than medicines but research demonstrates that CBT and medications can sometimes lead to similar changes in scanner images (Furmark, Tillfors, Marteinsdottir, Fischer, Pissiota, Langstrom, & Fredrikson, 2002). Adding CBT to medications can result in fewer relapses in BPD (Lam, Watkins, Hayward, Bright, Kerr, Parr-Davis, & Sham, 2003), and self-monitoring can be effective in preventing manic relapses (Perry, Tarrier, Morriss, McCarthy, & Limb, 1999; Colom, Vieta, Martinez-Aran, Reinarees, Goikolea, Benaba, Torrent, Comes, Corbella, Barramon, & Corominas, 2003; Dubovsky, 2003).

Cognitive therapy rests on the fact that not only do thoughts follow moods but the reverse is also true: challenge a discouraging thought by alternative interpretations and the associated mood dissipates (Beck, 1976; Beck, Shaw, & Emery, 1979). This tactic is direct, uncomplicated, and often successful with depressed, anxious, phobic, schizoid, bipolar, and even married clients (Beck & Freeman, 1990; Freeman, Pretzer, Fleming, & Simon, 1990; Dattilio & Padesky, 1990)!

Cognitive *behavior* therapy goes one step further: consequences supplement reasoning. CBT, thus, has a substantial technology from the procedures set up not only by Beck and his colleagues but also by a generation of behavior psychologists who followed Watson & Reyner (1920), Jones (1924), Eysenck (1960), and Wolpe (1973). Shaping, reinforcement, extinction, reinforcement of competing behaviors, and desensitization are applied to overt responses and to mental ones. Thus, CBT covers the dual realms of thought and action.

We should expect thoughts and actions to occur in emergent networks and CBT rests on hubs management even though, like bees that follow network rules when making a hive, Beck and his team knew nothing of emergent networks when they organized CBT. CBT pretends to be not modular but domain general and its success makes the questions, "Why consider evolution?" and "Why use networks?" all the more salient.

First,the value of evolutionary models is mentioned earlier in this chapter. (See also Beck, 1998.) Briefly, through *selection*, (emitting varied behaviors and repeating whatever

[18] Brody (1997) identified the likelihood of bait poisoning phenomena when children, who sometimes dislike taking stimulants, are given doses that are too large or too quickly introduced. Adults have a parallel difficulty. Nausea, sedation, and disorientation often occur with the sudden introduction of mood stabilizers or antidepressant. The client's reactions can parallel those of a rat that gets sick after a new food: aversive

works) we accumulate individually unique mental environments that seek, create, adapt, and link the strategies that pay off for us (Bouchard, Lykken, Tellegen, & McGue, 1996; Plomin et al, 1977; Scarr and McCartney, 1986).[19] Evolution defined the comparative salience of different response sequences: not all behaviors are equally likely in different contexts. Natural hierarchies between those strategies apply when we choose them as a part of therapy. Hugging a teddy bear can inhibit post surgical pain; thoughts of chili at an Arizona restaurant can inhibit jaw tension, plants in hospital rooms speed recovery, and mental images of the beach will settle many of us…all for evolutionary reasons.

Second, it is inevitable that we find emergent networks beneath our dilemmas: that is, there are some large thoughts but many smaller ones, thoughts clump by topic, some thoughts link to and amplify other thoughts and some thoughts can suppress, substitute for, or delay the ones that cause trouble. By whatever means, our goal is to disarm and fragment the hubs.

Third, the path of every therapy session can be viewed as the outcome of a selective experience: therapist and client make up an exploratory system wherein they test thoughts and repeat them according to their consequences (Kirschner and Gerhart, 1998; Gerhart and Kirschner, 1997). CBT, sooner or later, adjusts underlying networks of ideas (Beck 1976; Beck et al, 1979) and, conversely, we unwittingly use network models to summarize our procedures in CBT. *If networks accomplish information swaps between similar units and the speed of those exchanges guides network emergence, then relabeling or reclassifying ideas, cutting links to ancillary thoughts, or adding extra steps (and, therefore, delays) should deflate the importance of a troublesome hub.* CBT appears to do these very things.

NETWORKS AND INSTINCTS: BAMBI GOES TO SCHOOL

New Directions and Some Humility in the Bookstore

> I revised this chapter in a Barnes & Noble Café. Margie approached and mentioned that she has written four books and asked what I was writing.
> "A chapter on bipolar disorder."
> "Oh, how interesting. I've taken lithium for 20 years."
> Margie in that time has written no books nor has she worked in her former career but, instead, pursued a quest of correcting her medical records. Up against deadline and self-conscious, I switched from polite conversation to husband mode, first grunting and then turning mute. She returned three times with tidbits of her history and threw me a long look, a raised eyebrow, and a wave as she left the store. I considered how raise-the-stakes applied to our conversation and that we each have our obsessions despite lithium for her and caffeine for me.

Research in BPD is one more creation of power laws, one that consists of 20% established leaders and 80% tagalongs. There are also many promises and much activity but

conditioning occurs in a single experience and may never diminish (Garcia & Koelling, 1966, Garcia, Ervin, & Koelling, 1966; Brody, 1997; Buss, 1999).

[19] "Selection" is more inclusive than "reinforcement" which applies to shifts in the probability of a response as a function of its consequences. "Selection" often refers to "natural selection" but it also occurs within the development of an individual's life. For example, cellular components, neural hook ups, immune systems, and blood vessels develop in a similar manner: make lots of different responses and maintain those that pay off. Gerhart & Kirschner (1997) apply the term "exploratory system" to organizations that emerge through selection.

not a lot of achievement (Dubovsky, 1995; Goldberg, et al. 1995; Gitlin, et al, 1995; Frankle, et al. 2002; Judd, et al. 2003) Thus, research into BPD, despite the emergent order that we find in the relationships between its scientists, consists of an exploratory system, a pack of seasoned hounds still looking for a scent.

Emergent networks readily translate into modular organizations consistent with psychological adaptations and with nesting, cooperation, and conflict between them. Not only modular minds fit nicely into a network model, so does consciousness, even in *C. elegans*. Emergent networks were probably a vital part of our the environment that guided our evolution: that is, selection crafted genes, minds, and communities that conform to the statistical dynamics seen in networks. Lewontin (2000) considers organisms and their environment to represent a construction to which each partner contributes. "Emergent network" is probably a better term. We also face the interesting possibility of an intimate correspondence between the organizational patterns that we find in brains, thoughts and social conduct and the further interesting possibility that bidirectional links exist between each of these levels and its two companions, links that tend to bring all three of them into synchrony. Thus, network theory suggests not only that a surprising kind of order existed in Darwin's tangled bank, but an order identical to that in Darwin's own mind.

Benefits from Network Thinking

Bipolar disorder and its co-morbidities resemble an emergent network that has one or two dominant players accompanied by assorted needy friends. Common sense, cognitive-behavior therapy, corporate management, and even military strategy suggest procedures that align: make the hubs less influential and the rest of the organization fragments. Remove nodes that support the hubs: that is, delay or eliminate gratification, reinforce competing habits and concepts, grow a duplicate focus that does not have the same costs as the original, redirect an existing organization toward new purposes (cooption), levy costs, and finally, let it burn out. Any of these methods should adjust the relative strength of hubs and possibly erode the influence of a black hole.[20]

This chapter makes the case that mental networks have a statistical bias toward simplification and, thereby, towards dominance by a limited set of schema. This bias is ordinarily restrained by the competing tasks elicited by external and internal conditions but illness, depression, immaturity, and genetic variation narrow the list of choices, making stereotypic moods, conduct, and beliefs more likely.[21] The mind takes on a ratcheted existence after injury, infection, or developmental glitches: injuries rarely make someone more contemplative, circumspect, and wise but ties with friends, spouses, offspring, and children sometimes restrain hyperactive Gullivers who otherwise feel larger than life with BPD.

---

[20] They also parallel Raff's model of evolutionary change through isolation, specialization, duplication, cooption, and changes in the timing of parallel developmental cascades (Raff, 1996). These ideas align with network phenomena and, therefore, with CBT concepts and it would be an easy matter to arrange CBT with these ideas from evolutionary-developmental biology!

[21] Application is another matter. Margie has spent 20 years on her quests but her personal will and the networks behind it make her resilient not only to setbacks but also to cures. She and her occupants are attenuated but not silenced.

Network concepts:

1) Allow simulation, variation, and replication of experimental conditions and the opportunity to break away from correlational studies in social and psychological research,
2) Become a means to sharpen questions to be asked of molecular and behavior geneticists,
3) Reveal organizational detail that rearranges our views of schizophrenia, BPD, obsessions, and even addictions,
4) Allow reconstruction in simulations and eventually in clinical work. Organizations can be assembled but, under suitable conditions, they might also revert back into their original clusters for reassembly in new combinations,
5) Provide clues to the fundamental similarities and differences between normal behavior and BPD,
6) Give a different rationale for the effects of medication and CBT and let us find equivalencies between the two,
7) Fit hand-in-glove with brain research that reveals circuits in neural organizations and with the neurological disconnects that suggest modules in how we perceive and classify experiences (Sacks, 1987, 1992; Pinker, 2002),
8) Imply that cognitive-behavior manipulations, because of their specificity, immediacy, and availability for self-management, could have more impact than medicines for the many people who show lesser impairment in their executive functions.

Once you learn about networks you can almost see them play as you shift from one all-or-none task to another or, in rare moments, when you consider "what if" as you imagine the futures that might have been. I encounter networks when I make a decision on rational grounds but struggle later to implement it *in vivo*. I pretend to watch the networks in my cat's mind as he switches from eating his dinner to playing with my shoe lace or knocking my pen on the floor. He doesn't execute a little bit of each activity concurrently but shifts completely from one to the next. I can also watch networks more clearly in my own mind when broke, tired, alone, hungry, or preoccupied.

Bambi Resolved

> Bambi escaped from baseball when she became a Volunteer Mother in her daughter's elementary class. She did instinctive things and felt useful doing them, got the spotlight that she craved and, at the same time, saved money and silenced her self-nagging on three counts: the foolishness of her baseball ambitions, her failure to achieve them, and her guilt for being an irresponsible mother. Her daughter, other children, the teacher, and mothers of other children all reinforced her. Her son, perhaps developing his own grand schemes, was a little annoyed that he would not have a baseball player for his new dad.

Lorenz talks playfully about his "three little equations" for weather and other chaotic systems, equations beyond solution despite their apparent simplicity (Strogatz, 2003; Lorenz, 1993/2001). Clinicians not only try to predict weather-like events such as suicide or murder but also attempt to prevent them and are held to account if we fail. Imagine a forecaster who not only told us the path of a tornado but also changed it! Or was hauled before a review board for being wrong or not stopping it! Predicting and managing the course of human events is no simpler, but, fortunately, we sometimes have help from the storm itself, our client. Unfortunately, the factors that help him to resist his impairment also may help him to resist our help. The reasons appear to be simple.

Despite the structures handed to us by phylogeny, development makes no two brains identical in structure or in receptor-based preferences.[22] While evolution specifies reinforcement systems and environment offers choices, we each differ in our wants and the tactics that we use to achieve them. And genetic differences between individuals accounts for a substantial portion of the variance in the arrangements that we make (Plomin, 1994; Rowe, 1994). David Rowe, was a tall but reticent behavior geneticist and wrote outrageous but empirically supported ideas before his recent death from liver cancer:

> "Dawkins' examples [e. g., beavers' making dams: JB] are undeniably examples of instincts---of stereotyped inherent patterns of behavior...Such instincts are shared by most individuals in a species, but the present topic is individual differences in traits. *Yet the conceptual distance between the human expression of individual differences and the extended phenotype of a species may not be so great.* [Italics added, JB]" (Rowe, 1994, p. 91).

If Rowe and the other behavior geneticists are correct, then:

- No single template defines our clients. Their assets and liabilities as well as their PET scans will be unique for each of them. No one medicine or behavior trick will work for all of them.
- Each client selects experiences that meet her particular, sometimes peculiar allotment of psychological adaptations and experience-producing drives (Bouchard, et al., 1996). Many of our encounters with BPD may arise from a poor fit between what our client wants and what he has.
- Behavioral family histories may reveal how parents and grandparents with similar temperaments and talents found a place to be obsessed but without being locked up or divorced.
- Clients inevitably select from the therapist's offerings whether or not that is the therapist's intent. The closer the match between the menu and client aptitudes, the greater the chance for treatment success.
- While there will be substantial uniformity of automatic thoughts -- perhaps because we all came from the same theropod 160 mya -- there will also be substantial variation between us. The array of automatic thoughts available to the client will change with age, reproductive standing, access to resources, seasons of the year, and significant changes in his or her niche.
- Therapists help the client to discover opportunities that match his assets.

The obscure individual who wanted to go where the weather matched his clothes may have told all of us a powerful truth. As Popper (1992) observed, every creature searches for a better world. Further, that world that should be measured according to the closeness of fit

[22] "One part of the brain, the anterior commissure ... varies seven-fold in area between one person and the next ... the massa intermedia ... is not found at all in one in four people. The primary visual cortex can vary three-fold in area ... our amygdala ... can vary two-fold in volume – as can our hippocampus ... Most surprising, our cerebral cortex varies in non-learning impaired people nearly two-fold in volume." Skoyles, 2000, p. 143.)

between the traits of its occupants and the opportunities that those occupants achieve. Each one of us makes his personal unique environments (Plomin, 1994) while parents, spouses, employers, and sometimes police officers supply boundaries (common environments, Plomin, 1994) for them. *It is, therefore, essential to mobilize the client in their treatment rather than the clinician's assuming total responsibility for making some kind of repair.* This lesson applies to our treatment of anxiety and depression; it is also likely true for many manifestations of bipolar disorder. It was almost inevitable that Bambi solved her own dilemma while I helped her to identify options and to stay out of too much trouble until she found one that suited her.

REFERENCES

Albert, R. & Barabási, A-L. (2001) Statistical mechanics of complex networks. *Reviews of Modern Physics.* 74: 47-97.

Allport, G. (1955) Becoming: Basic Considerations for a Psychology of Personality. New Haven: Yale University Press.

American Psychiatric Association (1994) *Diagnostic and Statistical Manual of Mental Disorders.* 4th Ed., Washington, D.C.

Anderson P: Computing: Solving problems in finite time. *Nature,* 1999; 400: 115-116.

Ball, P. (1999) Transitions still to be made. *Nature*, 402, 73-76.

_____ . (2002) The Physics of society. *Nature*, 415: 371.

Barabási, A-L (2002) *Linked: The New Science of Networks.* NY: Perseus.

Barkley R. (1997) *ADHD and the Nature of Self Control.* NY: Guilford.

Barkow, J. Cosmides, L., & Tooby, J. (Eds.) (1992) *The Adapted Mind: Evolutionary Psychology and the Generation of Culture.* NY: Oxford.

Beck, A. (1976) *Cognitive Therapy and the Emotional Disorders.* NY: New American Library.

_____ . (1998) Cognitive aspects of personality disorders and their relation to syndromal disorders: A psychoevolutionary approach. In R. Cloninger (Ed.) *Personality and Psychopathology.* American Psychiatric Association, Washington, D. C., pp. 411-429.

Beck, A. & Emery, G. (1985) *Anxiety Disorders and Phobias: A Cognitive Perspective.* NY: Basic.

Beck, A. & Freeman, A. (1990) *Cognitive Therapy of Personality Disorders.* NY: Guilford.

Beck, A., Rush, J., Shaw, B., & Emery, G. (1979) *Cognitive Therapy of Depression.* NY: Guilford.

von Bekesy, G. (1967) Mach Band Type Lateral Inhibition in Different Sense Organs. *Journal of General Physiology*, 50(3), 519-532.

Bianconi, G. & Barabási, A-L (2000) Bose-Einstein condensation in complex networks. arXiv:cond-mat/0011224 v1 13 Nov.

Bouchard, T., Lykken, D., Tellegen, A., & McGue, M. (1996) Genes, Drives, Environment, and Experience. Chapter 1 in C.P. Benbow & D. Lubinski (eds.) Intellectual Talent: Psychometric and Social Issues. Baltimore: Johns Hopkins Press, pp 5-43.

Brody, J. F. (1997) Bait Poisoning and why kids complain about their medication. *Journal of Child and Adolescent Psychopharmacology*, 7(1), pp. 71-72.

_____ . (1999) Active Darwinism and Psychotherapy, NY Chapter, Association for Advancement of Philosophy and Psychiatry, Meeting held at St. John's Cathedral, NYC, November 13, 1999.

_____ . (2000) Active Darwinism offsets mismatch. Paper given at the annual meeting, Human Behavior & Evolution Society, Amherst, MA, 6/8/00.

_____ . (2001) Evolutionary recasting: ADHD, mania and its variants. *Journal of Affective Disorders*. 65: 197-215.

_____ . (2002) From Physics and Evolutionary Neuroscience to Psychotherapy: Phase Transitions and Adaptations, Diagnosis and Treatment. In G. Cory & R. Gardner (Eds.) *The Evolutionary Neuroethology of Paul MacLean: Convergences & Frontiers*, Praeger-Greenwood, pp. 231-259.

_____ . (2003) Seeds of Leviathan: Networks and Genomes. Presentation to the Association for Politics and the Life Sciences, Philadelphia, PA., August 30.

_____ . (under review) From networks to modular minds. Submitted to *Evolutionary Psychology*, December, 2003.

Brody, J., Bloom, H., & Turner, J. (June, 2002) "Alternatives to the Received View of Evolution" Human Behavior and Evolution Society, Rutgers, NJ. A panel consisting of 3 presentations: Brody (Alternatives to the Received View of Evolution: if Darwin had been a woman), Bloom (The Xerox effect: on the importance of pre-biotic evolution), and Turner (Darwinism's difficulties: extended organisms, constructed environments, and emergent physiology).

Bronowski, J. (1977) *A Sense of the Future*. Cambridge, MA: MIT Press.

Buchanan, M. (2002) Nexus: Small Worlds and the Groundbreaking Theory of Networks. NY: Norton.

Buss, D. (1999) *Evolutionary Psychology: The New Science of the Mind.* NY: Doubleday.

_____ . (2003) *Evolution of Desire: Strategies of Human Mating* (2nd Ed.) NY: Basic.

Camazine, S., Deneubourg, J-L., Franks, N., Sneyd, J., Theraulaz, G., & Bonabeau, E. (2001) *Self-Organization in Biological Systems*. Princeton, NJ: Princeton Univ. Press.

Cancho, R.F.I. & Solé, R. (2001) The small world of human language. *Proceedings of the Royal Society of London, Series B: Biological Sciences* . 268: 2261-2265.

Carroll, Sean, Grenier, J., & Weatherbee, S. (2001) *From DNA to Diversity: Molecular Genetics and the Evolution of Animal Design*. Malden, MA: Blackwell.

Cavanagh, J. Van Beck, M., Muir, W., & Blackwood, D. (2002) Case-control study of neurocognitive function in euthymic patients with bipolar disorder: An association with mania. *British Journal of Psychiatry*. 180: 320-6.

Clark, L., Iversen, S., & Goodwin, G. (2002) Sustained attention deficit in bipolar disorder, *British Journal of Psychiatry*. 180:313-9.

Colom, R., Vieta, E., Martinez-Aran, A., Reinares, M., Goikolea, J., Benaba, Torrent, C., Comes, M., Corbella, B., Barramon, G., Corominas, J. (2003) A randomized trial on the efficacy of group psychoeducation in prophylaxis of recurrences in bipolar patients whose disease is in remission. *Archives of General Psychiatry*. 60: 402-407.

Cosmides L. & Tooby, J. (1992) The psychological foundations of culture. In J. Barkow, L. Cosmides, & J. Tooby (Eds.) *The Adapted Mind: Evolutionary Psychology and the Generation of Culture*. NY: Oxford.

Darwin, C. (1879/1950) *Charles Darwin's Autobiography.* NY: Collier.

Dattilio, F. & Padesky, C. *Cognitive Therapy with Couples.* Sarasota, FL: Professional Resource Exchange.

Dawkins, R. (1976/1989) *The Selfish Gene.* New York: Oxford.

Dubovsky, S. (1995) Summary & Comment: Bipolar disorder does not always have a good outcome. *Journal Watch for Psychiatry.* April 1.

_____ . (1999) A mathematical model for mood swings. *Journal Watch for Psychiatry,* 5(5): 40-41. Review of Woyshville, M. et al. (1999) On the meaning and measurement of affective instability: clues from chaos theory. *Biological Psychiatry,* 1999; 45: 261-269.

_____ . (2003) Group psychoeducation as adjunctive maintenance therapy in bipolar disorder. *Journal Watch for Psychiatry.* 9: 60.

Eaves, L., Martin, N, & Heath, A. (1990) Religious affiliation in twins and their parents: Testing a model of cultural inheritance. *Behavior Genetics,* 20, 1-22.

Edelman, G. (1987) *Neural Darwinism: The Theory of Neuronal Group Selection.* NY: Basic.

_____ . (1992) *Bright Air, Brilliant Fire: On the Matter of the Mind.* NY: Basic.

Ertel, S. (1981) Wahrnehmung und Gesellschaft. Pragnanztendenzen in Wahrnehmung un Bewubtsein. *Semiotik.* 3: 107-141. Cited and discussed in Eibl-Eibesfeldt, I. (1989) *Human Ethology.* NY: Aldine de Gruyter.

Ewald, P. (1994) *The Evolution of Infectious Disease.* NY: Oxford.

_____ . (2000) *Plague Time.* NY: Basic Books.

Eysenck, H. (1960) *Behavior Therapy and the Neuroses.* Elmsford, NY: Pergamon.

Ferrier, I., & Thompson, J. (2002) Cognitive impairment in bipolar affective disorder: Implication for the bipolar diathesis. *British Journal of Psychiatry.* 180: 293-5.

Fewell, J. (2003) Social insect networks. *Science.* 301: 1867-1870.

Fodor, J. (1983) *The Modularity of Mind.* Cambridge, MA: MIT Press.

_____ . (2001) *The Mind Doesn't Work That Way.* Cambridge, MA: MIT Press.

Frank, R. & Cook, P. (1995) *The Winner-Take-All Society.* NY: Penguin.

Frankle, W., Perlis, R., Deckersbach, T., Grandin, L., Gray, S., Sachs, G., Nierenberg A. (2002) Bipolar depression: Relationship between episode length and antidepressant treatment. *Psychological Medicine.* 32: 1417-23.

Freeman, A., Pretzer, J., Fleming, B., & Simon, K. (1990) *Clinical Applications of Cognitive Therapy.* NY: Plenum.

Furmark, T., Tillfors, M., Marteinsdottir, I., Fischer, H., Pissiota, A., Langstrom, B., & Fredrikson, M. (2002) Common changes in cerebral blood flow in patients with social phobia treated with citalopram or cognitive-behavioral therapy. Archives of General Psychiatry. 59: 425-433.

Garcia, J. & Koelling, R. (1966) Relation of cue to consequence in avoidance learning. *Psychonomic Science.* 4, 123-124.

Garcia, J., Ervin, F., & Koelling, R. (1966) Learning with prolonged delay of reinforcement. *Psychonomic Science.* 5: 121-122.

Gardner, R. (1982) Mechanisms in manic depressive disorder: An evolutionary model. *Arch Gen Psychiatry.* 39: 1436-1441.

_____ . (1995) Sociobiology and its application to psychiatry. In H.I. Kaplan and B.J. Sadock (Eds.) *The Comprehensive Textbook of Psychiatry,* 6th Ed. Baltimore, MD: Williams & Wilkins, pp. 365-375.

Gazzaniga, M. (1992) *Nature's Mind.* NY: Basic Books.

Gerhart, J. & Kirschner, M. (1997) *Cells, Embryos, and Evolution.* Malden, MA: Blackwell.

Gilbert, P. (1989) *Human Nature and Suffering*. Mahwah, NJ: Erlbaum.
Gitlin, J., Swendsen, J., Heller, T., & Hammen, C. (1995) Relapse and impairment in bipolar disorder. *American Journal of Psychiatry*. 152: 1635-1640.
Glantz, K., & Pearce, J. (1989) *Exiles from Eden: Psychotherapy from an Evolutionary Perspective*. New York: Norton.
Gleick, James (1987) *Chaos: Making a New Science*. NY: Penguin.
_____. (1992) *Genius: The Life and Science of Richard Feynman*. NY: Vintage.
Goldberg, J., Harrow, M. & Grossman, L. (1995) Course and outcome in bipolar affective disorder: a longitudinal follow-up study. *American Journal of Psychiatry*. 152: 379-384.
Goodwin, F. & Jamison, K. (1990) *Manic-Depressive Illness*. NY: Oxford.
Gould, S. (2002) *The Structure of Evolutionary Theory*. Cambridge, MA: Harvard Belknap.
Granovetter, M. (1973) The strength of weak ties. *American Journal of Sociology*, 78, 1360-1380.
Hayes, B. (1997) Can't get no satisfaction. *American Scientist*, 85:108-112.
Hebb, D. (1949) *The Organization of Behavior: A Neurophysiological Approach*. NY: Wiley.
Hess, E. (1962) Ethology: An approach to the complete analysis of behavior. In Newcomb, T (Ed.) *New Directions in Psychology*. NY: Holt Rinehart, & Winston.
Holsinger, T., Steffens, D., Phillips, C., Helms, M., Havlik, R., Breitner, J., Guralnik, J., & Plassman, B. (2002) Head injury in early adulthood and the lifetime risk of depression. *Archives of General Psychiatry*. 59: 23-24.
Jamison, K. (1993) *Touched by Fire: Manic Depressive Illness and the Artistic Temperament*. NY: Free Press.
Jones, M. (1924) Elimination of children's fears. *Journal Experimental Psychology*. 7: 382-390.
Judd, L., Akiskal, H., Schettler, P., Coryell, W., Endicott, J., Maser, J., Leon, A., Keller, M. (2003) A prospective investigation of the natural history of the long-term weekly symptomatic status of bipolar II disorder. *Archives of General Psychiatry*. 60: 261-269.
Kauffman, S. (1993) *Origins of Order: Self-Organization and Selection in Evolution*. NY: Oxford.
_____. (1995) *At Home in the Universe: The Search for the Laws of Self Organization and Complexity*. NY: Oxford.
_____. (2000) *Investigations*. NY: Oxford.
Kirschner, M. & Gerhart, J. (1998) Perspective: Evolvability. *Proceedings National Academy of Science*, 95(15), 8420-8427.
Laland, K., Odling-Smee, F., & Feldman, M. (2000) Niche construction, biological evolution and cultural change. *Behavioral and Brain Sciences*. 23(1): 131-146.
Lam, D., Watkins, E., Hayward, P., Bright, J., Kerr, N., Parr-Davis, G., & Sham, P. (2003) A randomized controlled study of cognitive therapy for relapse prevention for bipolar affective disorder: outcome of the first year. *Archives of General Psychiatry*. 60: 145-152.
Laughlin, S. & Sejnowski, T. (2003) Communication in neuronal networks. *Science*. 301: 1870-1874.
Lewontin, R. (1998/2000) *Triple Helix: Gene, Organism, Environment*. Cambridge, MA, Harvard.
Lorenz, E. (1993/2001) *The Essence of Chaos*. Seattle, WA: University of Washington Press.

Lotka, A. (1926) The frequency distribution of scientific productivity. *Journal of the Washington Academy of Sciences* 16: 317-323. Cited in Murray, C. (2003) *Human Accomplishment: The Pursuit of Excellence in the Arts & Sciences, 800 B.C. to 1950* NY: Harper Collins.

Lusseau, D. (2003) The emergent properties of a dolphin social network. Biology Letters: *Proceedings of the Royal Society of London,* Series B (Suppl.)

Maes, H. H., Neale, M. C., Kendler, K. S., Hewitt, J. K., Silberg, J. L. Foley, D. L., Meyer, J. M., Rutter, M., Simonoff, E., Pickles A., & Eaves, L. (1998) Assortative mating for major psychiatric diagnoses in two population-based samples. *Psychological Medicine*, 28(6), 1389-1401.

Mackay, C. (1841) *Extraordinary Popular Delusions and the Madness of Crowds* (A. Tobias, Ed., 1980). NY: Three Rivers Press.

Martin, N. G., Eaves, L. J., Heath, A. C., Jardine, R., Feingold, L.M., & Eysenck, H.J. (1986) Transmission of social attitudes. *Proceedings National Academy of Science*, 83: 4364-4368.

Marquis, Donald. (1973/1990) archy and methitabel. NY: Anchor.

Mayr, E. (1976) *Evolution & the Diversity of Life: Selected Essays.* Cambridge, MA: Harvard Belknap.

McGuire, M., & Troisi, A. (1998) *Darwinian Psychiatry*. NY: Oxford.

Miller, G. (1999) "Human language and intelligence as sexually selected fitness indicators" Given at the Hunter School of Social Work, New York, NY. 4/14/99.

_____ . (2000) *The Mating Mind: How Sexual Choice Shaped the Evolution of Human Nature.* NY: Doubleday.

Nesse, R. & Williams G. (1995) *Why We Get Sick: The New Science of Darwinian Medicine.* NY: Vintage.

Odling-Smee F. J., Laland, K. N., & Feldman, M. W. (2003) *Niche Construction. The Neglected Process in Evolution.* Monographs in Population Biology. Princeton, NJ: Princeton University Press.

Pennington B. (1991) *Diagnosing Learning Disorders: A Neuropsychological Framework.* NY: Guilford.

Perry, A., Tarrier, N., Morriss, R., McCarthy, E., & Limb, K. (1999) Randomised controlled trial of efficacy of teaching patients with bipolar disorder to identify early symptoms of relapse and obtain treatment. *BMJ.* 318: 149-153.

Pinker, S. (1994) *The Language Instinct: How the Mind Creates Language.* NY: Morrow.

_____ . (2002) *The Blank Slate: The Modern Denial of Human Nature.* NY: Viking.

Plomin, R. (1994) *Genetics and Experience: The Interplay between Nature and Nurture.* Thousand Oaks, CA: Sage.

Plomin, R., DeFries, J., & Loehlin, J. (1977) Genotype-environment interaction and correlation in the analysis of human behavior. *Psychological Bulletin.* 84(2), 309-322.

Plomin, R., DeFries, J., McClearn, G., & McGuffin, P. (2000) *Behavioral Genetics* (4th Ed.) NY: Worth.

Popper, K. (1984/1992) *In Search of a Better World. Lectures & Essays from Thirty Years.* Routledge, London.

Price, J. (1967) Hypothesis: the dominance hierarchy and the evolution of mental illness. *Lancet*, 2, 243-246.

Price, J. & Sloman, L. (1987) Depression as yielding behaviour: an animal model based upon Schjelderup-Ebbe's pecking order. *Ethology and Sociobiology.* 8: 85-98.

Provine, W. (1986/1989) *Sewall Wright and Evolutionary Biology.* Chicago, IL: University of Chicago Press.

Robinson, R., & Jorge, R. (2002) Longitudinal course of mood disorders following traumatic brain injury. *Archives of General Psychiatry.* 59: 23-24. Reviewed by Dubovsky, S. (2002) More than a bump on the head. *Journal Watch for Psychiatry.* 8: 24.

Queitsch, C., Sangster, TA, & Lindquist, S. (2002) Hsp90 as a capacitor of phenotypic variation. *Nature.* 471, 618-624.

Raff, R. (1996) *The Shape of Life.* Chicago, IL: University of Chicago Press.

Roberts, G. & Sherratt, T. (1998) Development of cooperative relationships through increasing investment. *Nature*, 394, 175-179.

Rose, H. & Rose, S. (2001) *Alas, Poor Darwin: Arguments Against Evolutionary Psychology.* NY: Crown.

Rowe, D (1994) The Limits of Family Influence: Genes, Experience, and Behavior. NY: Guilford.

Rowe, D. (2002) *Biology and Crime.* Los Angeles, CA: Roxbury.

Roy-Byrne, P. (2003) Bipolar medication adherence: The patient-clinician gap revisited. *Journal Watch for Psychiatry.* 9(7), 55. Review of Pope, M. & Scott, J. (2003) Do clinicians understand why individuals stop taking lithium? *Journal of Affective Disorders.* 74: 287-291.

Rutherford, S. & Lindquist, S. (1998) Hsp90 as a capacitor for morphological evolution. *Nature.* 396: 336-342.

Sacks, O. (1992) *Migraine: Revised and Expanded.* Los Angeles: University of California Press.

_____ . (1987) *The Man Who Mistook His Wife for a Hat and Other Clinical Tales.* NY: Harper & Rowe.

Sagan, C., & Druyan, A. (1992) *Shadows of Forgotten Ancestors.* New York: Random House.

Scarr, S. & McCartney, K. (1983) How people make their own environments: A theory of genotype-->environment effects. *Child Development.* 54, 424-435.

Segestrale, U. (2000) *Defenders of the Truth: The Battle for Science in the Sociobiology Debate and Beyond.* NY: Oxford.

Singer, W. (1994) Coherence as an organizing principle of cortical functions. In O. Sporns & G.Tononi (Eds.) *Selectionism and the Brain: International Review of Neurobiology.* 37, 153-184. NY: Academic.

Skoyles, J. (2000) Quoted in Bloom, H. (2000) *Global Brain.* NY: Wiley, p. 143.

Sloman, L. & Gilbert, P. (Eds.) (2000) *Subordination and Defeat.* Hillsdale, NJ: Erlbaum.

Sporns, O. (1994) Selectionist and instructionist ideas in neurobiology. In O. Sporns & G.Tononi (Eds.) *Selectionism and the Brain: International Review of Neurobiology.* 37, 4-26. NY: Academic.

Sterelny, K., & Griffiths, P. (1999) *Sex and Death: An Introduction to the Philosophy of Biology.* Chicago: University of Chicago Press.

Stevens, A., & Price, J. (2000) *Evolutionary Psychiatry: A New Beginning.* Routledge, N.Y.

Strogatz, S. (2003) *Synch: The Emerging Science of Spontaneous Order.* NY: Hyperion.

Swann, A., Bowden, C., Calabrese, J., Dilsaver, S., & Morris, D. (2000) Mania: differential effects of previous depressive and manic episodes on response to treatment. *Acta Psychiatrica Scandinavica.* 101: 444-451.

Tononi, G. (1994) Reentry and the problem of cortical integration. In O. Sporns & G.Tononi (Eds.) *Selectionism and the Brain: International Review of Neurobiology.* 37, 127-152. NY: Academic.

Toroczkai, Z., & Bassler, K. (2004) Network dynamics: jamming is limited in scale-free systems. *Nature.* 428: 716.

Torrey, F. (2002) *The Invisible Plague: The Rise of Mental Illness from 1750 to the Present.* New Brunswick, NJ: Rutgers University Press.

Tucker, G. (2003) Antidepressants still don't seem to make a difference in bipolar depression. *Journal Watch for Psychiatry.* 9(2), 14.

Turner, J. (2000) *The Extended Organism: The Physiology of Animal-Built Structures.* Cambridge, MA: Harvard University Press.

Waldrop, M (1992) *Complexity: The Emerging Science at the Edge of Order and Chaos.* NY: Touchstone.

Watson, J. & Rayner, P. (1920) Conditioned emotional reactions, *Journal Experimental Psychology.* 3: 1-14.

Watts, D. (2003) *Six Degrees: The Science of a Connected Age.* NY: Norton.

Watts, D. (2004) *Small Worlds: The Dynamics of Networks between Order and Randomness.* Princeton, NJ: Princeton University Press.

Watts, D. & Strogatz, S. (1998) Collective dynamics of 'small-world' networks. *Nature.* 393: 440-442.

Wenegrat, B. (1990) *Sociobiological Psychiatry: A New Conceptual Framework.* Lexington, MA: Lexington Books.

White, J. G., Southgate, E., Thomson, J. & Brenner, S. (1986) The structure of the nervous system of *Caenorhabditis elegans. Proceedings of the Royal Society of London, Series B. Biological Sciences.* 314: 1-340.

Wilson, E. O. (1975/2000) *Sociobiology: The New Synthesis.* Cambridge, MA: Belknap, Harvard University Press.

_____. (1998) *Consilience: The Unity of Knowledge.* NY: Knopf.

Wolpe, J. (1973) *The Practice of Behavior Therapy.* Elmsford, NY: Pergamon.

Yook, S. H., Jeong, H., & Barabási, A-:L. Preprint. Cited in Albert & Barabási, 2001.

ACKNOWLEDGMENTS

Thanks to the staff of the Barnes and Noble store in Devon, PA. Please buy your books from a human that you can touch. Thanks also to Todd Stark, Howard Bloom and Alice Andrews for their steadfast encouragement. It helps when the cheering section understands what you mean…

In: Trends in Bipolar Disorder Research
Editor: Malcomb R. Brown, pp. 65-79

ISBN: 1-59454-060-8

Chapter 3

Bipolar Disorder, Migraine and 5-HT

Traiq Mahmood
Leeds Mental Health Teaching Trust
Trevor Silverstone
University of Toronto

Why Study this Association?

Ancient Greeks believed that migraine was caused by psychological dysfunction, and in more recent times Freud and Breuer considered headache to be a manifestation of neurotic conflict (Roy 1984). Clinical descriptions of affective changes in association with migraine started to appear in the late nineteenth century (Lieving 1873). An association between migraine and affective disorders was increasingly recognised (Wolff 1937, Alvarez 1947, Cassidy 1957, Markush et al 1975). Substantial evidence now exists to corroborate early anecdotal reports (Sandler et al 1990, Merikangas 1995). Although migraine is primarily a neurological condition, Lishman (1983) estimated that 10% of migraine patients who consulted a doctor complained of mood changes related to the migraine attack. Harvey and Hay (1983) in a small prospective study reported an overall improvement in mood on pre-headache days and worsening on days with headache in 8 out of 10 migraine patients. The premonitory symptoms of migraine, which are reported the night before by 25% of those affected with migraine, often include mood changes in the form of transient depression, or, occasionally elation (Harrigan et al 1984); however, the pathogenesis of these perturbations has not been well studied. Furthermore, headache is often a symptom of mood disorders particularly depression.

Prevalence of Migraine in General Population

The prevalence of migraine, based on more than 50 population studies (Stewart et al 1992), is most probably due to differences in case definition and in the age and gender distributions of study populations. One such study was carried out in Milton, a small New Zealand town (population, approximately 5000), which is situated 54 kilometers south of

Dunedin in the South Island (Paulin et al 1985). Five hundred and forty nine men and 590 women took part in this study. The sample was predominantly European (96%) with only 2% Maori and 2% Chinese. Interviews were conducted by the staff and students of Dunedin School of Medicine, and the subjects were asked "Do you ever have headaches e.g. in the past year". Those who answered in affirmative were asked a further 13 questions related to headache. In response to the question "Do you think you have migraine?" 15% of male headache sufferers (6% of total sample) and 30 % of female headache sufferers (19% of total sample) said yes. Three-percent men and 17% women experienced two out of three symptoms suggestive of migraine i.e. unilateral headache, flashing lights or nausea. One-percent men and 4% women experienced all three symptoms.

More recent population-based studies have used the diagnostic criteria of the International Headache Society (IHS) and have reported more consistent results (Breslau et al 1991, Henry et al 1992, Rasmussen et al 1991, Stewart et al 1992). The prevalence of migraine in these studies was 12.9% to 17.6% for women and 3.4% to 6.1% for men (Stewart et al 1992). These findings are similar to those reported in the Milton survey, which did not use the operational HIS (1988) criteria.

MIGRAINE AND DEPRESSION

A "bi-directional association" (Breslau et al 1994) between migraine and depression has been shown in studies carried out on populations selected from neurology clinics and psychiatric clinics as well as in community surveys. In a series of 100 patients with "functional headaches" Kashwagi et al (1972) found that 20% of migraine sufferers reported concomitant symptoms of depression. Selby & Lance (1960) in their study of 500 cases of migraine reported that a feeling of depression was not unusual after the migraine attack and 19 of their patients with anxiety states confessed to more prolonged episodes of depression. Their assessment, however, was limited to simple questions about patients' habits, reactions to stress, and tendency to check simple things or brood over trifles. Kudrow (1978) reported that the prevalence of depression in migraine sufferers was 10% or less. In a more recent study Devlen (1994) administered the Hospital Anxiety and Depression Scale to a sample of 648 subjects attending a migraine clinic and another sample of 87 migraine sufferers in the community. Approximately 20% in both groups scored as probable or possible / borderline cases of major depressive disorder.

Diamond (1964), Philips & Hunter (1982), Merikangas et al (1988) and Marchesi et al (1989) have all found an increased prevalence of migraine in cases of depression, and Serry and Serry (1965) noted that migraine was one of the common symptoms of "masked depression". Garvey et al (1984) compared depressed patients who had migraine with those who did not, using multiple variables of depressive illness e.g. affective polarity, length of depression, and age at onset of affective disorder etc. One hundred and sixteen consecutively admitted outpatients who met Research Diagnostic Criteria (Spitzer et al 1978) for major depressive disorder were given a structured interview that included a detailed psychiatric history and a current as well as past headache history. Diagnosis of migraine was based on the presence of episodic, unilateral, severe headaches with at least one of nausea/vomiting or pre-headache warning. There was no significant increase in prevalence of migraine in depressed women (26%) but it was significantly higher in depressed men (28%). In 35 (97%) of 36 patients who had both migraine and depression, the onset of migraine preceded the onset of depression. They concluded that depressed men with migraine might represent a distinct subgroup. It should be pointed out that 75% of their patients were suffering from unipolar depression, and the rest presumably had bipolar depression although this was not stated.

Crisp et al (1977) in a very careful inquiry of community samples drawn from the population of an English country market town and its surrounding villages found that migraine sufferers scored significantly higher than non-migrainous individuals on the depression scale of the Middlesex Hospital Questionnaire. The effect was more marked in women than in men. Their sample of male subjects was, however, not large enough to reveal significant differences between it and the non-migrainous population. Couch et al (1975) reported similar findings, and Merikangas et al (1988 & 1990) and Breslau et al (1991) have reported an association between migraine and depression in other community surveys.

Breslau et al (1994) examined the association between migraine and depression in a random sample of 1007 young adults registered with a large Health Maintenance Organization in Southeast Michigan. A structured diagnostic interview was used to elicit information on DSM-III-R major depression and IHS migraine. They estimated that the incidence of migraine per 1000 person years, based on prospectively gathered data, was 5.0 in males and 22.0 in females. The estimated relative risk for major depression associated with prior migraine was 3.2 and the adjusted relative risk for migraine associated with prior major depression was 3.1. This provided the first body of evidence to show that the previously observed cross-sectional association between migraine and major depression could result from bi-directional influences, with onset of each disorder increasing the risk for subsequent onset of the other. They concluded that the bi-directional association between migraine and depression tended to disprove the hypothesis that the association between migraine and depression was a psychological response to a chronic and disabling illness.

Migraine and Bipolar Affective Disorder

The great majority of investigations on migraine and affective disorders have focused on unipolar depression with relatively few examining bipolar patients specifically. Nevertheless, the studies of unipolar depression, particularly those of major depression, have often included cases of bipolar depression. Furthermore, 10 to 20% of patients with unipolar depression later go on to experience manic episodes (Kendell 1993). Therefore, findings of studies on major depression have potential relevance to bipolar disorder.

Cassidy et al (1957) found headache to be the most common somatic symptom in a group of 100 patients with manic depressive illness but did not specify the type of headache. The only study to have addressed this question specifically was that undertaken by Marchesi et al (1989), which evaluated the prevalence of headache and its subtypes (migraine, muscle tension headache, cluster headache and psychogenic headache) in 160 depressed patients that included 26 bipolar patients. They did not find an increased prevalence of migraine in bipolar patients.

MIGRAINE AMONG PATIENTS REGISTERED WITH A BIPOLAR REGISTER

Since there had been no large study of the association between migraine and bipolar disorder in a clinical sample, we decided to carry out a study based on Otago Bipolar Register. This register consists of cases of bipolar disorder attending the bipolar clinic at Dunedin Hospital, who have agreed to participate in research undertaken by the University of Otago Affective Disorders Research Group. The psychiatric diagnosis had been established on the basis of structured interviews using standardized instruments: the Schedule for Affective Disorders and Schizophrenia – Life Time Version (SADS – L) (Spitzer and Endicott 1978) or the Diagnostic Interview for Genetic Studies (DIGS) (Nurnberger 1994) and using DSM IIIR or DSM IV criteria. At the time of this study there were 117 bipolar patients on the bipolar register (61 males and 56 females aged between 20 to 70 years - mean = 42.6 years).

A postal questionnaire incorporating the international Headache Society's diagnostic criteria for headache disorders (IHS 1988) was sent to all cases on the Dunedin Bipolar Register. Completed questionnaires were obtained from 81 bipolar patients (69% of the sample). Twenty one (25.9%) patients met IHS criteria for a diagnosis of migraine. Only 2 cases met the criteria for migraine with aura. Another 16 patients (9 males, 7 females) complained of headaches, however, they did not meet all the criteria for migraine. Compared to general population the prevalence of migraine was strikingly higher in male (11/44 - 25%) than in female (10/37 - 27%) bipolar patients (**Table 1**). This was similar to the prevalence rate of migraine in men reported in an earlier study of 116 men who met Research Diagnostic Criteria (RDC) for major depressive disorder (Garvey et al 1984), some of whom were possibly bipolar cases. In a study of a relatively small sample of patients with bipolar and unipolar disorder, symptoms of migraine were common in both diagnostic groups (46% and 44%) and a lot more common in bipolar II group (77%) (Fasmer 2001).

Table 1. Prevalence of Migraine in Bipolar Patients

	Men (n=44)	Women (n=37)
Migraine	11 (25%)	10 (27%)
Migraine?	9 (20%)	7 (15%)

Bipolar patients who suffered from migraine tended to have an earlier onset of bipolar illness compared to those who did not experience migraine (**Table 2**). Twelve of the twenty one migraine sufferers (57%) had their first episode before the age of twenty five compared to 16/60 (21%) of those who did not suffer from migraine. Comorbidity of bipolar disorder and migraine was associated with greater psychosocial impairment than uncomplicated bipolar disorder. Patients with comorbid bipolar disorder and migrane were more likely to be single (42.8% vs. 34%), to be on a social welfare benefit (47.6% vs. 38%) and were less likely to have received tertiary education (38% vs. 54.5%).

Table 2. Comorbidity of Bipolar Disorder and Migraine and Degree of Social Adversity

	BP+Migraine	**BP**
Early onset	57%	21.6%
Unmarried	42.8%	34%
Unemployed	47.6%	38%
Higher education	38%	54.5%

A Possible Subtype of Bipolar Disorder and is Serotonin (5-HT) the Link?

Increased prevalence of migraine in bipolar patients and the earlier onset of bipolar disorder in those with history of migraine suggest that we may possibly be seeing a biologically determined subtype of bipolar disorder. One can postulate that bipolar disorder with co-morbid migraine is a severer variant of bipolar disorder with a common pathophysiological abnormality, possibly of the serotonergic system, because serotonin is known to play a role in the regulation of pain and cerebral perfusion as well as mood (Lucki 1998).

Several lines of pharmacological evidence suggest a relationship between serotonin and migraine (Ferrari and Saxena 1993, Silberstein 1994). Amitriptyline, an inhibitor of reuptake of monoamines including serotonin, is effective both as an antidepressant and as a prophylactic for migraine (Couch et al 1979). The fact that all antidepressants may not be effective against migraine indicates that the therapeutic effect is probably not due to a general improvement in mood (Martucci et al 1985). Conversely, reserpine, which depletes monoamine neurotransmitters, can precipitate headaches in migraine patients and has been associated with the onset of depression in approximately 20% patients who were using the drug regularly (Garvey et al 1984). Similarly, fenfluramine, which promotes serotonin release from nerve terminals, induced typical headaches in patients with migraine more frequently than in controls (Sicuteri et al 1976). M-CPP (m-chlorophenylpiperazine), a 5-HT_2 receptor agonist has also been observed to be a potent trigger of migraine-like headaches (Gordon et al 1995). Lithium, a widely used drug for the prevention of relapse in bipolar disorder, which is believed to enhance central serotonergic function, was found to be useful in the treatment of migraine (Nieper 1975). Two agents that are effective in the acute treatment of migraine namely dihydroergotamine and sumatriptan are agonists at the 5-HT_{1A} and 5-HT_{1D} receptors, and other prophylactic agents like methysergide, pizotifen and cyproheptadine are 5-HT_2 antagonists.

Sicuteri (1972) in a study involving 40 patients affected with migraine, who were drug free for six weeks, treated 20 with methysergide and the other 20 with L-5-hydroxytryptophan for 40 days. The efficiency of each agent was evaluated by the number of episodes of migraine that occurred in each group. Both drugs were equally effective. These findings are consistent with 5-HT deficiency leading to central monoamine supersensitivity.

SEROTONIN AND BIPOLAR DISORDER

As we have seen, abnormalities of serotonin metabolism have been implicated in migraine (Gordon et al 1995) and its role in pathogenesis of migraine has been well investigated. On the other hand, although reduced central serotonergic function is said to characterize both the manic and depressed phases of bipolar disorder (Goodwin and Jamison 1990), the role of serotonin in the pathogenesis of bipolar disorder has not been fully examined. Among the mood disorders the role of serotonin in the pathogenesis of major / unipolar (UP) depression has been widely researched; with most studies reporting decreased central serotonergic function in major depressive disorder (Maes and Meltzer 1994). As pointed out previously, a number of studies on the role of serotonin in major depression have included cases of bipolar depression (Asberg et al 1984, Lewis & McChesney 1985, Baron et al 1986, Coccaro et al 1989, Price et al 1990), although in the analysis little if any distinction was made between the two. Therefore, while it is fair to say that the findings of these studies may have some relevance to bipolar disorder, the degree to which this may apply is unclear.

A number of direct and indirect approaches have been used to study the role of 5-HT in the pathophysiology of bipolar disorder, which include: brain imaging, CSF analysis, neuroendocrine challenge, genetic studies, platelet function and psychopharmacological studies. These various investigations have yielded the following results:

- Low concentrations of 5-HT and 5-HIAA (Traskman et al 1981) and lower concentrations of seretonin uptake sites (Leake et al 1991) were found in the brains of depressed bipolar patients who completed suicide. Arranz et al (1994) found a significant decrease in 5-HT_{1D} binding sites in the brains of depressed as well as non-depressed suicide victims. They made no distinction between bipolar and unipolar cases. Baumann & Bogerts (2001) investigated the cyto-architecture of dorsal raphe nucleus in post-mortem brains of 12 patients with mood disorders (6 bipolar and 6 major depression) and 12 subjects without any neuropsychiatric disorder. The ventral parts of the mesencephalic dorsal raphe nucleus showed fewer serotonergic neurons in patients with a mood difference, and no difference was seen between major depression and bipolar disorder in this respect.
- An association with serotonin transporter gene has been reported in several genetic studies of bipolar disorder (Collier et al 1996).
- A preliminary SPECT study with a 5-HT ligand has shown low levels of serotonin transporter in brainstems of bipolar patients (Staley et al 1998). In another study (Ichimiya et al 2002) on 13 antidepressant-naïve or antidepressant-free patients with mood disorders (6 bipolar patients) with a selective ligand for 5-HTT, [11C](+)McN5652, binding potential was found to be significantly increased in the thalamus of patients with mood disorder.
- Absolute levels of the 5-HT metabolite (5-HIAA) were reduced in CSF of depressed bipolar patients (Asberg et al 1984) and raised in mania (Swan et al 1983).
- Significantly reduced hypothalamo-pituitary-axis response to 5-HT agonists has been found in the depressed as well as the manic phase of BP illness (Thakore et al 1996). Diminished cortisol response to a tryptophan challenge has been reported in euthymic bipolar patients (Nurnberger et al 1990).

- 5-HT transport is reduced in platelets of depressed bipolar patients (Meltzer et al 1989) as well as in platelets of bipolar patients in the manic phase (Marazziti et al 1991).
- Mood stabilizers such as lithium and valproate possibly act by enhancing central serotonergic transmission (Moorman & Leslie 1998, Maes et al 1997). The use of lithium leads to increased plasma serotonin levels (Artigas et al 1998).

The above findings indicate that serotonergic activity is reduced in bipolar depression, which is similar to but more extreme than that found in unipolar depression. In mania the findings are less consistent. In some cases the findings are the same as bipolar depression, in others the opposite. Euthymic bipolar cases, on the other hand, show reduced serotonin function, which suggests that diminished serotonergic activity may be a trait marker for bipolar disorder.

NEUROENDOCRINE PARADIGM AND THE STUDY OF CENTRAL SEROTONERGIC FUNCTION

The study of the activity of the hypothalamic-pituitary axis with the neuroendocrine challenge paradigm provides a window on the working of living brain (Gordon et al 1995). In this approach the challenge agent stimulates the release of a neurotransmitter in the hypothalamus, which promotes the secretion of a neuropeptide that in turn affects the hormone secretion from the pituitary gland. The resulting increased or decreased secretion of pituitary hormones is taken as an indirect measure of the activity of the relevant hypothalamic neurons.

There is extensive evidence that 5HT receptors in the brain participate in the hypothalamic control of pituitary hormone secretion (Fuller 1990). 5-HT containing nerve terminals make synaptic contact with corticotrophin-releasing factor (CRF) containing cells in the rat hypothalamus and both 5HT and 5HT receptor agonists can stimulate CRF release from isolated rat hypothalamus in vitro. In vivo, direct-acting 5-HT receptor agonists, 5-HT release uptake inhibitors, 5-HT releasers, and 5HT precursors all stimulate adrenocorticotrophin (ACTH) and cortisol release. Serotonergic neurons projecting to the hypothalamus also stimulate the secretion of prolactin. Rats with chemical lesions of brain serotonergic neurons have supersensitive cortisol and prolactin responses to direct 5-HT agonists (Van de Kar et al 1989).

Of the pituitary hormones, prolactin has been the most frequently measured in bipolar disorder, its secretion being stimulated by 5-HT and inhibited by dopamine. Serotonin is also thought to stimulate the secretion of growth hormone and adrenocorticotrophic hormone (ACTH). The most frequently employed neuroendocrine challenge agents for the study of central serotonergic systems have been fenfluramine/d-fenfluramine (which release 5-HT from presynaptic neurons), tryptophan/l-tryptophan (5-HT precursors), clomipramine/fluoxetine (inhibitors of 5-HT uptake) and buspirone (5-HT_{1A} receptor agonist) [Yatham & Steiner 1991]. More recently triptans, which are selective 5-HT_{1D} agonists, have also been employed for this purpose (Yatham et al 1997, Mahmood et al 2002).

Neuroendocrine Studies of 5-HT Function in Migrainous Patients

Brewerton et al (1988) found that m-chlorophenylpiperazine (m-CPP) provoked severe headache similar to migraine in 54% patients with eating disorder. In one such study using m-CPP as a neuroendocrine challenge Gordon et al (1993) investigated the neuroendocrine and headache responses in 8 subjects with migraine and 10 normal subjects. Employing a double-blind crossover design they found no significant differences between the migraine and the control groups in the ▲cortisol, ▲prolactin or area under the curve following m-CPP.

Leone et al (1997) reported a study on central serotonergic activity in cluster headache using m-CPP as the challenge agent. Cluster headache is a rare but distinct clinical and epidemiologic entity, which may share a similar neurobiology with migraine. It is characterized by male preponderance, periodicity, and responsiveness to lithium, and thus has some common ground with bipolar disorder. Both men and women (n=23) with cluster headache had a significantly lower cortisol delta maxima (maximum response - baseline level / baseline level) than the respective male and female controls (n=27), while the values of PRL delta maxima were significantly higher. These findings suggest that the central serotonergic system may be altered in patients with cluster headaches.

Pinessi et al (2001) studied the effects of subcutaneous sumatriptan on plasma growth hormone concentrations in migraine patients. They administered sumatriptan and placebo to 15 migraineurs and to 10 controls. Blood samples were collected at –15, 0, 15, 30, 45, 60 and 90 minutes after the injection. Sumatriptan induced an increase in growth hormone concentrations in both group with no significant difference between them.

Neuroendocrine Studies of Patients with Bipolar Disorder Mania

Only two studies have employed the fenfluramine challenge test in homogenous samples of manic patients (Newman et al 1998). Yatham (1996, 1997) found that prolactin or cortisol responses to d-fenfluramine (n = 10) and sumatriptan (n=9) in manic patients did not differ from normal controls. Thakore et al (1996), on the other hand, found increased basal cortisol levels and reduced prolactin responses to d-fenfluramine in 9 manic patients, compared with 9 healthy controls matched for age and sex. They suggest that mania is associated with a state of decreased 5-HT responsiveness, similar to that found in the depressed state.

Bipolar Depression

Whilst there have been no studies looking specifically at bipolar depression, studies of major depression have often included cases of bipolar depression (Mahmood & Silverstone 2001), or have included first episode cases (Cleare et al 1998), 20-30% of whom are likely to turn out to be bipolar. Of some relevance for bipolar disorder was the finding that the growth hormone release following subcutaneous administration of 6mg sumatriptan was significantly lower during winter depression and normalized following light therapy in 11 patients of seasonal affective disorder (Yatham et al 1997).

Table 3. Neuroendocrine Studies of Patients with Bipolar Disorder

	Mania	Depression	Euthymic
d-fenfluramine	=[a] ↓[b]		
Sumatriptan	=[c]	↓[c]	
Tryptophan			↓[d]

[a] Yatham 1996.
[b] Thakore et al 1996.
[c] Yatham et al 1997.
[d] Nurnberger et al 1990.
= No differenence.
↓ Reduced.

EUTHYMIC BIPOLAR PATIENTS

In a placebo-controlled study the serotonin precursor tryptophan was given intravenously to 11 remitted bipolar patients and 14 controls over a 20-minute period in the afternoon. Cortisol and ACTH release was significantly lower in bipolar patients (Nurnberger et al1990).

NEUROENDOCRINE CHALLENGE WITH SUMATRIPTAN IN BIPOLAR PATIENTS WITH AND WITHOUT MIGRAINE

As we have seen, sumatriptan, an antimigraine agent and a highly selective agonist of 5-HT1D/1B receptors, is reported to stimulate the release of growth hormone and to inhibit that of prolactin in normal subjects (Rolandi et al 1992; Franceschení et al 1994, Herdman et al 1994). It has been used to study affective disorders (Yatham et al 1997a; Yatham et al 1997b; Cleare et al 1998) and growth hormone response to sumatriptan was found to be diminished in cases of seasonal affective disorder (Yatham et al 1997). In our own studies we used sumatriptan to investigate further the biological basis of the association between bipolar disorder and migraine observed in clinical and population studies. We examined a series of 9 bipolar patients who also suffered from migraine (BP+MIGR), 9 who did not (BP), 7 migraine patients without affective disorder (MIGR), and 9 age, weight and gender matched control subjects (CONTR). Women controls were also matched for menstrual status. The bipolar patients were euthymic at the time of neuroendocrine challenge and were taking their prescribed mood stabilizers. Migraine patients were recruited from among the hospital staff and met the I.H.S. (1988) criteria for the diagnosis of migraine. Healthy controls were also recruited from among the hospital staff and were free of psychiatric disorder and migraine (Mahmood et al 2002). The main finding was a blunting of the GH response in patients who suffered from both migraine and bipolar disorder.

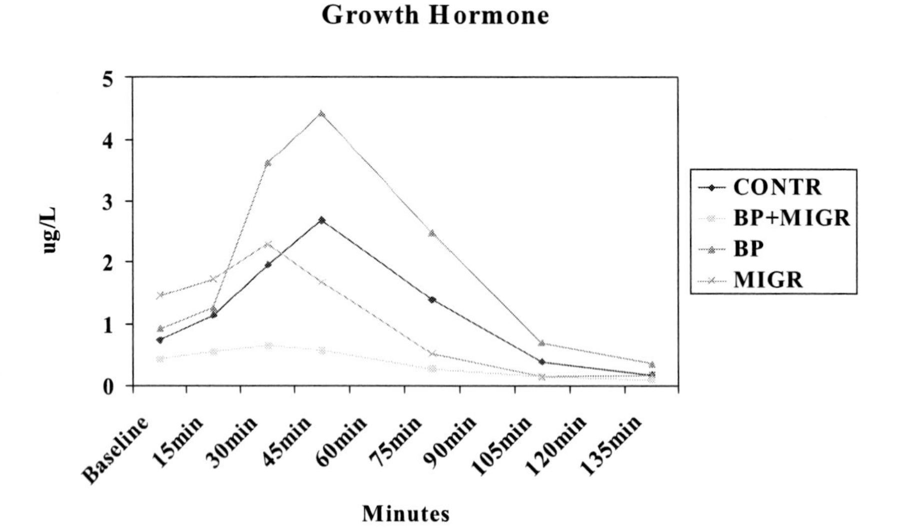

Graph 1. GH response in bipolar patients with and without migraine

SIGNIFICANCE OF 5-HT_{1D} RECEPTOR BLUNTING IN A GROUP OF BIPOLAR PATIENTS

Epidemiological association between mood disorders and migraine has often led to speculation that the two may be linked to a common underlying disturbance in the serotonergic system (Fasmer and Odeggaard 2001). This inference is based on the observation that serotonin seems to be involved in the pathogenesis of both migraine (Sicuteri and Nicoldi 1991) and bipolar disorder (Mahmood and Silverstone 2001). However, the question had not been addressed specifically in a formal biological investigation. We chose a to examine the central serotonergic function in euthymic bipolar patients with and without migraine by subjecting them to a neuroendocrine challenge with sumatriptan, a 5-HT_{1D} agonist. The evidence from neuroendocrine challenge studies shows reduced serotonergic activity in bipolar depressed patients as well as euthymic bipolar patients. Decreased 5-HT responsiveness has also been reported in some studies with manic patients. On the contrary, neuroendocrine studies of migraine patients have not shown the hormonal responses to be any different from the controls. Nevertheless, a recent study (Cassidy et al 2003) with a 5-HT1A receptor agonist namely buspirone, found that mean delta prolactin had a four-fold increase in migraine without aura patients. Buspirone, however, is a dopamine antagonist, and this effect may have contributed to the rise in prolactin levels seen by Cassidy et al in migraine patients without aura.

Yatham et al (1997) had studied growth hormone response to sumatriptan in manic patients and found it to be no different from depressed patients and controls. We found that growth hormone response after the administration of sumatriptan was blunted in euthymic bipolar patients with migraine, but not in those with bipolar disorder alone. Nor was it blunted in patients with migraine. Our findings, albeit in a subset of bipolar patients, are consistent with Thakore et al (1996) and Nurnberger et al (1990) who reported sub-sensitivity of central serotonergic system in manic patients. Our results suggest the possibility that bipolar patients with migraine represent a variant of bipolar disorder with an abnormal 5-HT_{1D} receptor function, and this abnormality is a trait rather than state marker. It is proposed that future genetic investigations of this receptor in bipolar patients (Mundo et al 2001) should give consideration to the presence or absence of migraine in probands.

REFERENCES

American Psychiatric Association (1994) Diagnostic and Statistical Manual of Mental Disorders, 4th ed. (DSM IV). APA, Washington, DC.

Arranz B, Eriksson A, Mellerup E, Plenge P, Marcusson J (1994) Brain 5-HT1A, 5-HT1D, and 5-HT2 receptors in suicide victims. *Biological Psychiatry 35,* 457-463.

Artigas F, Sarrias MJ, Martinez E, Gelpi E, Alvarez E, Udina C (1989) Increased plasma free serotonin but unchanged platelet serotonin in bipolar patients treated chronically with lithium. *Psychopharmacology 99*, 328-332.

Asberg M, Bertillsson L, Martensson B, Scalia-Tomba GP, Thoren P, Traskman-Bendz L (1984) CSF monoamine metabolites in melancholia. *Acta Psychiatrica Scandinavia 69*, 201-219.

Alvarez,W C. (1947) The migrainous personality and constitution: the essential features of the disease. American Journal of Medical Sciences 213, 2–8.

American Psychiatric Association (1989) Diagnostic and Statistical Manual of Mental Disorders (3rd edition revised) Washington DC: American Psychiatric Association.

Baron M, Barkai A, Gruen R, Peselow E, Fieve R, Quitken F (1986) Platelet ^{3}H imipramine binding in affective disorders: trait versus state characteristics. *American Journal of Psychiatry 143*, 711717.

Baumann B, Bogerts B (2001) Neuroanatomical studies on bipolar disorder. *British Journal of Psychiatry 178* (suppl. 41), s142-s147.

Breslau N, Davis G C, Andreski P. (1991) Migraine, psychiatric disorder, and suicide attempts: an epidemiologic study of young adults. Psychiatry Research 37, 11-23.

Breslau N, Davis G C, Schultz L R, Peterson E L (1994) Migraine and major depression: a longitudinal study. *Headache 34,* 387-393.

Brewerton TD, Murphy DL, Mueller EA, Jimerson DC (1988) Induction of migraine like headaches by the serotonin agonist m-chlorophenylpiperazine. *Clinical Pharmacology and Therapeutics 43*, 605-609.

Cassidy W L (1957) Clinical observations in manic depressive disease. *Journal of American Medical Association 164*, 1535-1546.

Cassidy F, Murry E, Carrol BJ (1998) Tryptophan depletion in recently manic patients treated with lithium. *Biological Psychiatry 43,* 230-232.

Couch J R and Hassanein R S (1979) Amitriptyline in the migraine prophylaxis. Archives of *Neurology 36,* 695-699.

Cleare AJ, Murray RM, Sherwood RA, O'Keane V (1998) Abnormal 5-HT_{1D} receptor function in major depression: a neuropharmacological challenge study using sumatriptan. *Psychological Medicine 28*, 295-300.

Coccaro EF, Siever LJ, Klar HM, Cochrane K, Cooper TB, Mohs RC, Davis KL (1989) Serotonergic studies in patients with affective and personality disorders: correlates with suicidal and impulsive-aggressive behaviour. *Archives of general psychiatry 46,* 587-599.

Collier DA, Arranz MJ, Battersby S, Vallada H, Gill P, Aitchison KJ, Sodhi M, Li T, Roberts GW, Smith B, Morton J, Murray RM, Smith D, Kirov G (1996) The serotonin transporter is a potential susceptibility factor for bipolar affective disorder. *NeuroReport 7,* 1675-1679.

Couch JR, Ziegler DK, Hassanein RS (1975) Evaluation of the relationship between migraine headache and depression. *Headache 15,* 41-50.

Crisp AH, Kalney RS, McGuinness B (1977) Some clinical, social and psychological characteristics of migraine subjects in the general population. Postgraduate Medical Journal 53, 691-697.

Devlen, J (1994) Anxiety and Depression in migrane. *Journal of Soc. Medicine, 87(6),* 338-341.

Diamond S (1964) Depressive headaches. Headache 4, 255-258.

Endicott J and Spitzer R L (1978) A diagnostic interview. The schedule for affective disorders and schizophrenia. *Archives of General Psychiatry 35*, 837-844.

Fasmer O B (2001) The prevalence of migraine in patients with bipolar and unipolar affective disorders. *Cephalalgia 21*, 894-899.

Fasmer OB, Odegaard KJ (2001) Clinical characteristics of patients with major affective disorders and comorbid migraine. World Biological Psychiatry 2, 149-155.

Ferrari MD, Saxena PR (1993) On serotonin and migraine: a clinical and pharmacological review. *Cephalalgia 13*, 151-165.

Franceschini R, Cataldi A, Garibaldi P, Scordamaglia A, Barreca T, Rolandi E (1994) The effects of sumatriptan on pituitary secretion in man. Neuropharmacology 33: 235-239.

Fuller RW (1990) Serotonin receptors and neuroendocrine responses. *Neuro-psychopharmacology 3,* 495-502.

Garvey M J, Tollefson G D, Schaffer C B (1984) Migraine headaches and depression. *American Journal of Psychiatry 141,* 986-988.

Goodwin F K and Jamison K R (1990) *Manic Depressive Illness*. New York: Oxford University Press.

Gordon M L, Lipton R B, Brown S C, van Pragg H M (1995) The neuroendocrine challenge paradigm in headache research. Cephalalgia 15, 292-296.

Harrigan JA, Kues JR, Ricks DF, Smith R (1984) Moods that predict coming migraine headaches. *Pain 20,* 385-396.

Headache Classification Committee of the International Headache Society (1988). Classification and diagnostic criteria for headache disorders, cranial neuralgias and facial pain. *Cephalalgia 8* (Suppl. 7), 1-96.

Henry P, Michel P, Brochet B, Dartiques J, Tison S, Salamon R (1992) A nationwide survey of migraine in France: prevalence and clinical features in adults. *Cephalalgia 12,* 229-237.

Herdman JR, Delva NJ, Hockney RE, Campling GM, Cowen PJ (1994) Neuroendocrine effects of sumatriptan. *Psychopharmacology 113*, 561-564.

Harvey P G and Hay K M (1984) Mood and migraine – a preliminary prospective study. *Headache, July 1984*, 225-228.

Ichimya T, Suhara T, Sudo Y, Okubo Y, Nakayama K, Nankai M, Inoue M, Yasuno F, Takano A, Maeda J, Shibuya H (2002) Serotonin transporter binding in patients with mood disorders: a PET study with [11C](+)McN5652). *Biological Psychiatry 51*, 715-722.

Kashiwagi T, McClure JN, Wetzel RD (1972) Headache and psychiatric disorders. *Disorders of Nervous System 33*, 659-663.

Kendell RE (1993) Mood affective disorders. In Companion to Psychiatric Studies 5t edition. Editors: R E Kendell & A K Zealley. London: Churchill Livingstone.

Kudrow L (1978) Current aspects of migraine headache. Psychosomatics 19, 48-57.

Lishman W A (1983) Organic Psychiatry. Blackwell: Oxford.

Lieving E (1873) On Megrim, Sick-Headache and Some Allied Disorders. A contribution in the Pathology of Nerve-Storms. Churchill: London.

Leake A, Fairbairn AF, McKeith IG, Ferrier IN (1991) Studies on the serotonin uptake binding site in major depressive disorder and control post-mortem brain: neurochemical and clinical correlates. Psychiatry Research 39, 155-165.

Leone M, Attanasio A, Croci D, Libro G, Grazzi L, D'Amico D, Nespolo A, Bussone G (1997) The m-chlorophenylpiperazine test in cluster headache: a study on central serotonergic activity. *Cephalalgia 17,* 666-672.

Lewis DA, McChesney C (1985) Tritiated imipramine binding distinguishes among subtypes of depression. *Archives of General Psychiatry 42,* 485-488.

Lucki I (1998) The spectrum of behaviours influenced by serotonin. *Biological Psychiatry 44,* 151-162.

Maes M, Meltzer HY (1994) The serotonin hypothesis of major depression, in *Psychopharmacology: The Fourth Generation of Progress*. Edited by Bloom FE, Kupfer DJ. New York, Raven Press, pp 933-944.

Maes M, Calabrese J, Jayathilake K, Meltzer HY (1997) Effects of subchronic treatment with valproate on L-5-HTP-induced cortisol responses in mania: evidence for increased central serotonergic neurotransmission. *Psychiatry Research 71,* 67-76.

Mahmood T, Romans S, Silverstone T (1999) Prevalence of migraine in bipolar disorder. *Journal of Affective Disorders* 52, 239-231.

Mahmood T, Silverstone T (2001) Serotonin and bipolar disorder. *Journal of Affective Disorders 66*, 1-11.

Mahmood T, Silverstone T, O'Connor R, Herbison P (2002) Sumatriptan challenge in bipolar patients with and without migraine – a neuroendocrine challenge study of 5-HT_{1D} receptor function. *International Clinical Psychopharmacology 17*, 33-36.

Marchesi C, Ferri A D, Petrolini N, Govi A, Manzoni G C, Coiro V, De Risio C (1989) Prevalence of migraine and muscle tension headache in depressive disorders. *Journal of Affective Disorders 6,* 33-36.

Markush R E, Karp H R, Heymen A et al (1975) Epidemiologic study of migraine symptoms in young women. *Neurology 25,* 430-435.

Martucci N, Manna V, Agnoli A (1985) Antidepressant drugs and migraine. *Cephalalgia 5*(suppl 2), 225-228.

Meltzer H, Arora RC, Goodnick P (1983) Effect of lithium carbonate on serotonin uptake in blood platelets of patients with affective disorders. *Journal of Affective Disorders 5,* 215-221.

Moorman JR, Leslie RA (1998) Paradoxical effects of lithium on serotonergic receptor function: an immunocytochemical, behavioural and autoradiographic study. *Neuropharmacology 37,* 357-370.

Merikangas K R, Merikangas J R, Angst J (1993) Migraine and depression: association and familial transmission. *Journal of Psychiatric Research 27*, 197-210.

Merikangas K R (1995) Association between psychopathology and headache syndromes. *Current Opinion in Neurology 8,* 248-251.

Merikangas KR (1996) Genetics of migraine and other headaches. Current Opinion in Neurology 9(3), 202-205.

Mundo E, Zai G, Lee L, Parikh SV, Kennedy JL (2001) The 5-$HT_{1D\beta}$ receptor gene in bipolar disorder: a family based association study. *Neuropsychopharmacology 25,* 608-13.

Nieper H A (1975) Clinical applications of lithium orotate: a two year study. Journal of *Academy of Preventive Medicine 2/2*, 18-22.

Nurnberger JI Jr, Berrettini W, Simmons-Alling S, Lawrence D, Brittain H (1990) Blunted ACTH and cortisol response to afternoon tryptophan infusion in euthymic bipolar patients. *Psychiatry Research (Ireland) 31 (1),* 57-67.

Nurnberger JI, Blehar MC, Kaufman CA, York-Cooler C, Simpson SG, Severe JB, Malaspina D (1994) Diagnostic interview for genetic studies. Rationale, unique features and training. *Archives of General Psychiatry 51,* 849-864.

Paulin JM, Wall-Manning HJ, Simpson FO, Knight RG (1985) The prevalence of headache in a small New Zealand Town. *Headache 25*, 147-151.

Philips C, Hunter M (1982) Headache in a psychiatric population. *Journal of Nervous and Mental Diseases 170*, 34-40.

Price LH, Charney DS, Delgado PD, Heninger GR (1989) Lithium treatment and serotonergic function. *Archives of General Psychiatry 46,* 13-19.

_____ . (1991) Serotonin function and depression: Neuroendocrine and mood responses to intravenous L-tryptophan in depressed patients and healthy comparison subjects. *American Journal of Psychiatry 148,* 1518-1525.

Rasmussen BK, Jensen R, Schroll M. Olesen J (1991) Epidemiology of headache in a general population: a prevalence study. *Journal of Clinical Epidemiology 44*, 1147-1157.

Roy R (1984) Migraine and muscle-contraction headache: psychiatry and personality issues – a review. *International Journal of Psychiatry in Medicine 14,* 157-170.

Sandler M (1990) *Migraine and depression.* Abstracts of 8th Migraine Trust International Symposium, pp. 176-177.

Selby G, Lance JW (1960) Observations on 500 cases of migraine and allied vascular headaches. *Journal of Neurology, Neurosurgery and Psychiatry 23*, 23-32.

Serry D and Serry M (1965) Masked depression and the use of antidepressants in general practice. *Medical Journal of Australia 1,* 334-338.

Sicuteri F (1972) 5-Hydroxytryptophan in the prophylaxis of migraine. *Pharmacological Research Communication 4,* 213-218.

Sicuteri F, Del Bene E, Anselmi B (1976) Fenfluramine headache. *Headache 6*, 185-188.

Sicuteri F and Nicoldi M (1991) Serotonin, a "Sphynx" in migraine *in* Headache and Depression: Serotonin Pathways as a Common Clue, *edited by* G. Nappi et al. New York: Raven Press, 225-236.

Silberstein SD (1994) Serotonin (5HT) and migraine. *Headache 34,* 408-417.

Spitzer RL, Endicott J, Robins E (1978) Research Diagnostic Criteria: rationale and reliability. *Archives of General Psychiatry 35,* 773-782.

Staley JK, Malison RT, Innis RB (1998) Imaging of the serotonergic system: interactions of neuroanatomical and functional abnormalities of depression. *Biological Psychiatry 44,* 534-549.

Spitzer RL, Endicott J, Robins E (1978) Research Diagnostic Criteria: rationale and reliability. *Archives of General Psychiatry 35*, 773-778.

Stewart WF, Reed ML, Lipton RB, Celentano DD (1992) Prevalence of migraine headache in the United States. *Journal of American Medical Association 267*, 64-69.

Swann AC, Secunda S, Davis JM, Robins E, Hanin I, Koslow SH, Maas JW (1983) CSF monoamine metabolites in mania. *American Journal of Psychiatry 140*, 396-400.

Stewart W F, Lipton R B, Celentano D et al (1992) Prevalence of migraine headache in the United States. *Journal of American Medical Association 267*, 64-69.

Thakore JH, O'Keane V, Dinan TG (1996) d-fenfluramine-induced prolactin responses in mania: evidence for serotonergic subsensitivity. *American Journal of Psychiatry 153,* 1460-1463.

Traskman L, Asberg M, Bertillsson L, Sjostrand L (1981) Monoamine metabolites in CSF and suicidal behaviour. *Archives of General Psychiatry 38,* 631-636.

Van de Kar LD, Carnes M, Masolowski RJ et al (1989) Neuroendocrine evidence for denervation supersensitivity of serotonin receptors: effects of the 5-HT agonist RU 24969 on corticotrophin, corticosterone, prolactin and renin secretion. *Journal of Pharmacology and Experimental Therapeutics 251*, 428-434.

Wolff H G (1937) Personality factors and reactions of subjects with migraine. *Archives of Neurology and Psychiatry 37,* 895-892.

Yatham LN & Steiner M (1993) Neuroendocrine probes of serotonergic function: a critical review. *Life Sciences 53,* 447-463.

Yatham LN (1996) Prolactin and cortisol responses to fenfluramine challenge in mania. *Biological Psychiatry 39*, 285-288.

Yatham LN, Lam RW, Zis AP (1997b) Growth hormone response to sumatriptan ($5\text{-}HT_{1D}$ agonist) challenge in seasonal affective disorder: effects of light therapy. *Biological Psychiatry 42*, 24-29.

Yatham LN, Zis AP, Lam RW, Tam E, Shiah IS (1997a) Sumatriptan-induced growth hormone release in patients with major depression, mania and normal controls. *Neuropsychopharmacology 17*, 258-263.

In: Trends in Bipolar Disorder Research
Editor: Malcomb R. Brown, pp. 81-96
ISBN: 1-59454-060-8

Chapter 4

GLUCOSE METABOLISM IN BIPOLAR DISORDER

William T. Regenold and Christopher Marano
Division of Geriatric Psychiatry, Department of Psychiatry, University of Maryland
School of Medicine and the Baltimore VA Medical Center, Maryland
University of Maryland Mood Disorders Program, Baltimore

INTRODUCTION

Bipolar mood disorder is ultimately a disorder of the brain. The brain relies almost exclusively on glucose as its substrate for energy metabolism, consuming glucose at a rate far exceeding that of any other bodily organ. It follows, therefore, that information about perturbations of glucose metabolism in bipolar disorder could contribute to our knowledge of the pathophysiology and treatment of the disorder. The aim of this chapter is to promote progress in the understanding and treatment of bipolar disorder by critically reviewing the literature, presenting data, and discussing theoretical and clinical issues regarding glucose metabolism in bipolar disorder. The literature on carbohydrate metabolism in bipolar disorder as well as on affective disorders and diabetes mellitus has been previously reviewed by Goodwin and Jamison [1] and by Geringer [2]. We are indebted to these authors. We will briefly and critically review the literature on glucose metabolism in psychiatric illness in general. This review will provide the background against which we will present our study of the relative frequencies of type-2 diabetes mellitus (T2DM) comorbidity among bipolar I, schizophrenic, and demented inpatients on an older adult psychiatric unit. Following the presentation of our study, we will discuss theoretical and clinical issues related to glucose metabolism in bipolar disorder such as the relationship of glucose metabolism to the etiology and pathophysiology of bipolar disorder, and the safety concerns when treating a patient taking medication for both diabetes mellitus and for bipolar disorder. Finally, we will close with a discussion of suggested future directions for research on glucose metabolism in bipolar disorder.

Discussion of the relationship between glucose metabolism and psychiatric illness has occurred for at least three hundred years. The eminent English physician, Thomas Willis, first documented observation of an interaction between psychiatric illness and diabetes mellitus in the late 17th century. In 1674, Willis, who coined the term "diabetes mellitus", made the following oft-quoted statement about diabetes mellitus. "Sadness, or long sorrow, as likewise convulsions, and other depressions and disorders of the animal spirits, are used to generate or foment this morbid disposition"[2, 3]. Although a brilliant physician and anatomist, Willis lived during an era of medical discovery before reliable psychiatric nomenclature and laboratory methods could codify and quantify his observations. As laboratory method developed and the more reliable diagnostic nomenclature of Kraepelin and Bleuler became widespread, reports of increased blood glucose concentration in patients with psychiatric disorders recognizable by today's nomenclature began to appear in the literature. In 1919 Kooy reported on "Hyperglycemia in Mental Disorders," in which he described blood glucose concentrations in "normal persons, psychoses, dementia praecox, dementia paralytica, epilepsy, melancholia, neurasthenia and psychasthenia, amentia, and mania" [4]. From these studies, he ultimately concluded that, "Emotions, especially those of a depressive character, cause an increase in blood-sugar" and that "Glycosuria and hyperglycemia are most frequent in melancholia." In addition to his conclusion that hyperglycemia was associated with disorders of emotion, particularly melancholic depression, it is important to point out two features of his study. First, Kooy drew his conclusions after studying psychiatric patients with a number of different disorders rather than focusing on a single disorder. Second, he performed his research long before the era of modern psychopharmacology when studies began linking psychiatric medication to hyperglycemia and diabetes mellitus onset. As was typical of practice at that time, most of his patients were prescribed opium and occasionally chloral hydrate for their calming effects. Kooy considered that these drugs could have contributed to hyperglycemia, but after reviewing the literature, concluded that this was very unlikely. Furthermore, given that these drugs were prescribed across diagnoses and that he found hyperglycemia to be most prevalent in patients with emotional disturbance, he concluded that the hyperglycemia was related to the emotional disturbance and not to the effects of medication.

Further reports with increasing technical sophistication followed throughout the 20th century as methods of measuring glucose tolerance and insulin resistance became readily available. These studies typically aimed to determine whether hyperglycemia was an enduring trait associated with particular psychiatric illnesses or whether it was a transitory state-related or medication-related phenomenon. Lorenz reported on "Sugar Tolerance in Dementia Praecox and other Mental Disorders" and drew a similar conclusion to that of Kooy: "Patients with cases of manic-depressive insanity—depressed phase—responded to the sugar test with a curve higher than that found in normal subjects" [5]. Using the insulin tolerance test, Langfeldt found variations in insulin tolerance across psychiatric disorders, but concluded that "…it was particularly the conditions characterized by severe melancholic, depressive, confusional or process-schizophrenic symptoms that were associated with an increased insulin tolerance" [6]. Van der Velde et al found that half of their manic-depressive patients over the age of 40 years had abnormal glucose tolerance tests, although there was no consistent relationship to phase of illness [7]. They speculated that repeated episodes of hyperglycemia associated with episodes of manic-depressive illness could eventually outstrip the pancreas' ability to secrete insulin, resulting in the onset of diabetes mellitus. Using the intravenous glucose tolerance test [8-11].

As epidemiologic data on general U.S. population rates of diabetes mellitus became available, studies comparing rates of diabetes mellitus in individuals with psychiatric illness to rates of diabetes mellitus in the general population began to appear in the literature.

Unfortunately, most of these studies focused on one diagnostic group--major depression, bipolar disorder, or schizophrenia—and typically reported increased rates of diabetes mellitus in the psychiatric group compared to the general population. Most studies of adult patients did not distinguish between Type-1 diabetes mellitus, a juvenile onset disease that involves destruction of the pancreas cells that secrete insulin, and T2DM, an adult onset disorder usually diagnosed after age 45, that begins with resistance to the effects of insulin. Since approximately 90 to 95% of adults with diabetes mellitus have T2DM, the reader should assume that diabetes mellitus diagnosis for a given patient in these studies was almost invariably T2DM. Major studies are reviewed below.

In the only prospective, population-based study reported to date, Eaton et al. (1996), as part of a 1994 follow-up to the original 1983 Epidemiological Catchment Area study of the community prevalence of psychiatric disorders, found that a diagnosis of major depression in 1983 was associated with a 2.23 relative risk of diabetes mellitus onset by 1994 [12]. In a study of the spouses and first-degree relatives of probands in the NIMH Collaborative Depression Study, Moldin et al. (1993) found that individuals diagnosed and treated for major depression had a 1.87 relative odds of also having a diagnosis of diabetes [13]. Conversely, in reviews of the many studies of depression prevalence in diabetics, Gavard et al. (1993) and Anderson et al (2001) reported rates of major depression twice that of non-diabetics [14, 15] . It is important to note that most of these studies did not attempt to distinguish unipolar from bipolar depression and none attempted to control for medication effects.

With regard to schizophrenia, there have been two large chart review studies reporting increased rates of diabetes mellitus. Tabata et al. (1987) found an increased rate of diabetes among Japanese schizophrenics compared to controls [16]. Mukherjee et al. (1996) found an increased prevalence of diabetes among Italian schizophrenic inpatients compared to the general population [17]. More recently, using Medicare and Medicaid data, Dixon et al. (2000) reported an increased rate of diabetes mellitus among schizophrenics compared to the general U.S. population [18]. It is noteworthy that none of these studies attempted to distinguish schizophrenia from schizoaffective disorder. Furthermore, most of the studies did not attempt to control for the effects of age, race, gender, psychotropic medications, and body weight on vulnerability to diabetes mellitus. Only the study by Tabata et al. (1987) attempted to control for body weight.

There have been three chart review studies of manic-depressive illness or bipolar disorder, all reporting an increased prevalence of diabetes mellitus in hospitalized patients. Lilliker (1980) who studied diabetes mellitus prevalence across diagnoses in state hospital inpatients found a five-fold increase in diabetes prevalence in manic-depressive inpatients (12.4%) compared to the rate expected in an age and gender-matched sample from the general U.S. population and a nearly four-fold increase compared to schizophrenic inpatients (3.3%) [19]. It is important to note, however, that this study used DSM-II nosology that did not distinguish manic-depression from unipolar depression nor from schizoaffective disorder. Cassidy et al. (1999) compared the rate of diabetes in hospitalized manic-depressives to the expected general U.S. population rate weighted for age, race and gender and found a three-fold elevation [20]. Neither study, however, attempted to control for the effects of medication or body weight. In a previously published study, we attempted to combine the best features of these two studies—the use of multiple diagnostic groups and the comparison to an age, race and gender-matched general population sample—as well as to control for the effects of body weight and medication on diabetes risk. Our goal was to determine whether increased T2DM comorbidity was relatively specific to a particular psychiatric diagnosis or group of diagnoses while controlling for factors that could confound the relationship between psychiatric diagnosis and T2DM diagnosis. We did a chart review study of older age (50 to 74 years) university hospital psychiatric inpatients and found that rates were significantly different as follows: schizoaffective (50%) > bipolar I (26%) > major depression (18%) = dementia (18%) > schizophrenia (13%) [21]. Only the bipolar and schizoaffective inpatients had significantly elevated rates of T2DM compared to the rate expected in an age, race and gender-matched sample from the general U.S. population. Using logistic regression, we were also able to simultaneously control for the effects of psychotropic medication, age, gender, race, and body weight on T2DM diagnosis. We controlled for body weight by entering body mass index (BMI) as a predictor variable into the logistic regression analysis. Medication effect was controlled by determining from discharge summaries whether patients were prescribed potentially hyperglycemic psychotropic medication (defined as phenothiazines, clozapine, or olanzapine) on discharge and entering the presence/absence of these medications as a predictor variable. Logistic regression found that only BMI and psychiatric diagnosis were significant, independent predictors of T2DM diagnosis.

Determining the Specificity of the Relationship amidst Bias

Tsuang et al have pointed out that determining the specificity of the relationships between particular psychiatric illnesses and particular physical diseases is necessary to the identification of common factors that could have etiologic significance [22]. Thus, determining whether T2DM favors one psychiatric diagnosis over another may help in understanding the etiologic significance of comorbid diabetes in psychiatric illness. The only way to establish that abnormal glucose metabolism or frank T2DM favors one diagnosis over another is to study, either retrospectively or prospectively, patients who have different diagnoses simultaneously using the same methods so that accurate comparisons can be made across diagnoses. An additional benefit of comparing different diagnostic groups is that it is one means of mitigating the ascertainment bias

that plagues most studies of diabetes mellitus prevalence in a single diagnostic group. Ascertainment bias, also called "detection bias" results from systematic differences between comparison groups in how outcomes are ascertained, diagnosed or verified [23]. It is inherent in all studies of diabetes mellitus prevalence that compare rates in patients with chronic psychiatric illness to rates in the general population. The reason for this is that patients with chronic psychiatric illness come into frequent contact with health care professionals who examine them and submit their blood for screening tests including measurement of blood glucose concentration. It is therefore inevitable that their diabetes mellitus will be detected sooner than the average person in the general population. This is particularly the case, because general U.S. population rates are derived from random phone interviews rather than laboratory assessment. If we compare patients with two different chronic psychiatric illnesses, such as schizophrenia and bipolar disorder, however, and find that one has a higher prevalence of T2DM, then we can infer that the finding is not the result of ascertainment bias and could suggest a specific relationship between the psychiatric disorder and T2DM. It is noteworthy that both studies published to date that examined diabetes mellitus prevalence across psychiatric diagnoses (Lilliker and Regenold et al) found that T2DM favored manic-depressive illness or bipolar disorder.

THE EFFECT OF MEDICATION

In addition to comparing groups of patients with different psychiatric diagnoses, studies must control for the hyperglycemic effects of particular psychotropic medications if they are to determine whether there is a specific relationship between hyperglycemia and a particular psychiatric disorder. As noted above, the hyperglycemic effects of medication were considered long before the recent controversy over atypical antipsychotics. As use of modern psychiatric drugs such as chlorpromazine and lithium became widespread in the 1950s and '60s, some investigators observed increased rates of hyperglycemia and diabetes mellitus among their patients and began to question whether these drugs might be involved. In the case of lithium, a definitive, prospective study by Vestergard and Schou has shown that treatment with lithium does not change fasting blood glucose nor increase the incidence of diabetes mellitus despite increases in body weight. In the case of chlorpromazine, however, Thonnard-Neumann's study of hospitalized women showed a four-fold increase in diabetes mellitus after the introduction of chlorpromazine [24]. In 25 percent of these patients diabetes mellitus remitted after chlorpromazine was withdrawn.

Given that weight gain is a risk factor for T2DM, weight gain secondary to psychotropic medications must be considered in any discussion of diabetes and psychiatric disorders. In addition to lithium and chlorpromazine, many psychotropic medications induce weight gain including tricyclic antidepressants, monoamine oxidase inhibitors, valproic acid, carbamazepine, typical antipsychotics and atypical antipsychotics [25]. However, atypical antipsychotics, particularly clozapine and olanzapine, appear to be diabetogenic beyond the effects of weight gain [26]. Numerous case reports and large epidemiological studies linking certain atypical antipsychotics to new onset diabetes mellitus have resulted in the U.S. Food and Drug Administration's (FDA) recent demand for a warning of increased diabetes mellitus risk to be included in the manufacturer's package insert for atypical antipsychotics [27-29]. This issue is relevant to bipolar disorder, as atypical antipsychotics are increasingly used in, and receiving FDA approval for use in, bipolar disorder patients [30]. Although we were able to show that the prescription of phenothiazines, clozapine, and olanzapine on hospital discharge did not predict T2DM diagnosis in our earlier study, this attempt to control for medication effect was imperfect and cannot replace a prospective study, such as Vestergaard and Schou's study of lithium, that followed blood glucose and medication use over six years. Short of such a prospective study, recent large-scale, retrospective studies using national and state databases suggest an alternative. Using a Veteran's Affairs (VA) national database, Sernyak et al found that the increased risk of T2DM onset in schizophrenic patients taking atypical antipsychotics such as clozapine, olanzapine and quetiapine was observed only in patients younger than 60 years of age and most prominently in patients under 40 years [29]. Similarly, Lund et al found that clozapine use was associated with diabetes mellitus among schizophrenic patients ages 20 to 34 years but not among older patients [31]. These findings are consistent with our finding no relationship between medication use and T2DM in our earlier study of patients between the ages of 50 to 74 years. Together, these findings suggest that the hyperglycemic effects of atypical antipsychotic medication may less confound the relationship between T2DM and psychiatric diagnosis in older patients. Given that the onset of T2DM is typically after 45 years of age, it could be that the patients who are vulnerable to developing T2DM will develop it, regardless of medication use, by the time they are in their fifth and sixth decades. Thus, by studying an older group of patients and by comparing rates across diagnoses, we may be able to mitigate both the confounding effect of medication as well as the ascertainment bias.

THE RELATIVE FREQUENCY OF T2DM DIAGNOSIS AMONG OLDER ADULT PSYCHIATRIC INPATIENTS

With the above discussion as introduction, we now present our study of the relative frequency of T2DM diagnosis among inpatients on an older adult psychiatric unit. The aim of the present study was to determine whether a specific association exists between bipolar I disorder and T2DM. To this end, we set out to determine the prevalence of T2DM among psychiatric inpatients with bipolar disorder compared to inpatients with schizophrenia and dementia and to the general U.S. population.

Methods

This was a retrospective, chart-review study in which we examined the medical records of all consecutive admissions to our older adult acute inpatient unit at the University of Maryland Medical Center (UMMC) from January 1993 to July 1999. Referral sources for admission included: the UMMC Emergency Department, 62%; private practice psychiatrists, 10%; the Psychiatry Consultation-Liaison Service, 9%; non-psychiatrist outpatient physicians and others, 19%. Diagnoses were determined by review of discharge summaries. T2DM diagnosis was obtained by examining charts for previously diagnosed diabetes or the use of insulin or oral hypoglycemic medications. Second-year psychiatry residents in conjunction with an attending geriatric psychiatrist made psychiatric discharge diagnoses. Patients admitted multiple times were counted only once. In cases where patients received more than one Axis I diagnosis over multiple admissions, a single DSM IV diagnosis was assigned according to Structured Clinical Interview for DSM-IV Axis I Disorders (SCID) criteria after review of the complete medical record by a board certified geriatric psychiatrist (W.T.R.) blinded to diabetes diagnosis.

469 patients were selected for inclusion in the study. Inclusion criteria were: 1) diagnosis of bipolar I disorder, schizophrenia, or dementia, 2) black or white race, and 3) complete data for age, gender, and hyperglycemic medication use. Based on review of the literature, psychotropic medications were defined as "hyperglycemic" if they had been repeatedly associated with new-onset diabetes. Hyperglycemic medications included clozapine, olanzapine and phenothiazines. Patients were categorized as using hyperglycemic medications if use of any one of these three medications was documented on at least one discharge summary. Patients were excluded if they had documented use of nonpsychotropic medications that were strongly associated with new-onset diabetes. Systemic glucocorticoids were the only such drugs identified. Selecting only patients meeting these criteria allowed for large enough numbers of diabetic and non-diabetic patients within each diagnostic group so

that patients could be further grouped by age, race, and gender and then compared to matched U.S. population dummy groups by chi square analysis using the following method. Patients categorized by Axis I diagnosis were subdivided by age (50-59, 60-74 years), race (black, white), and gender. Rates of diagnosed T2DM in the U.S. population used for comparison were obtained from the Third National Health and Nutrition Examination Survey, 1988-1994 (NHANES III), a survey of 18,825 adults 20 years of age or older [32]. Age categories for the NHANES III were: 20-39, 40-49, 50-59, 60-74, and ≥74 years. Racial categories included "Non-Hispanic white", "Non-Hispanic black", and "Mexican-American". We restricted our study group to the 50-59 and 60-74 years categories and only the first two racial groups, because these categories included sufficient numbers of diabetic and non-diabetic patients across the three diagnostic groups to permit valid statistical comparison. NHANES III did not distinguish type-1 from type-2 diabetes; however, it is expected that more than 95% of the diabetics in the 50-74 year age range are type-2 diabetics. Expected numbers of diabetics in the general U.S. population for each category were calculated as follows. If there were, for example, ten, 50-59 year old black, female schizophrenics, and the NHANES III rate of diabetes for black females in this age group was 15%, the expected number of diabetics in this category would be 1.5. Expected numbers were then summed to determine an expected total number of diabetics per diagnostic group, rounded to the nearest whole number. Expected frequencies were then compared to the actual diagnostic group frequencies using the chi square (χ^2) test. The three diagnostic groups were also compared to each other on T2DM prevalence and on characteristics that could affect their vulnerability to T2DM using χ^2 analysis, with Yates continuity correction for 2x2 analyses, for categorical variables and one-way analysis of variance (ANOVA) with post-hoc tests for continuous variables. Logistic regression analysis was performed to determine the independent contributions of variables to the prediction of T2DM diagnosis. All parametric tests were two-tailed, and statistical significance was set at $p< 0.05$.

Results

As shown in Table 1, rates of T2DM among the three diagnostic groups were significantly different by χ^2 test with bipolar patients having the highest rate. Groups also differed significantly in terms of hyperglycemic medication use with schizophrenic patients having the highest rate and demented patients the lowest. Racial and gender composition, however, did not differ significantly among the diagnostic groups. Mean age differed significantly, with demented patients having a significantly greater mean age than bipolar or schizophrenic patients.

Table 2 shows the inpatients grouped by T2DM diabetes diagnosis. Diabetic and non-diabetic patients did not differ significantly by racial and gender composition, by mean age, or by rates of hyperglycemic medication use. There was, however, a trend toward a greater frequency of black race patients in the T2DM group, consistent with findings in the general U.S. population [32].

Table 1. Characteristics of 469 Older Adult Psychiatric Inpatients, Grouped by Axis I Diagnosis

Variable	Bipolar Disorder		Schizophrenia		Dementia		Analysis
	N	%	N	%	N	%	
Gender							p=0.099
Female	124	70	88	63	90	59	χ^2=4.6,df=1
Male	53	30	51	37	63	41	
Race							p=0.147
Black	91	51	82	59	73	48	χ^2=3.8,df=1
White	86	49	57	41	80	52	
Type-2 Diabetes							p=0.031
Diabetic	37	21	18	13	17	11	χ^2=6.9, df=2
Nondiabetic	140	79	121	87	136	89	
Hyperglycemic medication use*	44	25	68	49	16	11	p<0.001 χ^2=55,df=2
	Mean	*SD*	*Mean*	*SD*	*Mean*	*SD*	
Age (years)	61.1	9.9	60.7	9.6	74.3**	10.9	p<0.001 F=89, df=2

* Hyperglycemic medications included clozapine, olanzapine, or phenothiazines.
** Significantly different (p<0.001) from all other diagnostic groups by least significant difference post-hoc test.

Table 2. Characteristics of 469 Older Adult Psychiatric Inpatients Grouped by Type-2 Diabetes Mellitus Diagnosis

Variable	All Patients			Diabetic Patients		Nondiabetic Patients		Analysis
	N	%		N	%	N	%	
Gender								p=0.87
Female	302	64		47	65	255	64	χ^2=0.29,df=1
Male	167	36		25	35	142	36	
Race								p=0.064
Black	246	57.5		45	62.5	201	51	χ^2=3.44, df=1
White	223	42.5		27	37.5	196	49	
Hyperglycemic medication use*	128	27		21	29	107	27	p=0.807 χ^2=0.06, df=1
		Mean	SD	Mean	SD	Mean	SD	p=0.634
Age (years)	469	65.3	11.9	64.7	10.3	65.4	12.2	t=0.477, df=467

* Hyperglycemic medications included clozapine, olanzapine, or phenothiazines.

Table 3 shows the results of logistic regression analysis to predict T2DM diagnosis. Of the five predictor variables, only bipolar disorder diagnosis significantly predicted T2DM diagnosis. As indicated by the odds ratio, bipolar patients had a two-fold increased risk of having T2DM. Black race nearly reached significance as a predictor of T2DM and was associated with a 1.67 risk of T2DM diagnosis.

Table 3. Results of Logistic Regression Analysis of Variables to Predict Type-2 Diabetes Mellitus Diagnosis in 469 Older Psychiatric Inpatients

Variable	Beta	Wald χ^2	df	P	R	Odds Ratio
Bipolar I Diagnosis*	0.724	7.00	1	0.008	0.112	2.06
Black Race	0.513	3.68	1	0.055	0.065	1.67
Female Gender	0.001	0.00	1	0.998	0.000	1.00
Age	0.006	0.29	1	0.594	0.000	1.00
Hyperglycemic medication use**	0.140	0.23	1	0.630	0.000	1.15

* The other diagnoses were schizophrenia and dementia.
** Hyperglycemic medications included clozapine, olanzapine, or phenothiazines.

Table 4 shows the results of comparing the rates of T2DM in the diagnostic groups to the expected rates based on age, race and gender-matched groups in the U.S. general population. For exact comparison to the age categories used by Harris et al [32], only patients aged 50 to 74 years were included in this analysis. Of the three diagnostic groups, only bipolar patients had a rate of T2DM that was significantly higher than the national norm. The odds ratios placed them at 1.87 times the general population's risk of being diagnosed with T2DM.

Table 4. Rates of Type-2 Diabetes Mellitus in Older Adult Psychiatric Inpatients, Ages 50-74, Grouped by Axis I Diagnosis, Compared to US General Population Rates[a]

Diagnosis	Total Inpatient	Diabetic Inpatient		Diabetic General U.S.*	Analysis			Odds Ratio
	N	N	%	%	χ^2	df	p	
Bipolar Disorder	147	32	22	13	4.0	1	0.045	1.87
Schizophrenia	112	17	15	15	0.0	1	1.0	1.00
Dementia	153	17	13	16	0.26	1	0.61	0.77

* US General Population rates are the expected rates, given the age, gender and race composition of each diagnostic group, calculated from rates reported by Harris et al (18).

DISCUSSION

Consistent with our previously reported findings, we found older adult bipolar inpatients to have a higher rate of T2DM compared to inpatients with non-affective, chronic psychiatric disorders on the same older adult inpatient unit and to a matched dummy sample from the general U.S. population. This finding is also consistent with the findings of Lilliker and Cassidy et al discussed above. As noted in the "Introduction", finding a higher rate of T2DM in bipolar inpatients compared to inpatients with other chronic psychiatric disorders suggests that increased T2DM comorbidity may be relatively specific to bipolar disorder and that the increased rate in comparison to the general U.S. population is not strictly the result of ascertainment bias. Just as in our previously reported study and that of Lilliker, we did not find an increased rate of T2DM in schizophrenia compared to other chronic psychiatric disorders and to the general U.S. population. This contrasts with the studies of Tabata, Mukergee and Dixon discussed above. There are numerous possible explanations for this difference. Firstly, since these studies made no attempt to control for ascertainment bias, the found increased rate in schizophrenia compared to the general population could be the result of earlier diagnosis in a group of patients whose diabetes mellitus would be diagnosed significantly sooner due to frequent contact with health care professionals. Secondly, these studies did not distinguish between schizophrenia and schizoaffective patients; both groups were included in the diagnostic category of "schizophrenia". In our previously reported study, schizoaffective inpatients had the highest rate of T2DM, suggesting that they are more like bipolar patients than schizophrenic patients as a whole with respect to glucose metabolism. Therefore, the inclusion of schizoaffective patients in these studies could have increased the rate of T2DM above that for schizophrenic patients alone. Thirdly, these studies made no attempt to control for the hyperglycemic effects of medication. This is important in light of Thonnard-Neumann and Sernyak et al's findings of an increased risk of diabetes mellitus in schizophrenic patients associated with phenothiazine and atypical antipsychotic prescription, respectively [24, 29]. Taken together, the studies could suggest that the increased rates of diabetes mellitus in schizophrenic patients may be due to a combination of ascertainment bias, inclusion of schizoaffective patients, and medication effect in younger adult patients.

Study Limitations

As a retrospective chart review of inpatient records, our study had significant limitations compared to an ideal, large-scale, prospective study. Firstly, we diagnosed patients on the basis of available information in the record rather than on the basis of information gathered by a SCID interview. Secondly, we did not attempt to control for the effect of body weight on the risk of T2DM diagnosis. We did attempt to control for body weight in our previous study that used a 243-patient sub-sample for whom heights and weights were available in the record. As previously noted, that study found that both BMI and psychiatric diagnosis predicted T2DM diagnosis. Thirdly, although we did attempt to control for the hyperglycemic effect of particular antipsychotic medications—clozapine, olanzapine and phenothiazines—some patients who may have taken these medications in the past without documentation in the records we reviewed may have been categorized as not having taken them. Furthermore, it remains a matter of debate as to which psychotropic medications increase the risk of T2DM , and it could be argued that our selection of these three medications is too conservative. Fourthly, the study sample size of 469 patients limited the power of statistical analyses. For example, the study was underpowered to detect a statistically significant relationship between race and T2DM diagnosis, finding only a trend-level effect. Fifthly, as a cross-sectional study, we cannot comment on the temporal relationship between bipolar disorder and T2DM diagnosis. Although, the findings of Eaton et al as well as the typical ages of onset of these disorders in the general population would suggest that bipolar disorder usually precedes T2DM diagnosis.

Theoretical Implications of Finding an Increased Rate of T2DM in Bipolar Patients

Our interest in glucose metabolism in bipolar disorder is driven by the observation of increased rates of T2DM in our patients and by the intriguing possibility that this observation reflects an intrinsic abnormality of glucose metabolism that could provide valuable insights into the pathophysiology and ultimate etiology of the disorder. We will now briefly discuss the theoretical implications of an increased rate of T2DM in bipolar patients in terms of both the pathophysiologic and the etiologic relationships between glucose metabolism and bipolar disorder.

Physiologic or Proximate Relationship

As reviewed above, the results of multiple studies over the previous eighty-five years suggest, but do not prove, that patients with bipolar disorder have a particular vulnerability to hyperglycemia and T2DM that is independent of body weight and medication effects. How is this the case? Numerous investigators have discussed the relationship between bipolar disorder and hyperglycemia or T2DM in terms of proximate causality, that is in physiologic terms. Kooy hypothesized that the hyperglycemia and glycosuria he observed most consistently in melancholic patients was a product of activation of the sympathetic nervous system in association with emotional disorder. This hypothesis has been further elaborated as an overall stress response that occurs in mood disorder and involves co-activation of the hypothalamus-pituitary-adrenal (HPA) axis. Activation of the sympathetic nervous system and the HPA axis results in increased blood concentrations of the anti-insulin hormones, adrenaline and cortisol. For example, both hyperglycemia and dexamethasone suppression test (DST) non-suppression, a clinical indicator of HPA axis hyperactivity, have both been observed most consistently in melancholic depression [33]. As some investigators have suggested, repeated episodes of hyperglycemia could, over time, outstrip the pancreas' ability to secrete insulin, resulting in glucose intolerance and eventually frank T2DM. The finding of significant rates of DST non-suppression in diabetic individuals without mood disorder could further suggest that hypercortisolism may be linked to T2DM onset irrespective of episodes of affective disorder[34].

Etiologic or Ultimate Relationship

Description of the proximate causal relationships among mood states, hormone secretion, and blood sugar begs the question, *why* do individuals with bipolar disorder have a vulnerability to hyperglycemia and T2DM? In answering this question, we will place the behavioral, emotional and physiologic phenomena that make up these disorders within the context of human evolution. There is considerable speculation about the evolutionary origins of bipolar disorder. Most of the discussion centers around the possible adaptive significance of certain manic and depressive behaviors. For example, the increased energy, confidence, and sexual drive of hypomania could promote reproduction and survival [1]. Depressive behaviors such as pessimism and inactivity could promote survival by conserving scarce resources and preventing risky behavior [1]. Although intriguing, these explanations do not provide any links to glucose metabolism. However, another hypothesis, entitled the "Evolutionary Origin of Bipolar Disorder" ("EOBD") together with the "carnivore connection" a hypothesis of the evolutionary origin of insulin resistance could account for the bipolar vulnerability to hyperglycemia and T2DM [35, 36]. It is important to note that neither hypothesis was intended to explain abnormal glucose metabolism in bipolar disorder. However, the hypotheses are remarkably complementary in terms of the evolutionary origin of bipolar disorder and T2DM. According to Sherman, who put forward the EOBD, "bipolar disorder behaviors evolved as highly derived adaptations to the selective pressures of extreme climactic conditions (long, severe winters and short summers)". These conditions occurred during a series of ice ages that existed over the course of the Pleistocene epoch approximately 1.8 million to 11, 000 years ago [35]. To make the most of brief summers it would have been advantageous for survival and reproduction to engage in intensely high levels of goal directed activity such as hunting, gathering, and procreating (mania). Conversely, to conserve resources over the long, harsh winter, it would have been advantageous to hunker down and engage in little activity (depression). The strong selective pressures of the harsh climate would therefore have selected for genes that contributed to the cyclical regulation of drives and emotions and the goal directed activity that follows from them.

In parallel to the EOBD, investigators of diabetes mellitus and nutrition have put forward the "carnivore connection" hypothesis of the evolutionary origin of insulin resistance that posits that insulin resistance was also an adaptation to ice age climactic conditions. According to Colagiuri and Miller, "The 'carnivore connection' postulates a critical role for the quantity of dietary protein and carbohydrate and the change in the glycemic index of dietary carbohydrate in the evolution of insulin resistance and hyperinsulinaemia. Insulin resistance offered survival and reproductive advantages during the Ice Ages which dominated human evolution, during which a high-protein low-carbohydrate diet was consumed" [36]. Insulin resistance is "...the phenotypic expression of the metabolic adaptation to a high protein/low carbohydrate diet with periodic starvation" that evolved as humans adapted to a series of severe ice ages that changed a temperate, moist climate with abundant edible plant life to a cold and dry climate with scarce edible plant life. Our primate ancestors had evolved prior to the ice ages when edible plant life was abundant and a high carbohydrate/low protein diet was the norm. Consequently, the primate brain and reproductive tissues evolved a specific requirement for glucose as an energy substrate. With the advent of the ice ages, humans had to become carnivores to survive. Therefore, human energy metabolism had to evolve a means of producing large amounts of glucose from the high protein/low carbohydrate and unpredictable diet of the hunter. An increased resistance to insulin evolved, because it promoted hepatic gluconeogenesis and decreased peripheral glucose utilization. They argue further that the increasing rates of insulin resistance and T2DM seen in modern times are the result of this inherited tendency toward insulin resistance and our modern diet, particularly the high content of refined carbohydrates that make great demands on insulin production.

Thus, taken together, the EOBD and the carnivore connection hypotheses suggest that the emotions, drives, and behaviors of bipolar disorder and the insulin resistance that results in T2DM may have co-evolved through strong selective pressures during human adaptation to the extreme climactic conditions throughout the Pleistocene epoch. It could be the case that individuals who have comorbid bipolar disorder and T2DM descended from ancestors who were consummately adapted to an ice age environment. It is therefore possible that the comorbidity of T2DM and bipolar disorder is to some extent rooted in genetic mutations that contribute to now outmoded metabolic, emotional, and behavioral adaptations. This explanation is analogous to the well-known evolutionary explanation for the origin of sickle cell anemia, a blood disorder derived from an adaptive erythrocyte defense to a lethal blood-borne parasite [37].

Clinical Implications of Finding an Increased Rate of T2DM in Bipolar Patients

Irrespective of its origin, the comorbidity of bipolar disorder and T2DM is a fact of life for a significant portion of bipolar patients. Furthermore, the work of Cassidy et al suggests that comorbid patients suffer a more severe course of illness, as indicated by a greater number of psychiatric hospitalizations [20]. It is therefore the responsibility of clinicians to help prevent the onset of T2DM and to safely and effectively manage patients with both disorders. The increasing use of atypical antipsychotic medications for bipolar disorder has made this a pressing clinical issue in the treatment of patients with bipolar disorder. As guidelines for the initial evaluation and follow-up of patients begun on potentially hyperglycemia-inducing atypical antipsychotics have been published, we will not discuss this topic here [28]. Rather, we will briefly present an approach to the comorbid patient that emphasizes clinician awareness of the hyper- and hypoglycemic effects of psychotropic medication, the misinterpretation of signs of hyper- and hypoglycemia, patient education, and particular safety issues.

Hyper- and Hypoglycemic Effects of Psychotropic Medication

Although much has been written recently about the adverse hyperglycemic effects of psychotropic medication, an awareness of the hypoglycemic effects of some psychotropic medications is very important to the safe management of the comorbid patient. Case reports as well as a prospective controlled trial have shown that selective serotonin reuptake inhibitor (SSRI) drugs can lower blood glucose in individuals with no history of glucose intolerance and in diabetic individuals taking insulin or oral hypoglycemics, possibly by increasing insulin secretion [38-40]. Controlled antidepressant trials for depression in individuals with diabetes have shown that an improvement of depressed mood with fluoxetine is associated with an improvement in glycemic control, while an improvement of depressed mood with nortriptyline is not associated with an improvement in glycemic control [40]. In fact, nortriptyline was found to have a hyperglycemic effect independent of its antidepressant effect [41]. Accordingly, antidepressant doses of tricyclic antidepressants should generally be avoided in diabetic patients due to their hyperglycemic effects [42]. Although SSRIs are among the preferred antidepressants for diabetic patients, clinicians should warn patients ahead of time that their requirement for insulin or oral hypoglycemics may decrease. Patients should monitor their blood glucose more carefully and keep a running journal to present at their next visit. Before this effect was recognized, one of our patients suffered several attacks of hypoglycemia requiring emergency medical assistance. The patient later reported that his requirement for insulin decreased nearly 40% while taking sertraline for the effective treatment of his major depression. Coordination of care with the clinician treating the diabetes is also very helpful, particularly for fine-tuning medications.

Finally, the misinterpretation of signs of hyperglycemia and hypoglycemia can complicate the management of the comorbid patient. The lethargy and malaise associated with hyperglycemia can be misinterpreted as a relapse in depressive symptoms, resulting in unnecessary medication changes. The misinterpretation of the anxiety and agitation that can result from hypoglycemia as symptoms of an exacerbation of bipolar disorder can be life-threatening. This misinterpretation can occur when hypoglycemic individuals with a known history of chronic psychiatric illness present to an emergency room with confusion and anxiety and are triaged for psychiatric evaluation without prior screening for medical causes of changed mental status. To help prevent this occurrence we recommend that comorbid patients wear some type of bracelet or necklace that alerts clinicians to their diabetes mellitus.

FUTURE DIRECTIONS

It is our hope that increased knowledge of glucose metabolism in bipolar disorder will eventually lead to a fuller understanding for the disorder and to improved treatments. The existing data on the metabolism of glucose in bipolar disorder suggests that, to some extent, bipolar disorder is a disorder of energy metabolism whose origin may lie in early man's adaptation to the cycles of a harsh climate. Studies aimed at discovering genes that confer a vulnerability to both bipolar disorder and T2DM would be very helpful in confirming or disputing this hypothesis. Further investigation of the relationship between glucose metabolism and bipolar disorder pathophysiology could lead to novel treatments that complement current therapy. Prospective studies examining the temporal relationship between insulin resistance and bipolar disorder onset and illness episodes would help to clarify whether abnormal glucose metabolism is a trait and/or a state feature of bipolar disorder. Certainly, the global rise in T2DM attributable to changing diet and physical activity level indicates that clinicians will need to become increasingly aware of the interrelationship of glucose metabolism and bipolar disorder.

REFERENCES

[1] Goodwin FK, Jamison KR. *Manic-depressive illness*. New York: Oxford University Press; 1990.

[2] Geringer ES. Affective disorders and diabetes mellitus. In: Holmes C, ed. *Neuropsychological and Behavioral Aspects of Diabetes*. New York: Springer-Verlag; 1990.

[3] Willis T. *Pharmaceutie rationali, sive diatriba de medicamentorum operationibus in humano corpore*. Oxford; 1674.

[4] Kooy FH. Hyperglycemia in mental disorders. *Brain.* 1919;42:214-289.

[5] Lorenz W. Sugar tolerance in dementia praecox and other mental disorders. *Arch Neurol Psychiatry.* 1922;8:184-196.

[6] Langfeldt G. The Insulin Tolerance Test in Mental Disorders. *Acta Psychiatr Neurol Scand.* 1952;80:189-199.

[7] Velde CDvd, Gordon MW. Manic-depressive illness, diabetes mellitus, and lithium carbonate. *Arch Gen Psychiatry.* 1969;21(4):478-485.

[8] Waitzkin L. A survey for unknown diabetics in a mental hospital. II. Men from age fifty. *Diabetes.* 1966;15(3):164-172.

[9] Mueller PS, Heninger GR, McDonald RK. Intravenous glucose tolerance test in depression. *Arch Gen Psychiatry.* 1969;21(4):470-477.

[10] Brambilla F, Guastalla A, Guerrini A, et al. Glucose-insulin metabolism in chronic schizophrenia. *Dis Nerv Syst.* 1976;37(2):98-103.

[11] Winokur A, Maislin G, Phillips JL, Amsterdam JD. Insulin resistance after oral glucose tolerance testing in patients with major depression. *Am J Psychiatry.* 1988;145(3):325-330.

[12] Eaton WW, Armenian H, Gallo J, Pratt L, Ford DE. Depression and risk for onset of type II diabetes. A prospective population-based study. *Diabetes Care.* 1996;19(10):1097-1102.

[13] Moldin SO, Scheftner WA, Rice JP, Nelson E, Knesevich MA, Akiskal H. Association between major depressive disorder and physical illness. *Psychol Med.* 1993;23(3):755-761.

[14] Gavard JA, Lustman PJ, Clouse RE. Prevalence of depression in adults with diabetes. An epidemiological evaluation. *Diabetes Care.* 1993;16(8):1167-1178.

[15] Anderson RJ, Freedland KE, Clouse RE, Lustman PJ. The Prevalence of Comorbid Depression in Adults With Diabetes: A meta-analysis. *Diabetes Care.* 2001;24(6):1069-1078.

[16] Tabata H, Kikuoka M, Kikuoka H, et al. Characteristics of diabetes mellitus in schizophrenic patients. *J Med Assoc Thai.* 1987;70 Suppl 2:90-93.

[17] Mukherjee S, Decina P, Bocola V, Saraceni F, Scapicchio PL. Diabetes mellitus in schizophrenic patients. *Compr Psychiatry.* 1996;37(1):68-73.

[18] Dixon L, Weiden P, Delahanty J, et al. Prevalence and correlates of diabetes in national schizophrenia samples [In Process Citation]. *Schizophr Bull.* 2000;26(4):903-912.

[19] Lilliker SL. Prevalence of diabetes in a manic-depressive population. *Compr Psychiatry.* 1980;21(4):270-275.

[20] Cassidy F, Ahearn E, Carroll BJ. Elevated frequency of diabetes mellitus in hospitalized manic-depressive patients. *Am J Psychiatry.* 1999;156(9):1417-1420.

[21] Regenold WT, Thapar RK, Marano C, Gavirneni S, Kondapavuluru PV. Increased prevalence of type 2 diabetes mellitus among psychiatric inpatients with bipolar I affective and schizoaffective disorders independent of psychotropic drug use. *J Affect Disord.* Jun 2002;70(1):19-26.

[22] Tsuang MT, Perkins K, Simpson JC. Physical diseases in schizophrenia and affective disorder. *J Clin Psychiatry.* 1983;44(2):42-46.

[23] Clarke M, Oxman AD. *Cochrane Reviewers' Handbook 4.2.0.* Oxford: Update software; 2003.

[24] Thonnard-Neumann E. Phenothiazines and diabetes in hospitalized women. *Am J Psychiatry.* 1968;124(7):978-982.

[25] Zimmermann U, Kraus T, Himmerich H, Schuld A, Pollmacher T. Epidemiology, implications and mechanisms underlying drug-induced weight gain in psychiatric patients. *J Psychiatr Res.* May-Jun 2003;37(3):193-220.

[26] ADA. Consensus development conference on antipsychotic drugs and obesity and diabetes. *J Clin Psychiatry.* Feb 2004;65(2):267-272.

[27] Goldstein LE, Sporn J, Brown S, et al. New-onset diabetes mellitus and diabetic ketoacidosis associated with olanzapine treatment [In Process Citation]. *Psychosomatics.* 1999;40(5):438-443.
[28] Henderson DC. Diabetes mellitus and other metabolic disturbances induced by atypical antipsychotic agents. *Curr Diab Rep.* Apr 2002;2(2):135-140.
[29] Sernyak MJ, Leslie DL, Alarcon RD, Losonczy MF, Rosenheck R. Association of diabetes mellitus with use of atypical neuroleptics in the treatment of schizophrenia. *Am J Psychiatry.* Apr 2002;159(4):561-566.
[30] Sachs GS, Printz DJ, Kahn DA, Carpenter D, Docherty JP. The Expert Consensus Guideline Series: Medication Treatment of Bipolar Disorder 2000. *Postgrad Med.* Apr 2000;Spec No:1-104.
[31] Lund BC, Perry PJ, Brooks JM, Arndt S. Clozapine use in patients with schizophrenia and the risk of diabetes, hyperlipidemia, and hypertension: a claims-based approach. *Arch Gen Psychiatry.* Dec 2001;58(12):1172-1176.
[32] Harris MI, Flegal KM, Cowie CC, et al. Prevalence of diabetes, impaired fasting glucose, and impaired glucose tolerance in U.S. adults. The Third National Health and Nutrition Examination Survey, 1988-1994 [see comments]. *Diabetes Care.* 1998;21(4):518-524.
[33] Carroll BJ, Feinberg M, Greden JF, et al. A specific laboratory test for the diagnosis of melancholia. Standardization, validation, and clinical utility. *Arch Gen Psychiatry.* 1981;38(1):15-22.
[34] Cameron OG, Kronfol Z, Greden JF, Carroll BJ. Hypothalamic-pituitary-adrenocortical activity in patients with diabetes mellitus. *Arch Gen Psychiatry.* 1984;41(11):1090-1095.
[35] Sherman J. Evolutionary Origin of Bipolar Disorder (eobd). *Psycoloquy.* 2001;12(28):online journal: http://psycprints.ecs.soton.ac.uk.
[36] Colagiuri S, Brand Miller J. The 'carnivore connection'--evolutionary aspects of insulin resistance. *Eur J Clin Nutr.* Mar 2002;56 Suppl 1:S30-35.
[37] Friedman MJ. Erythrocytic mechanism of sickle cell resistance to malaria. *Proc Natl Acad Sci U S A.* Apr 1978;75(4):1994-1997.
[38] Sugimoto Y, Kimura I, Yamada J, Watanabe Y, Takeuchi N, Horisaka K. Effects of serotonin on blood glucose and insulin levels of glucose- and streptozotocin-treated mice. *Jpn J Pharmacol.* Sep 1990;54(1):93-96.
[39] Pollak PT, Mukherjee SD, Fraser AD. Sertraline-induced hypoglycemia. *Ann Pharmacother.* Nov 2001;35(11):1371-1374.
[40] Lustman PJ, Freedland KE, Griffith LS, Clouse RE. Fluoxetine for depression in diabetes: a randomized double-blind placebo-controlled trial.PG - 618-23. *Diabetes Care.* May 2000;23(5).
[41] Lustman PJ, Griffith LS, Clouse RE, et al. Effects of nortriptyline on depression and glycemic control in diabetes: results of a double-blind, placebo-controlled trial. *Psychosom Med.* 1997;59(3):241-250.
[42] Goodnick PJ, Henry JH, Buki VM. Treatment of depression in patients with diabetes mellitus [see comments]. *J Clin Psychiatry.* 1995;56(4):128-136.

ACKNOWLEDGEMENTS

Preparation of this chapter was made possible through funds from the Stanley Medical Research Institute.

In: Trends in Bipolar Disorder Research
Editor: Malcomb R. Brown, pp. 97-118

ISBN: 1-59454-060-8

Chapter 5

ALBUMIN LEVELS IN BIPOLAR DISORDER AND MAJOR DEPRESSION: ACUTE PHASE REACTION AND INFLAMMATION/IMMUNITY

T. L. Huang
Chang Gung Memorial Hospital, Kaohsiung, Taiwan, ROC

ABSTRACT

Albumin plays an important role in physical functions, including serving as a transport and binding protein. At the same time, it is also a negative acute phase protein and related to the immune/inflammatory response in many diseases. Serum albumin levels had be a prognostic marker for mortality in elderly hospitalized patients, human immunodeficiency virus-infected women and prognosis of disease in patients with injury or inflammation. Perhaps, the level of serum albumin might also apply to be a predictive marker for the discussion of the prognosis of drug responses and clinical courses in patients with mood disorders. Previous papers had reported lower serum albumin levels in patients with major depression or schizophrenia. However, the data of albumin levels in bipolar disorder data are scarce. First, the relationships between serum albumin levels and mania, major depression, schizophrenia, physical violence and suicide attempts will be discussed in this chapter. Second, the relationships between the albumin (negative acute phase protein) and cytokines in bipolar disorder will also be mentioned. Finally, the importance of the combined data between clinical phenotypes and molecular levels in mood disorders should be emphasized.

INTRODUCTION

Albumin is a single peptide chain of 584 amino acids and is unique among major plasma proteins in containing no carbohydrate (Peters 1975;Whicher and Spence 1987). Albumin is formed exclusively in the liver and serves as a transport and binding protein for fatty acids, bilirubin, calcium, hormones, trace elements, vitamins, and drugs (Whicher and Spence 1987). Thus, albumin plays an important role in physical functions. It was also shown that determination of the CSF/serum albumin quotient permits diagnosis of barrier dysfunction and assessment of the local synthesis of other proteins within the central nervous system (Reiber and Felgenhauer 1987). Fleck et al. (1985) further showed that increased microvascular permeability is an important cause of hypoalbuminemia in serious acute and chronic disease. Furthermore, he suggested reductions in serum albumin levels may not be assumed to reflect primary malnutrition when there is evidence for an acute phase response (Fleck 1989).

The following contents had many parts, including (1) the clinical data of albumin levels in systemic diseases and mental disorders (2) possible mechanism of acute phase reaction and inflammation/immunity in mood disers (albumin, cytokines and albumin gene expression) (3) the roles of albumin which were applied to other fields (4) the conclusion was emphasized on the importance of linkage between the studies of clinical phenotypes and molecular mechanism in mood disorders.

Clinical Data of Albumin Levels in Systemic Diseases and Mental Disorders

Serum Albumin Levels and Systemic Diseases

Diminished serum albumin concentrations occur in severe impairment of hepatic synthesis capacity as well as in marked protein loss (Whicher and Spence 1987). The concentration of albumin in plasma is commonly below normal during infection (Grossman et al. 1960), after injury (including elective surgery) and myocardial infarction (Ballantyne and Fleck 1973; Fleck 1976), in patients with malignant disease (Waterhouse et al. 1951), in critically ill patients (Brandly et al. 1981), and in patients with psychiatric diseases (Roos et al. 1985; Gammack and Hector 1965). The factors which determine the concentration of circulating proteins include changes in circulating fluid volume, exchange with or loss to the extravascular tissue space, lymphatic return, catabolism, synthesis, and losses (Fleck 1985).

It has been demonstrated that the serum albumin concentration may be a prognostic marker for patients with myeloma (Peto 1971). It is also applied to the studies of mortality in elderly hospitalized patients (Hermann et al. 1992), survival in women infected with immunodeficiency virus (Feldman et al. 2000) and disease in patients with injury or inflammation (Fleck 1989). Therefore, the level of serum albumin might also be applied as a marker for the clinical courses in patients with mental disorders, especially in bipolar disorder, major depression and schizophrenia.

Serum Albumin Levels in Mental Disorders

There were many reports showed that depression is accompanied by an activation of the immune/inflammatory system, including an acute phase response as indicated by changes in serum acute phase protein (Roos et al. 1985; Swartz 1990; Maes et al.1991; Song et al. 1994; Maes et al. 1995; Maes et al. 1997). Some papers had reported that lower serum albumin (one of the negative acute phase proteins) levels were noted in patients with major depression in Western countries (Doumas et al. 1971; Maes et al. 1995; Maes et al. 1997; Maes, De Vos, Demedts et al. 1999; Gabay and Kushner 1999; Yao et al. 2000). However, most studies did not discuss the relationship between serum albumin level and patients with mania except other acute phase proteins (Maes et al. 1997; Hornig-Rohan et al. 1995; Hornig et al. 1998). Cassidy et al (2002) had shown that albumin levels were lower in mixed manic subjects as opposed to pure manic subjects and albumin levels were lower in females than males. However, there were still no data to compare the difference between manic patients and normal healthy group in that study.

In addition, there are also many reports showing that schizophrenia is accompanied by an activation of the immune/inflammatory system, including an acute phase response as indicated by changes in serum acute phase protein (Heinrich et al. 1990; Shintani et al. 1991; Wong et al. 1993; Maes et al. 1995; Wong et al.1996; Maes et al. 1997). These studies also reported lower serum albumin levels in patients with schizophrenia (Wong et al. 1993; Wong et al. 1996; Maes et al. 1997).

Age had been known to have significantly influence on the serum albumin levels. However, the above papers did not consider the effect of age for serum albumin. Huang (2002a, 2002b) use the method of analysis of covariance (ANCOVA) after age adjustment to compare the Taiwanese patients with mood disorder, schizophrenia and normal control. From January 1995 to December 1995, a total of 213 patients (including 61 with mood disorders, 106 with schizophrenia, 10 with organic disorder, 6 with drug dependence, 10 with alcohol dependence, 9 with delusion disorder and 11 with others) admitted to the acute psychiatric inpatient unit of Chang Gung Memorial Hospital in Kaohsiung was included in the study. All medical records were reviewed. The collected data included age, body mass index (BMI), albumin level, suicide attempt or physical violence on admission, and psychiatric diagnosis of schizophrenia and mood disorders with no other co-morbid illness according to DSM-III R criteria. Schizophrenic patients were subdivided into paranoid type and non-paranoid type (including disorganized, catatonic, undifferentiated and residual types). Mood disorders were subdivided into major depression and bipolar I disorder (mania). All subjects had normal blood tests, including serum sodium, potassium, blood urea nitrogen, creatinine and alanine aminotransaminase. The healthy control group data came from 32 healthy volunteers who are members of the staff in the same psychiatric ward. The serum albumin levels of these patients were noted in Table 1.

Of the 106 patients with schizophrenia, 84 had the paranoid subtype and 22 belonged to the non-paranoid type. Of the 106 patients with schizophrenia, 22 had physical violence on admission (84 patients without physical violence) and 14 had suicide attempts on admission (92 patients without suicide attempt). The mean age, BMI and levels of serum albumin in patients with schizophrenia were 30.6±10.8 years old (mean±standard deviation, SD), 23.0±4.5 kg/m^2 , and 40.6±3.8g/L. Of the 61 patients with mood disorders, 25 had mania and 36 had major depression (all cases were unipolar depression and 7 had attempted suicide before admission). The mean age, BMI and levels of serum albumin in patients with mania were 32.7±15.1 years old (mean±standard deviation, SD), 24.4±3.8 kg/m^2 , and 40.2±4.0g/L. The mean age, BMI and levels of serum albumin in patients with major depression 43.0±17.8 years old, 23.2±3.9 kg/m^2 , and 39.8±2.8g/L. The mean age, BMI and levels of serum albumin in control group were 30.1±4.9 years old, 22.2±2.4 kg/m^2 , and 45.8±2.0g/L. The data of serum albumin levels in patients with bipolar disorder (mania), major depression, schizophrenia, suicide attempt or violence behavior were noted in Table 2.

Table 1. Mean Levels of Albumin in Mental Disorders in Different Genders

Diagnosis	Mean±SD(g/L)		
	Men	Women	Total
Total	40.3±4.4 (n=99)	40.0±3.6 (n=114)	40.1±4.0 (n=213)
DSM III-R Axis I diagnosis			
Schizophrenia	41.3±3.5 (n=47)	40.0±3.9 (n=59)	40.6±3.8 (n=106)
Mania	40.1±5.0 (n=13)	40.3±2.7 (n=12)	40.2±4.0 (n=25)
Major depression	39.8±3.0 (n=13)	39.8±2.7 (n=23)	39.8±2.8 (n=36)
Organic mental disorder	42.0±3.5 (n=5)	40.2±4.1 (n=5)	41.1.±3.7 (n=10)
Drug dependence	41.3±3.9 (n=4)	34.5±5.0 (n=2)	39.0±5.0 (n=6)
Alcohol dependence	34.3±7.0 (n=9)	41.0 (n=1)	35.0±6.9 (n=10)
Delusion disorder	38.5±3.5 (n=4)	41.0±3.3 (n=5)	39.9±3.4 (n=9)
Others	42.0±2.7 (n=4)	40.9±4.7 (n=7)	41.3±4.0 (n=11)
DSM III-R Axis II diagnosis			
Mental retardation	39.4±3.0 (n=5)	41.5±3.4 (n=4)	40.3±3.2 (n=9)
Cluster B personality disorder	39.8±1.1 (n=5)	40.8±5.0 (n=5)	40.3±3.4 (n=10)
Normal control group	45.9±2.3 (n=14)	45.7±1.7 (n=18)	45.8±2.0 (n=32)

This retrospective study showed that there were significantly lower serum albumin levels in psychiatric inpatients with bipolar disorder, major depression and schizophrenia as compared to a healthy control group. This suggests that Taiwanese psychiatric inpatients with bipolar disorder, major depression (Huang 2002a) and schizophrenia (Huang 2002b) also suffered similar systemic responses in the acute phase during that illness which were noted in the previous studies in Western countries (Roos et al. 1985; Swartz 1990; Heinrich et al. 1990; Maes et al.1991; Shintani et al. 1991; Wong et al. 1993; Song et al. 1994; Maes et al. 1995; Maes et al. 1995; Wong et al. 1996; Maes et al. 1997; Maes et al. 1997; Hornig et al. 1998). It is thought that bipolar disorder, major depression and schizophrenia might be accompanied by an immunological or acute-phase protein (APP) response (Roos, Davis and Meltzer 1985; Heinrich et al. 1990; Swartz 1990; Maes et al.1991; Shintani et al. 1991; Song, Dinan and Leonard 1994; Maes et al. 1995; Maes et al. 1997).

Table 2. Serum Albumin Levels in Mood Disorder, Schizophrenia, Suicide and Violence

Diagnosis	Albumin (g/L)
Bipolar disorder (Mania) (n=25)	40.2±4.0
Major depression (n=36)	39.8±2.8
Suicide attempt (n=7)	38.7±4.0
Non-Suicide attempt (n=29)	40.1±3.0
Schizophrenia (n=106)	40.6±3.8
Paranoid (n=84)	40.6±3.6
Non-Paranoid (n=22)	40.7±4.6
Suicide attempt (n=14)	39.8±4.0
Non-Suicide attempt (n=92)	40.7±3.7
Physical violence (n=22)	40.1±2.5
Non-Physical violence (n=84)	40.8±4.1
Control group (n=32)	45.8±2.0

BMI: body mass index.

Gabay and Kushner (1999) had been described that there were "severe" changes in the plasma concentration of acute-phase proteins include infection, trauma, surgery, burns, tissue infarction and advanced cancer. "Moderate" changes occur after strenuous exercise, heatstroke, and childbirth. However, "small" changes occur after psychological stress and in several psychiatric illness (Ganguli et al.1993; Van Hunael et al.1998; Gabay and Kushner 1999;). In the above study, no significant differences were noted in mean serum albumin levels on admission between patients with and without suicide attempts and those with and without physical violence. This might mean that acute phase proteins show in only small changes in major depressive patients with these behaviors, even though these are thought to be severe behaviors in psychiatric disease. The same results were also seen in schizophrenic patients.

To my knowledge, there are reports showing a significant negative correlation between albumin concentration and severity of illness (Maes et al. 1995) and lower albumin levels in patients with treatment-resistant depression in Western countries (Van Hunsel et al. 1996). But, there was no discussion between serum albumin level and patients with mania except other acute phase proteins (Hornig-Rohan et al. 1995; Maes et al. 1997; Hornig et al. 1998). The finding of lower serum albumin levels in patient with mania than normal control by using ANCOVA with age adjustment in this study maybe was the first announce.

However, the data of serum albumin levels after the treatments of mood stabilizers were scarce.

Albumin and Kidney

There were papers to report the data of urine albumin level after the treatments of Lithium. Jensen et al. (1992) determined the urinary excretion of albumin and retinal-binding protein by means of sensitive immunochemical methods in a 2-year longitudinal study of 22 lithium-treated patients. During lithium treatment, there were no significant changes in the median albumin/creatinine ratios or retinal-binding protein/creatinine ratios. However, the median albumin/creatinine ratios were significantly higher in lithium-treated patients than in 22 normal subjects, which indicates that glomerular permeability is increased; no correlation with serum lithium level or duration of lithium treatment could be shown. The study supports the hypothesis that lithium treatment produces a small but significant and nonprogressive elevation of the urinary excretion of albumin. Jensen et al. (1995) also checked the urinary excretion of albumin and transferrin in 40 manic-depressive patients prior to and following 6 months of daily or alternate-day lithium carbonate treatment. He found the urinary excretion of albumin and transferrin was significantly elevated in the lithium-treated patients as compared to a control group. The change in urinary albumin/creatinine and transferrin/creatinine ratios did not correlate significantly with the lithium dosing schedule during the 6 months treatment, but did correlate with total lithium carbonate dose.

Serum albumin concentration as a means of assessing exogenous protein loss. The greatest losses of albumin can occur as a result of the minimal-change lesion in the kidney which carries the most favourable prognosis, while more serious forms of damage often give rise to less albumin loss. Serum albumin measurement is used as part of a selectivity index (Ellis and Buffone 1981) in the assessment of the nature of the glomerular lesion in children. This has largely been displaced by therapeutic trial of steroids when albumin concentrations in the urine may be used for monitoring the response. Return of serum albumin concentration to normal usually indicates recovery (Whicher and Spence 1987). We should assess the free component of substances which are albumin bound. A wide range of drugs are bound to albumin, the albumin bound fractions being inactive. If albumin levels are low, free drug levels increase and may cause toxic effects if the drugs involved are given in their normal dosage or if drugs which compete for binding sites are simultaneously administered (Whicher and Spence 1987). So, the more advanced data in this field should be investigated, including mood stablizers, antidepressants, and antipsychotics.

Albumin and CNS

Albumin also is applied to the study of the brain function. The quantitatively most pronounced component of the CSF-protein is albumin. The concentration is about 200 times lower in CSF compared to serum. Synthesis of albumin within the CNS has not been proved to occur (Frick and Scheid-Seydel 1958; Cutler et al.1967), and it can thus be assumed that albumin present in CSF derives from serum. Therefore, determination of CSF-albumin may be anticipated to give more adequate information when compared with determination of CSF-protein regarding presence of a blood-brain barrier damage. Protein parameters in CSF and serum have been studied in ninety-three reference subjects (Tibbling et al. 1977). CSF/S albumin ratio is proposed to be superior to CSF-protein or CSF-albumin as a test of the blood-brain barrier function, while IgG-index = (CSF/S IgG ratio)/(CSF/S albumin ratio) is superior to CSF IgG/protein ratio or CSF/albumin ratio for the demonstration of IgG elevation in CSF due to synthesis within CNS. The two quotients recommended correct for variations of albumin and IgG concentrations in serum. When the serum proteins are within reference range, the CSF protein concentrations are mainly regulated by the permeability of the blood-brain barrier, while the influence of S-albumin and S-IgG is only secondarily. The CSF/S albumin ratio is age dependent, while IgG-index is not. A proposed graphical presentation of CSF/S albumin and IgG-index may facilitate the interpretation of these parameters in routine clinical work (Tibbling et al. 1977).

Elevation of total protein is the most frequent pathologic finding in the cerebrospinal fluid (CSF) examination. It occurs in a variety of situations, such as inflammation or tumors of the central nervous system (CNS), subarachnoid hemorrhage, and degenerative disorder, or as a result of traumatic taps (Pitts et al. 1990).

However, no relationship was found between CSF protein levels and (1) the use of medication (tricyclic antidepressants, lithium carbonate, or monoamine oxidase inhibitors) or (2) post-dexamethasone suppression test cortisol levels (Pitts et al. 1990). They also suggest increased polyclonal production of CSF protein and/or increased blood-brain barrier permeability in male depressed patients, and a tendency to such in female depressed patients (Pitts et al. 1990). Quantitation of the connection to deep cervical lymph, using radio-iodinated albumin as tracer, indicates that the magnitude of outflow from CNS to major fraction (14-47%) of the radiolabeled albumin cleared from widely-dispersed regions of brain or intracranial CSF can be recovered from deep cervical lymph (Yamada et al. 1991). Further, there is a new view of the immunoreactivity in the normal brain to talk about the interaction between brain and the other tissues (Cserr and Knopf 1992). The theory is based on three key components. First, there is an active and highly-regulated communication between the brain and the central immune organs. Secondly, the connection from the brain to the draining nodes is much larger than previously appreciated. And third, the blood-brain barrier, by virtue of its selective permeability properties, contributes to the regulation of immunoregulatory cells and molecules in the brain cell microenvironment.

Simultaneous Changes in Serum Albumin and Other Chemical Substances

Sometimes, we could find both changes in albumin and other chemical levels in the clinical data. It may be both on the lower levels, or may be lower albumin level associated with increased levels in other chemical materials. This phenomenon was suggested to be related to the immune/inflammatory response by some authors (Maes et al. 1997; Maes et al. 1999; Gabay and Kushner 1999; Yao et al. 2000) For example, both anemia and hypoalbuminemia due to inflammation are common among hospitalized patients. Estimation of other changes in acute-phase proteins, despite the lack of diagnostic specificity, is useful to clinicians because such changes reflect the presence and intensity of an inflammatory process (Gabay and Kushner 1999).Some papers also reported lower serum zinc and albumin concentrations (zinc is closely bound to albumin in peripheral blood) were related to the immune/inflammatory response in major depression (Maes et al. 1997; Maes et al. 1999). Albumin is also a metal-binding protein shown to possess free radical scavenging properties, and may thus be a selective antioxidant (Yao et al. 2000). In addition, Cassidy et al.(2002) pointed that leucocytosis and hypoalbuminemia during mixed manic states suggest immune activation in mixed mania similar to depression. The finding also tends to support the recognition of mixed mania as a distinct bipolar state.

POSSIBLE MECHANISM : ACUTE PHASE REACTION AND INFLAMMATION/IMMUNITY

Acute Phase Reaction: Albumin Is a Negative Acute Phase Protein

Proteins with a transient increase in synthesis and plasma concentration are called positive acute-phase proteins (APP); examples include C-reactive protein, α_1-acid glycoprotein (AGP), α_2-macroglobulin, and haptoglobin. The proteins whose synthesis decreases are referred to as negative APP; examples include albumin, transferin and retinol-binding protein. (Lebreton et al. 1979; Schreiber and Howlett 1983; Koj 1985; Baumann and Gauldie 1994; Raynes 1994). The APPs are synthesized mainly in the liver and are secreted into the bloodstream (Aldred et al. 1992). The precise functions of many APPs are still largely unknown. It is generally believed that the APPs play an anti-inflammatory role to prevent ongoing tissue damage and to return the organism to normal function. The known functions of APPs can be classified into three categories, including the maintenance of homeostasis, the transport of a variety of factors, and defense against infection (Raynes 1994).

The changes in plasma concentrations of individual acute phase proteins are variable and probably reflect differences in the amount of each protein that is required to participate effectively in the acute phase response. Most positive acute phase proteins are induced between 50% and several-fold over normal levels. In contrast, the so-called 'major APRs' can include serum amyloid A (SAA) and other C-reactive protein (CRP) could increase to 1000-fold (Steel and Whitehead 1994; Gabay and Kushner 1999). On the other hand, the data of negative acute phase proteins were rare. It is not clear what functional advantages may arise from decreases in plasma concentrations of the negative acute-phase proteins. It is logical to presume that the need to divert available amino acids to the production of other acute-phase proteins explains the decreased production of plasma proteins not required for host defense (Gabay and Kushner 1999). Another point of view in "molecular economy of the hepatic acute-phase reaction" was suggested by some authors (Filkins 1985; Klasing 1988; Memon et al. 1994;Ramadori et al. 1999). They thought that the cytokine-stimulated burst synthesis of the positive acute-phase proteins in the liver requires an increased demand in amino acids and nucleotides during the acute-phase reaction. Whereas the demand in amino acids can be accomplished by external support from the cytokine-stimulated increase in muscle proteolysis and hepatic uptake, the demand in nucleotides can only be met by intrahepatic sources. According to the current view, this is achieved by the reduced expression of the negative acute-phase proteins (Mizock 1995).

The acute-phase reaction includes a variety systemic or local changes in response to tissue injury, infection or inflammation. A prominent feature of this response is the induction of acute phase proteins, which are involved in the restoration of homeostasis. Synthesis of several plasma proteins in the liver undergoes dramatic changes during the acute-phase reaction (Moshage 1997; Ramadori et al. 1999). The purposes of these responses are to keep homeostasis and to remove the cause of its disturbance. The phenomena of the systemic acute phase response comprise (1) fever, (2) neutrophilia, (3) hypoferranemia and hypozincaemia, (4) changes in lipid metabolism, (5) increased (muscle) protein catabolism and transfer of amino acids from muscle to liver, (6) increased gluconeogenesis, (7) hormonal changes, (8) activation of the complement and coagulation pathways, and (9) induction of acute phase proteins (Kushner 1982; Koj 1985; Baumann and Gauldie 1994; Moshage 1997; Ramadori et al. 1999; Rothermundt et al. 2001).

Two types of injury are used for explain the acute inflammatory reaction in animals (Lyoumi et al. 1998). The first is a localized inflammation induced by the formation of a sterile abscess after subcutaneous injection of turpentine oil (TO). The second is a systemic inflammation produced by intravenous injection of lipopolysaccharide (LPS). Systemic inflammation results in a systemic acute phase response. However, local inflammatory or injurious processes in the liver also can induce an acute phase response, for example during hepatic fibrosis and after partial hepatectomy. The acute phase proteins induced in these conditions probably act to limit proteolytic and/or fibrogenic activity and tissue damage (Moshage 1997).

Cytokins Regulation for Acute Phase Proteins

Acute-phase proteins have been studied extensively in humans and in the rat. Several studies *in vivo* and *in vitro* have been performed to analyse the response of acute-phase proteins to cytokine stimulation. Interleukin-6 (IL-6), IL-1 and IL-2 are the chief stimulators of the production of most acute-phase proteins in the recent researches (Gauldie et al. 1987; Gershenwald et al. 1990; Heinrich et al. 1990; Arend 1991; Dinarello and Thompson 1991;

McIntyre et al. 1991; Bevan and Raynes 1991; Dripps et al. 1991; Shintani et al. 1991; Maes et al. 1993; De Benedetti et al. 1994; Gabay et al. 1995; Maes et al. 1995; Geisterfer et al. 1993; Dinarello 1996; Moshage 1997). The papers showed the levels of both soluble interleukin-2 receptor (sIL-2R) and soluble interleukin-6 receptor (sIL-6R) were elevated in patients with major depression. However, Tsai et al. (1998) found that patients with manic episode had increased levels of sIL-2R but not sIL-6R in Taiwanese.

In my knowledge, the complex regulation of hepatic APP production is mediated by several classes of factors (Gauldie et al. 1992; Baumann and Gauldie 1994; Raynes 1994). The main action of cytokines, mainly interleukin-6 (IL-6) and interleukin-1(IL-1) type cytokines. Uncontrolled and prolonged action of cytokines is potentially harmful, therefore mechanisms exist which limit the activity of cytokines; these include soluble cytokine receptors and receptor antagonists. (Moshage 1997; Ramadori et al. 1999).

The binding affinity of IL-1 is 10-fold to 100-fold higher as compared with the IL-1 receptor antagonist. Thus, during the "initial" acute-phase reaction, while IL-1 serum concentration are elevated, the action of the IL-1 receptor antagonist is very likely without physiological relevance. Nevertheless, in the "late" phase of the acute-phase response, the IL-1 receptor antagonist might play an important role in downregulation (Arend 1991;Dayer and Burger 1994; Ramadori et al. 1999).

The assumption that the soluble forms of the TNF receptor and of the IL-1 receptor, as well as the IL-1 receptor antagonist, may be important for the downregulation of the acute-phase reaction, is corroborated by the findings that the anti-inflammatory cytokins IL-4 and IL-10 inhibited the production of TNFα and IL-1β and simultaneously increased IL-1 receptor antagonist production (Arend and Dayer 1995; Sugiyama et al. 1995; van Roon et al. 1996; Isomäki and Punnonen 1997; Choy and Panayi 2001) or that IL-6 increased circulating IL-1 receptor antagonist and soluble TNF receptor concentrations but decreased IL-1β and TNFα (Tilg et al. 1994). The anti-inflammatory cytokine IL-10 and the soluble forms of the 55-kDa and the 75-kDa TNFα receptor were also elevated in patients during the recovery phase from severe sepsis, indicating the potential role in the termination of the acute-phase reaction (Groeneveld et al. 1997). The role of IL-4 as an anti-inflammatory cytokine is also outlined by the inhibition of acute-phase protein production in human hepatocyte cultures (Loyer et al. 1993). However, the detailed mechanisms of cytokine in bipolar disorder and major depression were still unknown.

Other Factors Regulation for Acute Phase Proteins

Apart from the IL-1-like and IL-6-like cytokines, several other factors, usually associated with the regulation of proliferation, are able to modulate the synthesis of acute phase proteins, including transforming growth factor-β (TGF-β) and hepatocyte growth factor (HGF) (Moshage 1997;Lyoumi et al. 1998). The acute-phase protein (APP) response is regulated by cytokines such as interleukin-6 (IL-6), interleukin-1 (IL-1) and tumor necrosis factor (TNF), but may also be influenced by malnutrition (Geisterfer et al.1993; Scotté et al.1996;Lyoumi et al. 1998). In addition, bacterial endotoxins are known to be associated with the production of leukocytic pyrogens: peptides derived from peripheral phagocytic cells which act within the liver to increase acute phase protein synthesis (Atkins and Wood 1955; Gillman et al. 1961). Experimentally, the acute phase reaction can be induced by injection of animals with inflammatory agents such as turpentine (TO) or lipopolysaccharide (LPS) (Schreiber and Howlett 1983; Bauer et al. 1984; Lyoumi et al. 1998; Yirmiya et al. 2000;Dantzer 2001; Dunn and Swiergiel 2001). Glucocorticoids and insulin have also been implicated as a possible inducer of acute phase proteins within the liver (Horowitz et al. 1979; Turchik and Bornstein 1980; Whicher et al. 1980; Togari et al. 1986). Glucocorticoids generally enhance the stimulatory effects of cytokines on the production of acute-phase proteins (Baumann et al. 1987), whereas insulin decreases their effects on the production of some acute-phase proteins (Campos et al. 1994).

Cytokine Signal Transduction and Cell-mediated Immunity

The cytokine signal is transmitted into the cell via membrane-bound receptors. Different intracellular signaling pathways are activated by different cytokine-receptor interactions. Eventually, cytokine-inducible transcription factors interact with their response elements in the promotor region of acute phase genes and transcription is induced (Moshage 1997). For example, from the study of rheumatoid arthritis, antigen-activated CD4+ T cells could stimulate monocytes, macrophages, and synovial fibroblasts to produce the cytokins interleukin-1, interleukin-6, and TNF-α and to secrete matrix metalloproteinases through cell-surface signaling by means of CD69 and CD11 (Isler et al. 1993) as well as through the release of soluble mediators such as interferon-γ and interleukin-17. Interleukin-1, interleukin-6, and TNF-α are the key cytokines that drive inflammation. And activated CD4+ T cells also could stimulate B cells , through cell-surface contract and through the binding of $\alpha_L\beta_2$ integrin, CD154 (CD40 ligand), and CD28, to produce immunoglobulins, including rheumatoid factor (Choy and Panayi 2001).

However, the detailed mechanisms of cytokine signal transduction in bipolar disorder and major depression were still known. There are numerous papers on the function of T cells and B cells in mood disorder, particular major depression, yet data are inconsistent. Activation of T and B cells has been reports by some authors (Maes et al. 1995c; Muller et al. 1993), although others (Haack et al. 1999) could not confirm this. With regard to bipolar disorder, it appears that acute episodes of bipolar disorder are accompanied by cell-mediated immune (CMI) activation and an acute phase response. Both phenomena often (Maes et al. 1997; Hornig et al. 1998; Rapaport et al. 1999; Tsai et al. 1999), but not always (Maes et al. 1995c), normalize with treatment and /or remission. Breunis et al. (2003) use the T cell marker CD3 in combination with the activation markers MHC-class II, CD25, CD69 or CD71 and measure serum soluble IL-2(sIL-2R) receptor to study bipolar outpatients. They found that significantly higher numbers of circulating activated T cells and raised sIL-2 receptor in euthymic, manic, and depressed bipolar patients when compared with healthy controls.

Albumin Gene Expression and Signal Transduction

The expression of the negative acute-phase protein genes, which comprise prealbumin, albumin, transferrin, α1-inhibitor 3, and α1-lipoprotein (Heinrich et al. 1990; Milland et al. 1990; Baumann and Gauldie 1994; Ramadori et al. 1999).

During the hepatic acute-phase reaction, not only is the expression of secretory acute-phase proteins subjected to changes, but also the expression of key enzymes of liver-specific metabolic functions. In LPS-treated Syrian hamsters, the expression of the rate-limiting enzyme in cholesterol synthesis, HMG-CoA reductase, was increased in endotoxin-treated rats, the subtypes 2C11, 3A2, and 2E1 were decreased (Sewer et al. 1996), very likely attributable to the action of IL-1 and IL-6 (Morgan et al. 1994). In rat hepatocytes, the expression of glutatione S-transferase was inhibited by IL-1β, but not by a variety of other cytokines including IL-6 and TNF-α (Maheo et al. 1997). In rat and mice, endotocin treatment attenuated the expression of the key gluconerogenic enzyme phosphoenolpyruvate carboxykinase (Hill and McCallum 1991; Hill and McCallum 1992). The stimulation of gene expression of phosphoenolpyruvate carboxykinase by glucagon was inhibited by IL-6, IL-1β, or TNF-α in cultured rat hepatocytes. Changes in the expression of control enzymes of metabolism might cause severe dysregulation of whole body homeostasis during the acute-phase reaction. In patients with septicemia, increased serum triglycerides, increased hepatic fatty acid synthesis, decreased serum glucose concentrations caused by decreased hepatic glucose output, and increased peripheral glucose utilization can be observed (Ramadori et al. 1999).

The Roles of Albumin on Other Fields

Recently, albumin had the new role in the study of human disease. For example, albumin is a necessary stabilizer of TBE-vaccine to avoid fever in children after vaccination (Marth and Kleinhappl 2001).Treatment of TNF-alpha mice with antioxidants or NOS inhibitors prevented phosphorylation of C/EBPbeta on Ser239 and its nuclear export, and rescued the abnormal albumin gene expression (Buck et al. 2001). The mortality rate in hemodialysis patients remains extremely high, and reduced serum albumin concentration resulting from malnutrition is the strongest predictor of mortality and morbidity. Vitamin D deficiency in patients with end-stage renal disease might be involved in reduced serum albumin concentrations (Yonemura et al. 2000). TNF-alpha promotes the clearance of protein macromolecules from the CSF to the venous blood in the rat by (125) I-labeled human serum albumin ((125)I-HSA)(Dickstein et al. 2000).

Si et al. (1997) had showed that a serum factor, albumin, increased O(2)(-) production by cultured Microglia. Further, they also found that serum could enhanced lipopolysaccharide (LPS)-induced production of nitric oxide and tumor necrosis factor-alpha, which are other important neurotoxins released by activated microglia (Si 2000). Several purified serum proteins including albumin could not minic the enhancing effect of serum. However, the acute-phase serum showed a potent enhancing effect at a 10 times lower concentration than the normal serum (Si 2000). These studies suggest that some serum protein infiltrates into brain parenchyma after blood-brain barrier disruption and such protein may result system diseases (Si 2000). Some albumin solutions directly modulate adhesion molecule expression on endothelial cells. This may explain the previous finding of increased soluble adhesion molecules and a decreased PO2/FIO2 ratio in critically ill patients undergoing volume replacement with human albumin (Nohe et al. 1999). Time-dependent changes in brain and spinal cord were studied in mice in a cardiac arrest model. A transient decrease in body weight and a prolonged decrease in brain weight occurred after arrest whereas spinal cord weight was unchanged. The permeability of the blood-brain barrier (BBB) to I131-albumin and I131 tumor necrosis factor-alpha (TNF) showed maximal, non-significant increases on day 5 after cardiac arrest, but the permeability of the blood-spinal cord barrier (BSCB) to both materials was unchanged with time. They conclude that selective weight loss occurs in the brain after cardiac arrest with the integrity of the BBB and BSCB remaining intact to serum proteins and minimal alteration in the blood to CNS transport of TNF (Mizushima et al. 1999).

Hypoalbuminemia and hypocholesterolemia individually are well known predictors of mortality in the older population, and although they are often interpreted as markers of poor nutrition, it has recently been speculated that these variables can also be altered as part of a cytokine-mediated acute-phase reaction to acute or chronic inflammation. (Ettinger et al. 1995; Ranieri et al. 1999). C-reactive protein and interleukin-6 have each been found to be powerful predictors of both serum albumin concentration and of mortality (Ridker et al.1998; Koenig et al. 1999). Kaysen et al. (2000) also found that the acute-phase response varies with time and predicts serum albumin levels in hemodialysis patients.

CONCLUSION

The relationship between serum albumin levels and clinical subgroups in bipolar disorder and major depression should be explored. Although activation of an immune response during major depressive episodes has been reported, less is known about changes during manic and mixed bipolar episodes. Albumin and leukocyte levels were compared between subjects in manic and mixed bipolar episodes (Cassidy et al. 2002). The result supports the recognition of the mixed mania as a distinct bipolar state.

Melancholic depression is not simply a more severe form of non-melancholic depression. It represents a distinct clinical subtype with an episodic rather than a chronic course. Research results and clinical presentation have led to melancholic depression being considered as the most 'biological' form of depression . There is evidence that patients with major depression (MD) also suffer an inflammatory immune reaction. Since melancholic depression is psychopathologically and possibly etiologically different from non-melancholic MD, Rothermundt et al (2001) focused on investigating immune parameters in these two subgroups. They suggested melancholic and non-melancholic patients show different immune patterns. However, the data of serum albumin levels in the subtypes of major depression were not been explored.

From the above statements, we knew that the role of albumin in psychiatric disease is important. The combined data in clinical and basic researches would be needed to be investigated simultaneously in future. And then we could give a more detailed description for the possible invloved mechanism in bipolar I disorder and major depression.

REFERENCES

Aldred AR, Southwell B, Schreiber G. Extrahepatic synthesis of acute phase proteins and their functions. *Folia Histochem Cytobiol 1992*; 30:223-232.

Arend WP. Interleukin-1 receptor antagonist. *J Clin Invest 1991; 88:* 1445-1451.

Arend WP, Dayer JM. Inhibition of the production and effects of interleukin-1 and tumor necrosis factor alpha in rheumatoid arthritis. *Arthritis Rheum 1995; 38:*151-160.

Atkins K, Wood WB Jr. Studies on the pathogenesis of fever. Identification of an endogenous pyrogen in the blood stream following the injection of typhoid vaccine. *J Exp Med 1955;* 102: 499-503.

Ballantyne FC, Fleck A. The effects of environmental temperature (20 and 30 degrees) after injury on the concentration of serum proteins in man. *Clin Chim Acta 1973;*44:341-347.

Bauer J, Birmelin M, Northoff GH, Northemann W, Tran-Thi T, Ueberberg H, Decker K, Heinrich P.C. Induction of rat alpha 2-macroglobulin in vivo and in hepatocyte primary cultures: synergistic action of glucocorticoids and a Kupffer cell-derived factor. *FEBS Lett. 1984; 177*:89-94.

Baumann H, Gauldie J. The acute phase response. *Immunol Today 1994; 15*:74-80.

Baumann H, Richard C, Gauldie J. Interzction among hepatocyte-stimulating factors, interleukin 1, and glucocorticoids for regulation of acute phase plasma proteins in human hepatoma (HepG2) cells. *J Immunol 1987; 139*: 4122-4128.

Bevan S, Raynes JG. IL-1receptor antagonist regulation of acute phase protein synthesis in human hepatoma cells. J Immunol 1991; 147: 2574-2578.

Bradly JA, Cunningham KJ, Jackson VJ, Halmiton DNH, Ledingham ImcA. Serum protein levels in critically ill surgical patients. *Intensive Care Med 1981: 7;*291-295.

Breunis MN, Kupka RW, Nolen WA, Suppes T, Denicoff KD, Leverich GS, Post RM, Drexhage HA. High numbers of circulating activated T cells and raised levels of serum IL-2 receptor in bipolar disorder. *Biol Psychiatry 2003;53(2):*157-165

Buck M, Zhang L, Halasz NA, Hunter T. Chojkier M. Nuclear export of phosphorylated C/EBPbeta mediates the inhibition of albumin expression by TNF-alpha. *EMBO J 2001*; 20(23): 6712-6723.

Campos SP, Wang Y, Koj A, Baumann H. Insulin cooperates with IL-1 in regulating expression of α1-acid glycoprotein gene in rat hepatoma cells. *Cytokine 1994;* 6: 485-492.5.

Cassidy F, Wilson WH, Carroll BJ. Leukocytosis and hypoalbuminemia in mixed bipolar states: evidence for immune activation. *Acta Psychiatr Scand 2002; 105(1):*60-64.

Choy EHS, Panayi GS. Cytokine Pathways and Joint Inflammation in Rheumatoid Arthritis. *N Engl J Med 2001; 344*:907-916.

Cserr HF, Knopf PM. Cervical lymphatics, the blood-brain barrier and the immunoreactivity of the brain: a new view. *Immunol Today 1992; 13*:507-512.

Cutler RWP, Deuel RK, Barlow CF. Albumin exchange between plasma and cerebro-spinal fluid. *Arch.Neurol. 1967; 17*:261

Dantzer R. Cytokine-induced sickness behavior : mechanisms and implications (Review) (65 refs) *Ann N Y Acad Sci. 2001;* 933:222-34.

Dayer JM, Burger D. Interleukin-1, tumor necrosis factor and their specific inhibitors. *Eur Cytokine Netw 1994; 5*: 563-571.

De Benedetti F, Massa M, Pignatti P, Albani S, Novick D, Martini A. Serum soluble interleukin-6 (IL-6) receptor and IL-6/soluble IL-6 receptor complex in systemic juvenile rheumatoid arthritis. *J Clin Invest 1994; 93:*2114-2119.

Dickstein JB, Moldofsky H, Hay JB. Brain-blood permeability: TNF-alpha promotes escape of protein tracer from CSF to blood. *Am J Physiol Regul Integr Comp Physiol 2000; 279(1):* R148-R151.

Dinarello CA. Biologic basis for interleukin-1 in disease. *Blood 1996;87:* 2095- 2147.

Dinarello CA, Thompson RC. Blocking IL-1:interleukin 1 receptor antagonist in vivo and in vitro. *Immunol Today 1991; 12*: 404-410.

Doumas BT, Watson WA, Biggs HG. Albumin standards and the measurement of serum albumin with bromcresol green. *Clin Chim Acta 1971;*31:87-96.

Dripps DJ, Verderber E, Hg RK, Thompson RC, Eisenberg SP. Interleukin-1 receptor antagonist binds to the type interleukin-1receptor on B cells and neutrophils. *J Biol Chem 1991; 266:* 20311-20315.

Dunn AJ, Swiergiel AH. The reductions in sweetened milk intake induced by interleukin-1 and endotoxin are not prevented by chronic antidepressant treatment. *Neuroimmunomodulation 2001*;9:163-9.

Ellis D, Buffone GJ. Protein clearances and selectivity determinations in childhood nephrosis: a reappraisal. *Clin Chem 1981; 27:* 1397-1400.

Ettinger WH, Harris T, Verdery RB et al. Evidence of inflammation as a cause of hypocholesterolemia in older people. *J Am Geriatr Soc 1995; 43*: 264-266.

Feldman JG, Burns DN, Gange SJ, Bacchetti P, Cohen M, Anastos K, Nowicki M, Delapena R, Miotti P. *AIDS 2000;14*:863-870.

Filkins JP. Monokines and the metabolic pathophysiology of septic shock. *Fed Proc 1985; 44:* 300-304.

Fleck A. The influence of the nature, severity and environmental temperature on the response to injury. In: Wilkinson AW, Cuthbertson D, eds. *Metabolism and the Response to Injury.* London: Pitman Medical, 1976: 44-48.

Fleck A. Computer models for metabolic studies on plasma proteins. *Ann Clin Biochem 1985;22:*33-49.

Fleck A. Clinical and nutritional aspects of changes in acute-phase proteins during inflammation. *Proc Nutr Soc 1989;48*:347-354.

Frick E, Scheid-Seydel L. Untersuchungen mit 131J-markiertem Albumin über Austauschvorgänge zwischen Plasma und Liquor Cerebrospinalis. *Klin Wochenschr 1958;* 36:66.

Gabay C, Kushner I. Acute-phase proteins and other systemic responses to inflammation. *N Engl J Med 1999;340*:448-454.

Gabay C, Silacci P, Genin B, Mentha G, Le Coultre C, Guerne P-A. Souble IL-6 receptor strongly increases the production of acute-phase protein by hepatoma cells but exerts minimal changes on human primary hepatocytes. *Eur J Immunol 1995; 25:* 2378-2383.

Gammack DB, Hector RI. A study of serum proteins in acute schizophrenia. *Clin Sci 1965; 28*:469-475.

Ganguli R, Brar JS, Chengappa KNR, Zan WY, Nimgoankar VL, Rabin BS. Autoimmunity in schizophrenia: a review of recent findings. *Ann Med 1993;25*:489-496.

Gauldie J, Richards C, Baumann H. IL6 and the acute phase reaction. *Res Immunol Cytobiol 1992; 143*:755-759.

Gauldie J, Richards C, Harnish D, Lansdorp P, Baumann H. Interferon β2/B-cell stimulatory factor type 2 shares identify with monocyte-derived hepatocyte-stimulating factor and regulates the major acute phase protein response in liver cells. *Proc Natl Acad Sci USA 1987;84:*7251-7255.

Geisterfer M, Richards C, Baumann M, Fey G, Gywnne D, Gauldie J. Regulation of IL-6 and the hepatic IL-6 receptor in acute inflammation in vivo. *Cytokine 1993; 5:* 1-7.

Gershenwald JE, Fong Y, Fathey TJ, Calvano SE, Chizzonite R, Kilian PL, Lowry SF, Moldawer LL. Interleukin 1 receptor blockade attenuates the host inflammatory response. *Proc Natl Acad Sci USA 1990; 87:* 4966-4970.

Gillman SM, Bornstein DL, Wood WB Jr. Studies on the pathogenesis of fever. Further observations on the role of endogenous pyrogen in endotoxin fever. *J Exp Med 1961; 114:* 729-739.

Groeneveld PH, Kwappenberg KM, Langermans JA, Nibbering PH, Curtis L. Relation between pro- and anti- inflammatory cytokines and the production of nitric oxide (NO) in severe sepsis. *Cytokine 1997; 9:* 138-142.

Grossman J, Yalow AA, Weston RE. Albumin degradation and synthesis as influenced by hydrocortisone, corticotrophin and infection. *Metabolism 1960; 9:*528-550.

Haack M, Hinze-Selch D, Fenzel T, Kraus T, Kuhn M, Schuld A, Pollmacher T. Plasma levels of cytokines and soluble cytokine receptors in psychiatric patients upon hospital admission: Effects of confounding factors and diagnosis. *J Psychiatr Res 1999; 33:* 407-418.

Heinrich PC, Castell JV, Andus T. Interleukin-6 and the acute phase response. *Biochem J 1990;265:*621-636.

Hermann FR, Safran C, Levkoff SE, Minaker KL. Serum albumin level on admission as a predictor of death, length of stay, and readmission. *Arch Intern Med 1992;152:*125-130.

Hill M, McCallum R. Altered transcriptional regulation of phosphoenolpyruvate carboxykinase in rats following endotoxin treatment. *J Clin Invest 1991; 88:*81-816.

Hill MR, McCallum RE. Identification of tumor necrosis factor as a transcriptional regulator of the phosphoenolpyuvate carboxykinase gene following endotoxin treatment of mice. *Infect Immun 1992; 60:* 4040-4050.

Hornig M, Goodman DBP, Kamoun M, Amsterdam JD. Positive and negative acute phase proteins in affective subtypes. *J Affect Disord 1998*;49:9-18.

Hornig-Rohan M, Van Bell CT, Kuhn P, Amsterdam JD. Acute phase proteins in affective illness. *Biol Psychiatry 1995;*37:607

Horowitz J, Volanakis JE, Stroud RM. Rabbit CRP production after insulin injection. Proc Soc *Exp Biol Med 1979; 160*:222-225.

Huang TL. Lower serum albumin levels in patients with mood disorders. *Chang Gung Med J 2002a; 25*:509-513.

Huang TL. Decreased serum albumin levels in Taiwanese patients with schizophrenia. *Psychiatry Clin Neurosci 2002b;* 56:627-630.

Isler P, Vey E, Zhang JH, Dayer JM. Cell surface glycoproteins expressed on activated human T cells induce production of interleukin-1 beta by monocytic cells: a possible role o CD69. *Eur Cytokine Netw 1993; 4:* 15-23.

Isomäki P, Punnonen J. Pro- and anti-inflammatory cytokines in rheumatoid arthritis. *Ann Med 1997; 29:* 499-507.

Jensen HV, Hemmingsen L, Holm J, Christensen E.M. Aggernaes H. Urinary excretion of albumin and retinol-binding protein in lithium-treated patients : a longitudinal study. *Acta Psychiatr Scand 1992; 85:*480-483.

Jensen HV, Holm J, Davidsen K, Toftegaard L, Aggernaes H, Bjorum N. Urinary excretion of albumin and transferrin in lithium maintenance treatment: daily versus alternate-day lithium dosing schedule. *Psychopharmacology. 1995; 122:*317-320.

Kaysen GA, Dubin JA, Muller HG, Rosales LM, Levin NW. The acute-phase response varies with time and predicts serum albumin levels in hemodialysis patients. *Kidney Int. 2000; 58:* 346-352.

Klasing KC. Nutritional aspects of leukocytic cytokines. *J Nutr 1988; 118:* 1436-1446.

Koenig W, Sund M, Frohlich M, Fischer HG, Lowel H, Doring A, Hutchinson WL, Pepys MB: C-reactive protein, a sensitive marker of inflammation, predicts future risk of coronary heart disease in initially healthy middle-aged men: Results from the MONICA (Monitoring Trends and Determinants in Cardiovascular Disease) Augsburg Cohort Study, 1984 to 1992. *Circulation 1999;* 19: 237-242.

Koj A. Biological functions of acute-phase proteins. In: Gordon AH. Koj A. eds. The Acute Phase Response to Injury and Infection. *Amsterdam: Elsevier. 1985;* 145 –160.

Koj A. Definition and classification of acute-phase proteis. In: *The Acute-Phase Response to Injury and infection* (Gordon A.H. and Koj A, eds.), Elsevier, Amsterdam, The Netherlands. 1985; 189-197.

Kushner I. The phenomenon of the acute phase response. *Ann NY Acad Sci 1982; 389:* 39-48.

Lebreton JP, Joisel F, Raoult JP, Lannuzel M, Rogez JP. and Humbert G. Serum concentration of human alpha-2HS glycoprotein during the inflammation process: evidence that alpha-2HS glycoprotein is a negative acute phase reactant. J Clin Invest 1979; 64:1118-1129.

Loyer P, Ilyin G, Abdel Razzak Z, Banchereau J, Dezier JF, Campion JP, Guguen-Guillouzo C, Guillouzo A. Interleukin 4 inhibits the production of some acute-phase proteins by human hepatocytes in primary culture. *FEBS Lett 1993; 336:* 215-20.

Lyoumi S, Tamion F, Petit J, Déchelotte P, Dauguet C. et al. Induction and Modulation of Acute-Phase Response by Protein Malnutrition in Rats: Comparative Effect of Systemic and Localized Inflammation on Interleukin-6 and Acute-Phase Protein Synthesis. *J Nutr 1998; 128*:166-174.

Maes M, Bosmans E, Suy E, DeJonckheere C, Raus J. Depression-related disturbances in mitogen-induced lymphocyte responses and interleukin-1β and soluble interleukin-2 receptor production. *Acta Psychiatr Seand 1991;* 84, 379-386.

Maes M, Vandewwoude M, Scharp'e S, DeClercq L, Stevens W, Lepoutre L, Schotte C. Anthropometric and biochemical assessment of the nutritional state in depression: evidence for lower visceral protein plasma levels in depression. *J Affect Disord 1991;*23:25-33.

Maes M, Scharp'e S, Meltzer HY, Bosman E, Suy E, Calabrese J, Cosyns P. Relationships between interleukin-6 activity, acute phase proteins and HPA-axis function in severe depression. *Psychiatry Res 1993;*49:11-27.

Maes M, Bosman E, Calabrese J, Meltzer HY. Plasma interleukin-2 and –6 in schizophrenia and mania: effects of neuroleptics and mood stabilizers. *J Psychiatr Res 1995c;29:*141-152.

Maes M, Meltzer HY, Bosman E, Vandoolaeghe E, Ranjan R, Desnyder R. Increased plasma concentrations of interleukin-6, soluble interleukin-6, soluble interleukin-2, and transferrin receptor in major depression. *J Affect Disord 1995;34:*301-309.

Maes M, Wauters A, Neels H, Scharp'e S, Van Gastel A, D'Hondt P, Peeters D, Cosyns P, Desnyder R. Total serum protein and serum protein fractions in depression: relationships to depressive symptoms and glucocorticoid activity. *J Affect Disord 1995;34:*61-69.

Maes M, Delange J, Ranjan R, Meltzer HY, Desnyder R, Cooremans W, Scharp'e S. Acute phase proteins in schizophrenia, mania and major depression: modulation by psychotropic drugs. *Psychiatry Res 1997;*66:1-11.

Maes M, Hendrinks D, Van Gastel A, Demedts P, Wauters A, Neels H. Effects of psychological stress on serum immunoglobulin, complement and acute phase protein concentrations in normal volunteers. *Psychoneuroendocrinology 1997; 22:* 397-409.

Maes M, Smith R, Christophe A, Vandoolaeghe E, Van Gastel A, Neels H, Demedts P, Wauters A, Meltzer HY. Lower serum high-density lipoprotein cholesterol (HDL-C) in major depression and in depressed men with serious suicidal attempts: relationship with immune-inflammatory markers. *Acta Psychiar Scand 1997; 95(3):* 212-221.

Maes M, Vandoolaeghe E, Neels H, Demedts P, Annick Wauters, Meltzer HY, Aitamura C, Desnyder R. Lower serum zinc in major depression is a sensitive marker of treatment resistance and of the immune/inflammatory response in that illness. *Biol Psychiatry 1997;42:*349-358.

Maes M. The immune pathophysiology of major depression. In: Honing A, Van Praag HM, Editors. *Depression: Neurobiological, Psychopathological and Therapeutic Advances.* London: Wiley & Sons. 1997; pp 197-215.

Maes M, De Vos N, Demedts P, Annick Wauters, Neels H. Lower serum zinc in major depression in relation to changes in serum acute phase proteins. *J Affect Disord 1999;56:*189-94.

Maes M, DeVos N, Wauters A, Demedts P, et al. Inflammatory markers in younger vs elderly normal volunteers and in patients with Alzheimer's disease. *J Psychiatr Res 1999; 33(5):* 397-405.

Maheo K, Antras-Ferry J, Morel F. et al. Modulation of glutathione S-transferase subunits A2, M1, and P1 expression by interleukin-1 beta in rat hepatocytes in primary culture. *J Biol Chem 1997; 272:* 16125-16132.

Marth E, Kleinhappl B. Albumin is a necessary stabilizer of TBE-vaccine to avoid fever in children after vaccination. *Vaccine 2001; 20(3-4):* 532-537.

McIntyre KW, Stepan GJ, Kolinsky KD. et al. Inhibition of interleukin 1 (IL-1) binding and bioactivity in vitro and modulation of acute inflammation in vivo by IL-1 receptor antagonist and anti-IL-1 receptor monoclonal antibody. *J Exp Med 1991; 173:* 931-939.

Memon RA, Feingold KR, Grunfeld C. The effect of cytokines on intermediary metabolism. *Endocrinologist 1994; 4:* 56-63.

Milland J, Tsykin A, Thomas T. et al. Gene expression in regenerating and acute-phase rat liver. *Am J Physiol 1990; 259:* G340-G347.

Mizock BA. Alterations in carbohydrate metabolism during stress: A review of the literature. *Am J Med 1995; 98:* 75-84.

Mizushima H, Bank WA, Dohi K, Shioda S, Matsumoto K. Effect of cardiac arrest on brain weight and the permeability of the blood-brain and blood-spinal cord barrier to albumin and tumor necrosis factor-alpha. *Life Sci 1999; 65(20):*2127-2134.

Morgan ET, Thomas KB, Swanson R, Vales T, Hwang J, Wright K. Selective suppression of cytochrome P-450 gene expression by interleukins 1 and 6 in rat liver. *Biochem Biophys Acta 1994; 1219:* 475-483.

Moshage H. Cytokines and the hepatic acute phase response. *J Pathol 1997; 181:* 257-266.

Muller N, Hofschuster E, Ackenheil M, Mempel W, Eckstein R. Investigations of the cellular immunity during depression and the free interval: Evidence for an immune activation in affective psychosis. *Prog Neuropsychopharmacol Biol Psychiatry 1993;* 17:713-730.

Nohe B, Dieterich HJ, Eichner M, Unertl K. Certain batches of albumin solutions influence the expression of endothelial cell adhesion molecules. *Intensive Care Med 1999; 25(12):* 1381-1385.

Peters T Jnr. Serum albumin. In: *The Plasma Proteins. Vol. 1.* (Putnam FW, ed.) New York: Academic Press, 1975; 133-81.

Peto R. Urea, albumin and response rates. *Br Med J 1971; 2:* 324.

Pitts AF, Carroll BT, Gehris TL, Kathol R. G, Samuelson SD. Elevated CSF Protein in Male Patients with Depression. *Biol Psychiatry 1990;28:*629-637.

Ramadori G, Chirst B. Cytokines and the Hepatic Acute-Phase Response. *Semin Liver Dis 1999; 19:*141-155.

Ranieri P, Rozzini R, Franzoni S, Trabucchi M. Comeined Hypoalbuminemia and Hypocholesterolemia as a Predictor of Mortality in Older Patients in a Short-Term Period. *J Am Geriatr Soc 1999; 47(11):*1386-1387.

Rapaport MH, Guylai L, Whybrow P. Immune parameters in rapid cycling bipolar patients before and after lithium treatment. *J Psychiatr Res 1999; 33:* 335-340.

Raynes JG. The acute phase response. Biochem Soc Trans 1994; 22:69-74.

Reiber H, Felgenhauer K. Protein transfer at the blood cerebrospinal fluid barrier and the quantitation of the humoral immune response within the central nervous system. *Clin Chim Acta 1987;163:*319-328.

Ridker PM, Buring JE, Shih J, Matias M, Jennekens CH: Prospective study of C-reactive protein and the risk of future cardiovascular events among apparently healthy women. *Circulation 1998; 98:*731-733.

Roos RP, Davis K, Meltzer HY. Immunoglobulin studies in patients with psychiatric diseases. *Arch Gen Psychiatry 1985;42:*124-128.

Rothermundt M, Arolt V, Peters M, Gutbrodt H, Fenker J, Kersting A, Kirchner H. Inflammatory makers in major depression and melancholia. *J Affect Disord 2001;* 63:93-102.

Schreiber G, Howlett G. in *Plasma Protein Secretion by the Liver* (Blaumann H, Peters T. Jr, Redman C, eds) Academic Press,Inc, London 1983.

Scotté M, Hiron M, Maddon S, Lyoumi S, Banine F, Ténière P, Lebreton JP. and Daveau M. Differential expression of cytokine genes in monocytes, peritoneal macrophages and liver following endotoxin or turpen-tine-induced inflammation in rat. *Cytokine 1996; 8:* 115-120.

Sewer MB, Koop DR, Morgan ET. Endotoxemia in rats is associated with induction of the P4504A subfamily and suppression of several other forms of cytochrome P450. *Drug Metab Dispos 1996; 24:* 401-407.

Shintani F, Kanba S, Maruo N et al. Serum interleukin-6 in schizophrenic patients. *Life Sci 1991;49:*661-664.

Si Q, Nakamura Y, Kataoka K. Albumin enhances superoxide production in cultured microglia. *Glia 1997; 21:*413-418.

Si Q, Nakamura Y, Kataoka K. A serum factor enhances production of nitric oxide and tumor necrosis factor-alpha from cultured microglia. *Exp Neurol 2000;* 162:89-97.

Song C, Dinan T, Leonard BE. Changes in immunoglobulin, complement and acute phase protein levels in the depressed patients and normal controls. *J Affect Disord 1994;30*:283-288.

Steel DM, Whitehead AS. The major acute phase reactions: C-reactive protein, serum amyloid P component and serum amyloid A protein. *Immunol Today 1994; 15:*81-88.

Sugiyama E, Kuroda A, Taki H. et al. Interkine 10 cooperates with interleukin 4 to suppress inflammatory cytokine production by freshly prepared adherent rheumatoid synovial cells. *J Rheumatol 1995; 22:* 2020-2026.

Swartz CM. Albumin decrement in depression and cholesterol decrement in mania. *J Affect Disord 1990;*19:173-176.

Tibbling G, Link H, Öhman S. Principles of albumin and IgG analyses in neurological disorders. I. Establishment of reference values. *Scand J clin Lab Invest 1977; 37:*385-390.

Tilg H, Trehu E, Atkins MB. et al. Interleukin-6 (IL-6) as an anti-inflammatory cytokine: Induction of circulating IL-1 receptor antagonist and soluble tumor necrosis factor receptor p55. *Blood 1994; 83:* 113-118.

Togari H, Sugiyama S, Ogino T, Suzuki S, Ito T, Ichiki T, Kamiya K, Watanabe I, Ogawa Y, Wada Y, Takaoka T. Interactions of Endotoxin with Cortisol and Acute Phase Proteins in Septic Shock Neonates. *Acta Paediatr Scand 1986;75:*69-74.

Tsai SY, Chen KP, Yang YY, Chen CC, Lee JC, Leu SJC. Activation of Cell-mediated immunity during manic episodes in bipolar disorder. Taiwanese *J Psychiatry 1998;12:*207-217.

Tsai SY, Chen KP, Yang YY, Chen CC, Lee JC, Singh VK, Leu SJ. Activation of indices of sell-mediated immunity in bipolar mania. *Biol Psychiatry 1999; 45:*989-994.

Turchik JB, Bornstein DL. Role of the central nervous system in acute-phase responses to leukocytic pyrogen. *Infect Immun 1980; 30:* 439-444.

Van Hunsel A, Van Gastel A, Neels H, Wauters A, Demedts P, Bruyland K, DeMeeter I, Scharp'e S, Janca A, Song C, Maes M. The influence of psychological stress on total serum protein and patterns obstained in serum protein electrophorosis. *Psychol Med 1998;28:*301-309.

Van Hunsel F. Wauters A. Vandoolaeghe E. Neels H. Demedts P. Maes M. Lower total serum protein, albumin, and beta- and gamma-globulin in major and treatment-resistant depression: effects of antidepressant treatments. *Psychiatry Res 1996;65:*159-169.

van Roon JA. van Roy JL. Gmelig-Meyling FH. Lafeber FP. Bijlsma JW. Prevention and reversal of cartilage degradation in rheumatoid arthritis by interleukin-10 and interleukin-4. *Arthritis Rheum 1996; 39:*829-835.

Waterhouse C, Fenninger LD, Keutmann EH. Nitrogen exchange and caloric expenditure in patients with malignant neoplasias. *Cancer 1951; 4*:500-514.

Whicher JT, Martin MFR,m Dieppe PA. Absence of prostaglandin stimulated increase in acute phase proteins in systemic sclerosis. *Lancet 1980; 2:*1187-1188.

Whicher J, Spence C. When is serum albumin worth measuring? *Ann Clin Biochem 1987;24*:572-580.

Wong CT, Tsoi WF, Saha N. Serum immunoglobin levels in Chinese male schizophrenics. Schizophr Res 1993;10:61-66.

Wong CT, Tsoi WF, Saha N. Acute phase proteins in male Chinese schizophrenic patients in Singapore. *Schizophr Res 1996;22:*165-171.

Yamada S, DePasquale M, Parlak SC, Cserr HF. *Am. J. Physiol.1991; 261:* H1197-H1204.

Yao JK, Reddy R, van Kammen DP. Abnormal age-related changes of plasma antioxidant proteins in schizophrenia. *Psychiatry Res 2000;*97:137-151.

Yirmiya R, Pollak Y, Morag M, Reichenberg A, Barak O, Avitsur R, Shavit Y, Ovadia H, Weidenfeld J, Morag A, Newman ME, Pollmacher T. Illness, cytokines, and depression. *Ann N Y Acad Sci 2000; 917:*478-487.

Yonemura K. Fujimoto T. Fujigaki Y. Hishida A. Vitamin D deficiency is implicated in reduced serum albumin concentrations in patients with end-stage renal disease. *Am J Kidney Dis 2000;36(2):*337-344.

In: Trends in Bipolar Disorder Research
Editor: Malcomb R. Brown, pp. 117-138
ISBN: 1-59454-060-8

Chapter 6

TOPIRAMATE IN THE TREATMENT OF BIPOLAR DISORDERS

Vasilis P. Bozikas, Christina Andreou and Athanasios Karavatos
1st Department of Psychiatry, Aristotle University of Thessaloniki, Thessaloniki, Greece

ABSTRACT

Bipolar disorder is a mental illness that often requires lifetime treatment. Lithium has revolutionized the treatment of the disorder; however, it is associated with a 20-40% rate of treatment failures, and its use is limited by some of its adverse effects as well as by its narrow therapeutic index, requiring constant monitoring of plasma levels. First-generation anticonvulsants, such as carbamazepine and valproate, have proved themselves quite efficient and, generally, well tolerated alternatives to lithium therapy. However, they too are associated with severe adverse events, especially idiosyncratic ones, while their pharmacokinetic characteristics complicate their use. The newer antiepileptic agents (lamotrigine, gabapentin and topiramate) have recently received increasing attention as candidate mood-stabilizing agents, since they combine more favorable pharmacokinetic properties with fewer side effects. In this chapter, we will focus on the role of topiramate in the acute and maintenance treatment of bipolar disorder. Data on general characteristics of the drug (mechanisms of action, pharmacokinetic properties, and drug interactions) are provided. Studies assessing the efficacy of topiramate in bipolar disorder are reviewed. We discuss the efficacy of topiramate in mania, depression, rapid-cycling, and maintenance treatment of bipolar disorder, along with optimal dosages and titration schedules. Finally, safety and tolerability data from clinical experience with topiramate in bipolar patients are summarized, and evidence regarding the weight-reducing properties of topiramate is separately mentioned.

INTRODUCTION

Bipolar disorder is a major public health problem, associated with significant morbidity and mortality, which often requires lifetime treatment (Hilty et al., 1999). For quite a long time, lithium has been the agent of choice for the acute and maintenance treatment of the illness. The introduction of lithium remains a watershed event in the field of psychopharmacology, and lithium still is the best-studied agent for the treatment of bipolar disorder (Schou, 1997). However, it is associated with a 20-40% rate of treatment failures (Dubovsky and Buzan, 1997), particularly in certain subgroups of patients (dysphoric mania, substance abuse, secondary bipolar disorders) (Bowden, 1995); in patients with rapid-cycling disorder, lithium treatment fails at a rate of 72-82% (Chengappa et al., 2001a). In addition, the use of lithium is limited through some of its adverse events, such as neurotoxicity, nephrotoxicity, thyroid dysfunction, and weight gain (Ketter et al., 1999a), which lead to dose reductions or treatment discontinuations in a proportion as high as 25-50% of patients (Dubovsky and Buzan, 1997), on the other hand, the narrow therapeutic index for lithium makes it quite problematic to use in an illness with a life-long course, such as bipolar disorder (Chengappa et al., 2001a).

In the search for alternative therapies, the first-generation anticonvulsant agents, valproate and carbamazepine, were tested as mood-stabilizing agents for the treatment of bipolar disorder. Both of these drugs have proven themselves quite efficient –even in lithium-resistant cases- and generally well tolerated, offering new potentials for a more efficient treatment of the disorder (Post et al., 1996; Post et al., 1998a; Post et al., 1998b). Although they show a more favorable side-effect profile than lithium, first-generation antiepileptic drugs do not lack serious adverse events either, especially from the central nervous system, as well as idiosyncratic reactions (APA, 1994). In addition, their pharmacokinetic characteristics complicate their use, and they also require monitoring of blood levels, as well as liver functions (APA, 1994; Ketter et al., 1999a). The newer antiepileptic agents (lamotrigine, gabapentin and topiramate) have recently received increasing attention as candidate mood-stabilizing agents, since they combine more favorable pharmacokinetic properties with fewer side effects (Ketter et al., 1999a). So far, the study of the efficacy of second-generation anticonvulsants in bipolar disorders has shown that these agents may be of use in the treatment of mania and bipolar depression.

In this chapter, we will focus on the role of topiramate in the acute and prophylactic treatment of bipolar disorder. Topiramate was developed as an antiepileptic drug, and is approved by the United States Food and Drug Administration as add-on therapy for partial onset seizures or primary generalized tonic-clonic seizures in adults, as well as in children age 2 and over (Chengappa et al, 2001a; Suppes, 2002). Topiramate as monotherapy has been demonstrated to be as effective as carbamazepine and valproate in newly diagnosed patients with epilepsy, both children and adults, for all seizure types (Kwan and Brodie, 2003). Moreover, it has been suggested for the treatment of patients with neuropathic pain resistant to conventional treatments (Chong and Libretto, 2003) as well as for the preventive treatment of episodic migraine headaches (Edwards et al., 2003).

Mechanism of Action

Topiramate is a sulfamate-substituted monosaccharide derivative of fructose. It inhibits voltage-dependent sodium channels, although it seems to be less effective than phenytoin, carbamazepine and lamotrigine in this regard. It enhances the activity of GABA through interaction with the GABA-A receptor, with a different way of action than benzodiazepines and barbiturates, and it has been found to increase cerebral GABA concentration within hours of administration. In addition, it is an antagonist at the AMPA and kainate type glutamate receptors, and it has inhibitory effects on high voltage-activated calcium channels. All the above properties of topiramate are hypothesized to contribute to its anticonvulsant actions (Perucca, 1997; Bazil, 2002; Shank et al., 2000; Li et al., 2002); the rationale for its use in bipolar disorder rests on the fact that, although the pathophysiology of the disorder is not as yet completely clarified, it appears to share a similar substrate with epilepsy, such as an imbalance between inhibitory and excitatory amino acids and the altered function of cellular cation pumps (Chengappa et al., 2001a; Li et al., 2002). Finally, topiramate inhibits type II and IV isoenzymes of carbonic anhydrase, which is of relevance in determining some of the adverse effects of topiramate, such as increased risk of nephrolothiasis (Perucca, 1997; Shank et al., 2000).

An interesting view, proposed by Ketter et al. (1999b), suggests that antiepileptic drugs can be conceived as belonging to two main groups. The first group –which includes barbiturates, benzodiazepines, valproate, gabapentin, tiagabine and vigabatrine- is assumed to enhance GABAergic inhibitory neurotransmission; this group demonstrates "sedating" properties, causing fatigue, cognitive slowing and weight gain, and possibly also antimanic and anxiolytic effects. The second group, which includes felbamate and lamotrigine, demonstrates "stimulating" properties –activation, weight loss- and possibly also anxiogenic and antidepressant actions, which are associated with a decrease in glutamatergic excitatory neurotransmition. The combined GABAergic and glutamatergic effects of topiramate may provide it with a "mixed" profile.

Pharmacokinetic Properties and Drug Interactions

The pharmacokinetic profile of topiramate is generally favorable and linear in relation to dose, at least in a dose range between 100 and 1200 mg. Topiramate is rapidly absorbed, and the maximum plasma concentration is achieved within 1-3 hours from oral administration; co-administration with food slows down absorption by approximately 2 hours, but it does not affect the extent of absorption. After oral ingestion, the bioavailability of topiramate ranges between 80-95%; its plasma protein binding is minimal (less than 20%), and its elimination half-life is between 19 and 25 hours, permitting once- or twice-daily dosing (Perucca, 1996; Perucca, 1997; Ketter et al., 1999a; Patsalos, 1999; Shank et al., 2000; Bazil, 2002; Bazil and Pedley, 2003).

When administered alone, topiramate is mostly eliminated via the kidneys, with approximately 70% of the dose excreted unchanged in the urine; the rest of the drug is metabolized in the liver, without producing any active metabolites (Perucca, 1996; Perucca 1997; Ketter et al., 1999a; Patsalos, 1999; Shank et al., 2000; Bazil, 2002; Bazil and Pedley, 2003). Moderate increases in plasma concentrations have been observed in the presence of hepatic disease, about 29% compared to healthy age-matched individuals, but they are not considered clinically significant (Doose et al., 1994). However, as topiramate is predominantly excreted through the kidneys, downward adjustments, about 50%, of its dose may be required in renally impaired patients; dosage reduction may not be necessary in renally impaired patients taking concomitant enzyme-inducing antiepileptic drugs as in such patients hepatic metabolism plays a more prominent role in the elimination of topiramate (Perruca 1997; Patsalos, 1999; Bazil and Pedley, 2003).

In children, topiramate, like most other antiepileptic drugs, is eliminated at a faster rate than in adults. Specifically, for any given mg/kg dosage, plasma topiramate concentrations will be approximately 30% lower in children than in adults (Perruca 1997; Patsalos, 1999). In elderly patients, in the absence of renal impairment, age alone had no effect on renal clearance or on the elimination half-life of topiramate (Doose et al., 1998). However, caution is needed whenever topiramate is prescribed to elderly patients because they are more sensitive to such brain active drugs (Perruca 1997; Patsalos, 1999).

It is not known whether topiramate undergoes metabolism by the P450 cytochrome enzyme system in the liver but there are data suggesting that it is a weak inhibitor of CYP2C9/19 and inducer of CYP2A4 (Mula and Monaco, 2002; Patsalos and Perucca, 2003). When topiramate is co-administered with enzyme inducing antiepileptic drugs, such as carbamazepine, barbiturates, and phenytoin, its hepatic metabolism increases (Hachad et al., 2002), about 2- to 3- fold (Chengappa et al., 2001a). In these patients, the fraction of the dose excreted unchanged in the urine decreases from 55% to 30% (Sachdeo et al., 1996). Also, valproic acid induces topiramate metabolism through an unknown mechanism, decreasing its levels by 14% (Rosenfeld et al., 1997b). Topiramate dosages may need to be adjusted when used in combination with carbamazepine or phenytoin (Hachad et al., 2002), but such adjustments may not be necessary when the drug is combined with valproate (Chengappa et al., 2001a). Conversely, topiramate does not appear to affect the steady state levels of either carbamazepine (Sachdeo et al., 1996) or valproate (Rosenfeld et al., 1997b).

Topiramate does not cause any clinically significant changes in the pharmacokinetics of haloperidol (Doose et al., 1999a); it may slightly decrease lithium levels, when the two drugs are administered in combination (Doose et al., 1999b). The latter effect is likely mediated through topiramate's weak carbonic anhydrase inhibitory activity; carbonic anhydrase inhibition is known to increase the renal clearance of monovalent cations, such as lithium (Doose et al., 1999b).

When topiramate is administered along with digoxin, digoxin levels decrease by 13%; however, the dose of digoxin may need to be adjusted in this case, due to its narrow therapeutic index (Liao and Palmer, 1993). Topiramate also compromises the efficacy of oral contraceptives by decreasing the concentration of the estrogenic component, therefore, women taking topiramate and oral contraceptives should be monitored for changes in bleeding patterns (Rosenfeld et al., 1997). Finally, given the high dependence of topiramate clearance on renal function, there exists a potential for pharmacokinetic interactions with drugs that affect renal function, such as NSAIDs, ACE inhibitors, thiazide diuretics, loop diuretics etc; however, no such interactions have as yet been reported (Chengappa et al., 2001a).

Table 1. Clinical Studies of Topiramate in Patients with Bipolar Disorders

	Add-on or monotherapy	Study design and population	Mood symptoms (No of patients)	Mean daily dose (range)	Duration	Response* (measure)
Marcotte (1998)	Add-on	Chart review BD (I, II, NOS), CD, Sch/Aff, dementia, psychosis	RC (44)	200 mg (25-400)	mean=16 weeks	23/44 (marked-to-moderate improvement as rated by the investigator in a Likert scale)
Chengappa et al. (1999)	Add-on	Open-label BD I, Sch/Aff	Manic (20) RC (6)	210.5 mg (50-300)	5 weeks	Mania: 11/18 (YMRS†+ CGI††) RC: 4/6 (YMRS† + CGI††)
Kusumakar et al. (1999)	Add-on	Open-label BD (I, II)	RC (27)	105.2 mg (up to 150)	16 weeks	15/27 achieved euthymia
McElroy et al. (2000)	Add-on	Open-label BD (I, II), Sch/Aff	Manic, mixed or extremely RC (32) Depressive (11) Euthymic (13)	121.9 mg (25-350) 193.2 mg (25-500)	4 weeks 10 weeks	Mania: 9/30 (CGI)†† Depression: 3/11(CGI)†† Mania: 19/30 (CGI)†† Depression: 3/11 (CGI)††
Calabrese et al. (2001)	Monotherapy	Open-label BD I	Manic or mixed (11)	313 mg (30-1300)	2-29 days (mean=16 days)	5/10 (CGI)†††
Ghaemi et al. (2001)	Add-on (n=70) Monotherapy (n=6)	Chart review BD (I, II, NOS)	Depressive (33) RC (24) Mixed (8) Hypomanic (3) Prophylaxis (8)	96.1 mg (12.5-400)	0.5-65 weeks (mean= 17.5 weeks)	Overall: 46/76 (CGI)††† Depression: 5/33 (CGI)††† RC: 3/24 (CGI)†††
Grunze et al. (2001)	Add-on	On-off-on BD I	Manic or mixed (11)	25-200 mg	22 days (10 days "on" 5 days "off" 7 days "on")	8/9 on day 22 of the study (YMRS)†
Hussain et al. (2001)	Add-on	Open-label BD (I, II)	Depressive (135)	400-600 mg	24 months	69/135 achieved HDRS≤5 23/135 achieved 5<HDRS≤8
Bozikas et al. (2002)	Monotherapy (9) Add-on / combination (5)	Open-label BD (I, NOS)	Manic or mixed (14)	310 mg (150-700)	4 weeks	Overall: 8/13 (BMRS)† Monotherapy: 4/8 (BMRS)†
Carpenter et al. (2002)	Add-on	Chart review Unipolar depression BD (II, NOS)	Depressive (16)	277 mg (100-400)	4-8 weeks 1-40 weeks	4/11 (CGI)†† 7/16 (CGI)††

Table 1. Clinical Studies of Topiramate in Patients with Bipolar Disorders (Continued)

	Add-on or monotherapy	Study design and population	Mood symptoms (No of patients)	Mean daily dose (range)	Duration	Response* (measure)
Guille and Sachs (2002)	Add-on	Chart review BD (I,II) Various comorbidities	Manic (6) Depressive (4) RC (8)	100 mg (25-300)	1-64 weeks (mean=22.4 weeks)	Mania: 3/6 (CGI)⊗ Depression 1/4 (CGI)⊗ RC: 3/8 (CGI)⊗
McIntyre et al. (2002)	Add-on	Single-blind (rater-blind) topiramate vs bupropion BD (I,II)	Depressive (36)	Topiramate: 176 mg (50-300) Bupropion: 250 mg (100-400)	8 weeks	Comparable results for topiramate and bupropion
Vietta et al. (2002)	Add-on	Open-label BD (I, II, NOS), Sch/Aff	Manic (17) Hypomanic (3) Mixed (3) Depressive (11)	202 mg (100-400)	24 weeks	Mania: 13/23 (YMRS)† Depression: 6/11 (HDRS)† Total: 19/34 (CGI)††

"Mania" refers to manic, mixed or hypomanic symptoms, BD: bipolar disorder, NOS: not otherwise specified, CD: cyclothymic disorder, Sch/Aff: schizoaffective disorder, RC: rapid-cycling

* In the calculation of response, patients with schizoaffective disorder were eliminated when it was possible, in order to achieve comparability of results.

†YMRS: ≥50% improvement on the Young Mania Rating Scale †BMRS: ≥50% improvement on the Bech and Rafaelsen Mania Scale †HDRS: ≥50% improvement on the Hamilton Depression Rating Scale

††CGI: moderate-to-marked improvement as measured by the Clinical Global Impression †††CGI: mild-to-marked improvement as measured by the Clinical Global Impression

⊗CGI: decrease in the severity of illness by at least one CGI point.

EFFICACY

Given the similarities in the mode of action with other antiepileptic agents, it has been suggested that topiramate might be of use in the treatment of bipolar disorder. Until now, the efficacy of topiramate has been mainly evaluated in small, nonrandomized, open-label studies, in most cases as adjunctive therapy in patients inadequately responsive to or intolerant of standard mood stabilizers (Table 1).

Topiramate as Adjunctive Treatment in the Management of Refractory Bipolar Disorder

Marcotte (1998) studied retrospectively the actions of topiramate as adjunctive therapy in a sample of 58 patients refractory to conventional mood stabilizers (44 with rapid-cycling bipolar disorder, 9 with schizoaffective disorder, 3 with dementia, and 2 with psychosis), at a mean daily dose of 200 mg (25-400 mg) and for a mean duration of 16 weeks. Response to topiramate was rated on a Likert scale; improvement was investigator rated and included a qualitative assessment of changes in sleep, appetite, mood and concentration during therapy. Measured according to these criteria, a total of 35 patients (62%) exhibited marked or moderate improvement, usually within days or weeks – the majority of responders showed improvement within 72 hours after starting drug while only on a daily dosage of 50 mg. Eighteen of 34 patients (53%) with bipolar disorder and 5 of 10 patients (50%) with cyclothymic disorder exhibited marked or moderate improvement. Improvement rates were also significant for patients with rapid cycling bipolar disorder (23 of 44 patients or 52%). Adverse effects were mild in general, and included paresthesias, somnolence, fatigue, impaired concentration and memory, as well as minor gastrointestinal side effects. Adverse effects lead to topiramate discontinuation in 6 patients (10%).

McElroy et al. (2000) administered topiramate as adjunctive therapy in 56 patients with bipolar (n=54) or schizoaffective (n=2) disorder, which were either resistant to or intolerant of at least one standard mood stabilizer (lithium, valproate or carbamazepine). Thirty two patients had manic, mixed or extremely rapid mood symptoms, 11 were depressed, and 13 were relatively euthymic at the time topiramate was started; all the patients of the latter group received topiramate for its putative weight-reducing properties. The efficacy of topiramate was measured by means of the Clinical Global Impression Scale modified for Bipolar Disorder (CGI-BP) for the acute phase (10 weeks, n=56) in daily doses of 25-500 mg (mean: 193.2mg). Additionally, 37 patients continued open maintenance treatment with topiramate for a mean 294.6 days in a daily dose of 25-1200 mg (mean: 244.7 mg). Of the latter patients, 22 had manic mood symptoms at topiramate initiation, 11 were depressed and 10 were euthymic. During the acute phase, patients with manic symptoms generally responded well to treatment: of 30 patients who completed at least one week of treatment, 9 (34.6%) showed much or very much improvement in their manic symptoms on the CGI-BP at week 4; after 10 weeks of treatment, 19 patients (63.3%) showed much or very much improvement, as measured by means of the CGI-BP. Patients with mania as a group exhibited a significant decrease in the CGI-BP-Mania and Young Mania Rating Scale (YMRS) at 4 weeks of treatment, as well as in the Inventory of Depressive Symptoms (IDS) at week 2. Depressed and euthymic patients did not demonstrate any significant changes in their scores as a group in the 10-week follow-up; only three depressed patients (27.3%) exhibited much or very much improvement in their depressive symptoms (as measured by means of the CGI-BP) at 10 weeks.

During the maintenance phase of the study, 12 (55%) of the 22 patients with initially manic symptoms were rated as much or very much improved at their last evaluation; 11 of the 12 acute phase responders remained well throughout the maintenance phase. On the opposite, of 5 initially depressed patients, which continued maintenance treatment with topiramate, only one was rated as much or very much improved. Of the 10 initially euthymic patients, nine remained euthymic throughout the maintenance phase, but one worsened, with development of mixed symptoms. A substantial proportion of patients (n=29, 52%) discontinued topiramate treatment, 19 patients (34%) before week 10, and 10 (27%) of the 37 entering the maintenance phase. Reasons for discontinuation during acute treatment were increase in manic (n=4) or depressive (n=7) symptoms, and side effects (n=6, 11%). Of the patients entering the maintenance phase, four (11%) discontinued treatment due to side effects and four (11%) due to lack of efficacy or worsening of symptoms. Although 10 patients (18%) discontinued topiramate because of side effects, many patients tolerated the drug well. The most common side effects were neurological and gastrointestinal; side effects leading to discontinuation of treatment were cognitive impairment (n=2), poor appetite and weight loss (n=2), sedation (n=1), paresthesia (n=1), psychosis (n=1), anxiety (n=1), dysgeusia (n=1), tremors (n=1), nausea (n=1) and rash (n=1). Topiramate treatment was associated with significant decreases in both body weight and BMI at 4 (-0.7±1.9 kg or -0.1%) and 10 weeks of treatment (-1.6±2.9 kg or -1.7%), as well as at the last evaluation of patients as a group (-4.5±6.7 kg or –4.9%). For patients remaining on topiramate in the maintenance phase, weight loss continued (-6.2±7.5% kg at 1 year). Weight loss was neither associated with baseline weight nor with BMI, and was judged beneficial by most patients.

In a retrospective chart review (Ghaemi et al., 2001), the effects of topiramate were assessed in a sample 76 bipolar (I, II and NOS) patients, who were resistant to or intolerant of current treatments. Indications for treatment included depressive symptoms (n=33), rapid-cycling (n=24), mixed episodes (n=8), and hypomania (n=3), while 8 subjects received topiramate as prophylaxis. Most patients (n=70) received topiramate as adjunctive treatment; only 6 patients took the medication for less than 2 weeks. Response rate, defined as moderate-to-marked improvement in the Clinical Global Impressions Scale of Improvement (CGI-I), was 13.2% (10/76 patients); however, mild improvement was noted in 47.4% of patients (36/76 patients). Response appeared to correlate with topiramate dose; patients receiving ≥150 mg daily presented a greater response rate (29.4%) than those receiving smaller doses (8.5%). Response rates remained similar in the subsamples of patients with acute major depressive symptoms (15.2% or 5/33 patients) or rapid-cycling (12.5% or 3/24 patients). Side effects were reported quite frequently (81.6% of patients), and lead to discontinuation of treatment in approximately one-third of patients (n=27). The most common side effects were cognitive impairment (36.8%), sedation (14.5%) and paresthesias (10.5%); other side effects were usually related to the central nervous or the gastrointestinal system. Weight loss, defined as loss of 5 lbs (2.27 kg) or greater, was reported by 51.6% of 62 patients, for whom data was available; the mean weight loss was 6.45±2.9 kg (range: 2.27-11.35 kg). Topiramate dose appeared to influence whether or not patients lost weight, but it did not correlate with the amount of weight loss.

Vietta et al. (2002) administered open-label topiramate in a total of 34 bipolar-spectrum patients, all of which had failed adequate trials of at least two mood stabilizers (lithium, carbamazepine or valproate), either in monotherapy or in combination. The patients received topiramate as adjunctive treatment for their manic (n=17), depressive (n=11), hypomanic (n=3) or mixed (n=3) symptoms. The dose of topiramate was gradually titrated up to 100-400 mg daily (mean: 202±65 mg), and outcome was measured over a period of 6 months. Twenty-five patients (74%) completed the 6-month follow-up, whereas 9 withdrew from the study due to subject lost to follow-up (n=4), worsening of symptoms (n=2), hospitalization due to intercurrent illness (n=1), non-compliance (n=1), and one due to side effects (paraesthesia, anxiety and impaired concentration). Of the 23 manic, hypomanic and mixed patients, 13 or 56.5% (10 manic, 2 hypomanic, and 1 mixed) responded well to topiramate administration, defined as a ≥50% reduction in the YMRS score between the initial and final visits. The number of depressed patients demonstrating a similar improvement in the Hamilton Depression Rating Scale (HDRS) was 6 (55%). In total, 19 patients (56%) improved by 2 or more points in the Clinical Global Impressions Scale of Severity (CGS-S); the most relevant decline in CGI-S ratings was seen between week 2 and 6, and accounted for 65% of total improvement. During the follow-up period, 15 (44%) patients experienced a new affective episode, which was depressive in 9 (26%) patients, manic in 3 (9%), hypomanic in 2 (6%) and mixed in 1 (3%) patient. Seven of these relapses occurred before week 7, while the rest occurred after this period. It is noted that due to study design, relapsing patients could well be considered responders at the end of the study (week 24). In general, a significant reduction in YMRS, HDRS and CGI-S scores was observed after the introduction of topiramate ($p<0.0001$ for all measures at endpoint). Topiramate was generally well tolerated; only one patient discontinued due to adverse effects (paraesthesia, anxiety and impaired concentration). Eight patients (24%) reported one or more adverse events, usually of mild or moderate severity. The most common side effects were from the central nervous system (paraesthesias, somnolence, impaired concentration, headache) and the gastrointestinal system (anorexia, nausea, vomiting, gastric discomfort, diarrhea). Ten patients (29%) experienced moderate weight loss during the follow-up period (mean: -2.3±1.3 kg), but only two of them (6%) complained of it.

A retrospective chart review, which was conducted by Guille and Sachs (2002), assessed the effects of topiramate in 14 patients with bipolar disorder, 13 of which also suffered from one or more comorbid conditions (anxiety disorders, eating disorders, OCD-spectrum disorders, migraine, alcohol/substance abuse and obesity); 8 of these patients were rapid cycling. The patients had received topiramate for 1-64 weeks (mean: 22.4) at a final daily dose of 25-300 mg (mean: 100 mg); in all patients, topiramate was added to previous treatment (1-5 medications, mean: 3). Eleven patients remained on topiramate for longer than 2 weeks; four of them (28%) experienced a decrease in the severity of their bipolar illness by one or more CGI points, and 8 (61%) also exhibited clinically significant improvements in their primary comorbid condition, as measured by the CGI-I. The majority of the patients (13/14) showed improvement in their Global Assessment Scale (GAS) scores. Patient response to topiramate was 50% (3/6) for the subgroup with mania, 25% (1/4) for depression, and 38% (3/8) for rapid-cycling patients. During treatment with topiramate, 4 patients with a body mass index (BMI) >28 experienced a mean weight loss of 13.5 kg (range: 2.3-34 kg). Five patients (35%) were forced to discontinue treatment due to adverse events (rash, paresthesia, cognitive impairment or sedation).

DelBello et al. (2002) evaluated the effectiveness of topiramate as adjunctive treatment for children and adolescents with bipolar disorders. Twenty-six patients, with a mean age of 14±3.5 years with bipolar disorder, type I (n=23) or II (n=3), were included in this study. The mean dose of topiramate was 104±77 mg/day and the mean duration of treatment was 4.1±6.1 months. Response rate, defined by a CGI-I score of ≤2 at the end, was 73% for mania and 62% for overall illness. No serious adverse events were reported.

Topiramate for the Treatment of Acute Mania

Chengappa et al. (1999) assessed the efficacy of topiramate as adjunctive therapy in 20 patients with bipolar or schizoaffective disorder; all patients had failed to respond to combination treatments with mood-stabilizing and/or antipsychotic agents, and all suffered from mania prior to starting treatment with topiramate. The mean daily dose of topiramate at the end of the study was 210.5 mg (50-300 mg), and assessments were carried out weekly until week 5; response to topiramate was a priori defined as a ≥50% reduction in the YMRS baseline score and a CGI-I score of 2 or less (i.e. "much improved" or "very much improved"). According to these criteria, 12 patients or 60% (11 with bipolar disorder and 1 with schizoaffective disorder) were responders to topiramate, with time to response ranging between 2 and 4 weeks; another 3 subjects improved on the YMRS scores by 25-50%. It is worth noting that improvement was also observed in psychotic symptoms, as well as in aggressive behavior. Adverse events were seen in the first 3-4 weeks, and resolved either without treatment or by dosage reduction; in one patient, who was concomitantly receiving clozapine and valproate, topiramate was discontinued due to acute mental changes (confusion), but it was reintroduced 2 weeks later with a slower titration without untoward events. Side effects included paresthesias, anorexia, fatigue, sedation, slowed thinking, word finding difficulty, tremor, and nausea. All adverse effects occurred singly or in combination in only nine subjects, whereas none were noted in 11 subjects. No particular clinical characteristics distinguished either group, although the group without adverse effects appeared to have fewer concomitant medications overall. There was a significant weight loss (mean: 4.3 kg over 5 weeks) for the group; all patients lost weight, although three subjects initially gained weight during the first 2 weeks. Similarly, significant decreases in the BMI were noted.

Calabrese et al. (2001) assessed the efficacy of topiramate monotherapy in 11 inpatients with severe refractory mania or mixed episode. Topiramate was administered in a mean daily dose of 313 mg (50-1300 mg), for a mean of 16 days (2-29 days). Four patients completed 28 days in the study; one patient only received two days of study medication, and six patients withdrew early from the study (one of which due to lack of efficacy and five due to patient choice). Among 10 evaluable patients, three showed an improvement of 50% or more in the YMRS scores, and two more had scores that improved by 25-50%. At the final evaluation with the CGI-I, 3 patients were judged markedly improved, one was moderately improved and another one was minimally improved. The adverse events that occurred were paresthesias (n=5), decreased appetite (n=2), nausea (n=2) and constipation (n=2). No patient withdrew from the study because of adverse events. In the four patients completing the 28-treatment period, mean body weight decreased from 93.6 kg to 91.5 kg.

Grunze et al. (2001) investigated the antimanic efficacy of topiramate in 11 patients with acute manic episode refractory to treatment with mood stabilizers and/or antipsychotics, in a study with an on-off-on design. Topiramate was titrated within 1 week to a final dose in the range of 25 to 200 mg/day, depending on clinical efficacy and tolerability. After 10 days of treatment, topiramate was discontinued, while concomitant medication remained unchanged. Five days later (on day 16) topiramate was reintroduced at similar or increased doses for another 7 days. Seven of the 11 patients initially showed a good antimanic response with more than 50% reduction in YMRS scores by day 10; one patient, who showed psychotic features following rapid increase in topiramate dose, dropped out at this point. After discontinuation, 7 of the remaining 10 patients worsened (increase of at least 25% in YMRS scores), 2 remained stable, and 1 discontinued follow-up after good recovery. Finally, on day 22, after the reintroduction of topiramate, eight of the remaining 9 patients met the responder criterion of at least 50% reduction on YMRS scores compared with baseline values. With the exception of the patient who developed psychosis, topiramate was well tolerated. Two patients experienced sedation with topiramate at a dose of 50 mg/day. One of them, who was also receiving carbamazepine, presented a transient carbamazepine plasma level increase, and sedation reversed after readjusting the carbamazepine dose; the other patient was receiving concomitant valproate with no change in valproate plasma level.

Bozikas et al. (2002) evaluated the effectiveness of topiramate in 14 inpatients with an acute manic episode. Nine patients received topiramate as monotherapy, in 3 patients topiramate was added to previous treatment (valproate, carbamazepine or risperidone), and 2 patients received topiramate along with an antipsychotic agent (zuclopenthixol and risperidone, respectively). The mean dose of topiramate was 310 mg daily (150-400 mg, except for one patient who received 700 mg). The duration of the study was 4 weeks; one patient withdrew from the study, discontinuing hospitalization and psychiatric treatment. At the end of the study, 61.5% (8/13) patients showed a ≥50% reduction in the Bech and Rafaelsen Mania Scale (BMRS); in the subgroup of patients receiving topiramate as monotherapy, response rate was 50% (4/8). All patients needed benzodiazepines or antipsychotics as rescue medication, due to psychomotor agitation and other disruptive symptoms. Four patients –three women and one man, all of them obese- reported weight loss (1-8 kg); two patients gained weight, one man receiving topiramate in combination with risperidone (3 kg) and one woman in topiramate monotherapy (2 kg). No other adverse effects were observed in this sample of patients.

Recently, an unpublished, 3-week, prospective, double blind, placebo controlled study assessed the effects of topiramate in a sample of 97 patients with bipolar I disorder and manic or mixed symptoms (YMRS score≥20). Patients were randomly assigned into two active treatment arms (topiramate 256 mg/day or 512 mg/day) and a placebo arm; rescue medication (benzodiazepines) was permitted for up to 10 days. Primary efficacy analyses did not provide any statistically significant differences among the three groups for the mean change from baseline YMRS total scores; however, when all subjects receiving antidepressants prior to study entry were eliminated from the analyses, results were statistically significant for patients receiving 512 mg/d topiramate, compared to those receiving placebo (this study, performed by D. van Kammen, R. Reife and the Topimate Team at Robert Wood Johnson Pharmaceutical Research Institute, New Jersey, USA, is referred by Chengappa et al., 2001a and Suppes, 2002).

Topiramate in Depression

Hussain et al. (2001) studied the effects of open-label adjunctive topiramate in 135 individuals with bipolar (type I or II) depression, who had failed to respond adequately to previous treatment trials with mood stabilizers and antidepressants. The daily dose of topiramate was titrated up to 600 mg/day, and patients were evaluated with the HDRS for a period of 24 months. Of the 92 patients completing the 24-month follow-up, 75% were full responders (HDRS score 0-5), and the rest were close-to-full responders (HDRS score 6-8). Clinically significant responses were seen within 2-4 weeks of treatment. There was no instance of affective switch; five patients developed hypomania, but responded well to dosage adjustment.

In another study (Carpenter et al., 2002), the efficacy of adjunctive topiramate was retrospectively evaluated through chart review in 16 patients suffering from major depressive episode of mild or moderate severity. Twelve patients suffered from unipolar depression, 3 had bipolar II disorder, and one patient suffered from bipolar disorder NOS. Topiramate was added to the previous treatment with antidepressants, in a dose of 100-400 mg/day (mean: 277 mg/day); its efficacy was assessed over a period of 1-40 weeks for all patients (mean: 17.7±13.4), but also for the acute phase (mean: 5.5±1.2 weeks) in a subset of 11 patients. Acute phase patients demonstrated significant improvement, when self-evaluated with the Inventory for Depressive Symptomatology-Self Report (IDS-SR), but only two 2 of them (18%) achieved a ≥50% decrease in IDS-SR total score at acute phase endpoint. CGI illness severity scores also showed significant improvement during the acute phase, as did GAS and Social and Occupational Functioning Assessment (SOFAS) scores; however, only four patients (36%) met a priori CGI criteria for positive response at the end of the acute phase, defined as much or very much improved on CGI change score. In the extended phase data for the larger sample, 44% (7/16) of patients were judged responders; in five of them, improvement was noted within 2-4 weeks after starting topiramate. Of the nonresponders, four (25%) were rated "minimally worse" and one (6.25%) "very much worse". Adverse events documented included impaired concentration or word-finding difficulties (n=6, 38%), paresthesias (n=6, 38%), memory disturbance (n=4, 25%), dysgeusia (n=3, 19%) and hematuria (n=2, 13%). Adverse events lead to discontinuation of treatment in four patients, two with hematuria and two with impaired cognition; side effects resolved fully after drug discontinuation, which was accomplished by gradual taper without significant withdrawal symptoms. During topiramate treatment, a significant decrease of mean patient body weight and BMI was observed. The mean percent weight loss from baseline was 6.1±8.2%, with 6 patients (38%) experiencing marked weight loss (≥5% of baseline). Weight loss was correlated with topiramate treatment duration and tended to correlate with final topiramate dose, but was uncorrelated with other measures of clinical status.

In a single-blind (rater-blind), 8-week study conducted by McIntyre et al. (2002) the efficacy of topiramate was compared to that of bupropion XR in 36 patients with bipolar depression. The study medications were administered as adjunctive treatment, in a daily dose of 50-300 mg (mean: 176 mg) for topiramate and 100-400 mg (mean: 250 mg) for bupropion. Patient response, defined as a ≥50% from baseline score in mean HDRS-total score, was similar for topiramate (56%) and bupropion (59%); time to response ranged from 2 to 4 weeks for both treatment groups. The observed improvement, which was also reflected in the

CGI-scores, did not differ significantly between the two groups. Adverse events were reported in 61% of patients receiving topiramate and 50% of patients receiving bupropion; the only adverse event, the frequency of which differed significantly between groups, was difficulty in sleeping (greater in the bupropion group). It is noted that paresthesia and tremors were experienced by a higher percentage (but not significantly) of patients receiving bupropion. In total, 44% of patients receiving topiramate discontinued prematurely from the 8-week study phase, compared with 28% of patients receiving bupropion; the percentage of withdrawal due to adverse effects was 33% for topiramate and 22% for bupropion. Weight loss was recorded in both treatment groups, but it was greater for topiramate (5.8 kg for topiramate versus 1.2 kg for bupropion).

Topiramate in Rapid-cycling Bipolar Disorder

Three of the studies, which assessed adjunctive topiramate in refractory patients, observed a beneficial effect in patients with rapid-cycling bipolar disorder. Marcotte (1998) reported improvement in 23 of 44 (52%) rapid cycling patients. The success rates were 38% (3 of 8 patients) and 67% (4 of 6 patients) in the studies by Guille and Sachs (2002) and Chengappa et al. (1999), respectively.

Kusumakar et al. (1999) evaluated topiramate in 27 female patients with a diagnosis of bipolar I or II disorder and ultra-rapid, ultradian or chaotic biphasic mood instability; patients had been refractory to previous mood-stabilizer therapies and had suffered significant weight gain (>20%) from previous treatment. Patients received either lithium or valproate, followed after 3 weeks by the addition of topiramate, which was gradually titrated up to 150 mg/day (mean, 105.2 mg/day); lorazepam (up to 4 mg/day) was permitted during the study for anxiety or insomnia. Outcome was measured by means of the HDRS and YMRS, as well as through assessments of sleep, weight loss and mood (daily mood chart held by subjects). Twenty-three patients completed the study; four patients discontinued due to adverse events (drowsiness, ataxia, confusion and reemergence of psychosis). Fifteen patients (56%) showed a significant improvement in mood and achieved euthymia at the 4th-12th week of the study. During the 16-week study period, 14 patients (52%) experienced weight loss, which exceeded 5% of baseline body weight in 9 patients (33%), and one patient experienced weight gain.

Topiramate as Maintenance Therapy in Bipolar Disorder

Few studies have followed the long-term course of patients treated with topiramate, usually as adjunctive treatment, and report positive results. Although they mainly focused on the acute treatment of patients with manic symptoms, Chengappa et al. (1999) also reported on their outcome during a two- to ten-month follow-up period. Generally, the 12 patients who were considered to be responders during the initial phase of the study kept on improving; however, two subjects with a rapid cycling course experienced a manic and a hypomanic episode 7 and 6 months later, respectively, and responded to an increment in the topiramate dosage. Four individuals achieved an eventual reduction in polypharmacy, benzodiazepines were discontinued in four subjects, and antipsychotic agents were discontinued in three subjects. McElroy et al. (2000) also provided data for 37 patients in their study, who continued open maintenance treatment with topiramate for a mean period of more than 7 months; as previously noted, they obtained satisfactory results for manic and euthymic patients, but rather not so for depressed patients. In the study by Vietta et al. (2002), a gradual reduction in YMRS, HDRS and CGI scores was observed during the 24-week study period; this reduction reached significance at endpoint for patients as a group, as well as for the separate subsamples of manic and depressed patients. Two retrospective studies (Carpenter et al., 2002; Guille and Sachs, 2002) also included some data for patients who received topiramate for a longer period of time (up to 64 and 40 weeks, respectively); although the researchers do not report separately on the outcome of these patients, the benefits of topiramate appeared to endure, and maybe increase, in the long-term.

Chengappa et al. (2001b), in a small case series, reported 3 patients with bipolar I disorder, obesity and diabetes mellitus type II, who received topiramate as adjunctive treatment in a daily dose of 300 mg for 1-2 years. All patients demonstrated a reduction in the frequency of episodes while on topiramate, as compared to the past 12 months, i.e. before starting treatment; for two of these patients, who where rapid-cycling, the reduction was quite considerable.

Efficacy and Tolerability of Topiramate in Review

Efficacy

Existing data do not permit an accurate assessment of topiramate efficacy. So far, the effects of topiramate have been mostly evaluated in open-label, non-randomized trials. Moreover, few studies have assessed topiramate as monotherapy, and most studies focus on patients refractory to, or intolerant of, previous therapies, thus limiting the interpretation of results. On the other hand, results are often not comparable due to differences in patient characteristics, methodology, length of follow-up and outcome measures. However, these limitations do not invalidate the fact that preliminary studies generally report positive results. Seven recent trials (Chengappa et al., 1999; McElroy et al., 2000; Calabrese et al., 2001; Grunze et al., 2001; Bozikas et al., 2002; Guille and Sachs, 2002; Vietta et al., 2002) report efficacy rates of 50% to 89% for manic, hypomanic or mixed symptoms in patients with bipolar disorder; overall, 67 of 109 patients (61.5%) with such symptoms experienced significant improvement, as measured with the CGI, YMRS or BRMS. In 80 of these patients the effects of topiramate were assessed in the acute (up to 10 weeks) treatment period; 51 of them (64%) exhibited significant improvement of their symptomatology. The reported efficacy rates in bipolar depression and in rapid-cycling range somewhat more widely. In five studies, which included bipolar patients with depressive symptoms (McElroy et al., 2000; Ghaemi et al., 2001; Hussain et al., 2001; Guille and Sachs, 2002; Vietta et al., 2002), topiramate treatment was judged beneficial, as measured with the CGI or the HDRS, in 15% to 68% of patients; out of a total of 194 patients in these studies, 107 (55%) experienced some decrease in their symptoms. The results are similar in the five studies (Marcotte, 1998; Chengappa et al., 1999; Kusumakar et al., 1999; Ghaemi et al., 2001; Guille and Sachs, 2002) reporting separately on rapid-cycling patients: efficacy rates range between 12.5% and 67%, providing a mean of 44% (48 out of 109 patients).

It is also worth noting that, among the subjects with manic psychoses in the study by Chengappa et al. (1999), topiramate treatment led to a clinically important reduction in aggressive behaviour, as well as to an improvement in psychotic symptoms (mood-congruent and –incongruent delusional ideas and hallucinations, measured by means of the YMRS); the latter findings were not confirmed by means of separate scales, but they certainly warrant more extensive investigation. Another point that merits emphasis is the potential utility of topiramate in bipolar patients with comorbid conditions, as suggested by the positive results obtained by Guille and Sachs (2002) in a sample of bipolar patients with various comorbidities: as mentioned earlier, 8 of 11 (73%) of these patients exhibited clinically significant improvement in their primary comorbid condition as measured by the CGI-I; a wide range of comorbid conditions appeared to respond to some extent to topiramate treatment, including bulimia and anorexia nervosa; obsessive-compulsive disorder, Tourette's syndrome and other OCD spectrum disorders; post-traumatic stress and panic disorder; alcohol and substance abuse; migraine; and psychotic features. Similar findings regarding the efficacy of topiramate in patients with history of alcohol and substance abuse or dependence were also reported in other studies (Marcotte, 1998; Chengappa et al., 1999). Naturally, due to the small number of patients no definite judgements can be made, but these observations offer yet another promising direction for future research.

Optimal Dosages and Titration Schedule

In the clinical studies described above, topiramate daily dose ranged between 12.5 and 1300 mg (mean doses approximately 100-300 mg). Topiramate was generally started at a low dose of 25-50 mg, and gradually titrated in 25-50 mg increments at 2- to 14-day intervals, most usually every 3-7 days; the rate of topiramate titration was determined by clinical status and tolerance in most studies. Regarding optimal dosages, it should be noted that the only double-blind study as yet available observed a superiority of the effects topiramate over placebo only at a dose of 512 mg/day, and not at 256 mg/day. On the other hand, Ghaemi et al. (2001) report that a significantly greater proportion of patients receiving higher daily doses of topiramate (≥150 mg daily) were judged responders (29%), than patients receiving lower doses (8%). It is thus possible that the optimal dosages of topiramate might be higher than initially thought.

Safety Profile

In the clinical studies assessing topiramate in patients with bipolar disorder, the drug appeared to be quite well tolerated. The most common adverse effects of topiramate involved the central nervous system and the gastrointestinal system (Table 2). Topiramate treatment was quite frequently related to cognitive impairment (disturbed attention and concentration, memory impairment and word-finding difficulty). In a prospective multicenter, postmarketing study, the prevalence in general of cognitive adverse events in patients with epilepsy treated with topiramate, was 41.4%, yet 5.8% of those discontinued the drug solely for that reason, mainly because of psychomotor slowing. However, the vast majority of the patients were receiving at least two antiepileptic drugs (Tatum et al., 2001). Other common CNS effects include paresthesias, sedation and fatigue. The CNS adverse effects of topiramate are often reported to be associated with higher doses, aggressive titration schedules, or with the combination of topiramate with other central-acting drugs (Chengappa et al., 1999; Guille and Sachs, 2002), and it has been suggested that a more gradual introduction of topiramate can reduce the extent of cognitive impairment (Elger and Bauer, 1998; Chengappa et al., 2001a; Smith et al., 2001; Tatum et al., 2001; Carpenter et al., 2002; Suppes, 2002). Nevertheless, there are also studies that could not confirm the association of word finding difficulties with rapid titration (Mula et al., 2003) and alternatively it was speculated that some properties of topiramate, e.g. sulfa moiety or carbonic acid inhibition, might be related to the word finding difficulties (Ojemann et al., 2001). Chengappa et al. (1999) reported that in one of their patients, who was initially forced to discontinue topiramate treatment due to confusion, a re-challenge with the drug at a slower titration rate was possible without any problems.

Gastrointestinal complications of topiramate treatment included anorexia, nausea and vomiting, diarrhea or constipation and gastric discomfort. Other adverse effects that have been observed, although not frequently, include dysgeusia, dry mouth and increased thirst, pruritis, and rash.

Table 2. Reported Side Effects from 7 Studies of Patients with Mood Disorders (N=270) on Topiramate Treatment (Marcotte, 1998; Chengappa et al., 1999; McElroy et al., 2000; Calabrese et al., 2001; Ghaemi et al., 2001; Carpenter et al., 2002 Vieta et al., 2002)*

Side effects	N	%
Cognitive impairment-slowed thinking	41	15
Paresthesias	38	14
Anorexia	20	7.5
Sedation	18	7
Nausea	10	4
Fatigue	11	4
Dizziness	8	3
Word-finding difficulty	8	3
Dysgeusia	7	2.5
Weight loss	6	2
Insomnia	5	2
Somnolence	5	2
Headache	4	1.5
Dyspepsia	4	1.5
Polydipsia	4	1.5
Ataxia	4	1.5
Itching	4	1.5
Memory disturbance	4	1.5
Dry mouth	4	1.5
Constipation	2	1
Vomiting	2	1
Hematuria	2	1
Tremor	1	0.5
Acute confusional state	1	0.5
Rash	1	0.5

* Only side effects with incidence rate of at least 5% per study were included.

Adverse effects of topiramate are usually of mild to moderate severity; they appear mainly at the beginning of the treatment and are often reported to resolve spontaneously or with small dosage adjustments (McElroy et al., 2000; Chengappa et al., 2001a; Suppes, 2002), although drop-out rates as high as 36% (Ghaemi et al., 2001; Guille and Sachs, 2002) have been reported because of side effects. In three trials that provided relevant data (Chengappa et al., 1999; Ghaemi et al., 2001; Vietta et al., 2002), 79 out of a total of 130 patients (61%) reported at least one adverse event; approximately one-third of them discontinued treatment because of side effects.

An infrequent but troublesome adverse effect of topiramate is the formation of renal stones, estimated to occur in 1.5% of patients on topiramate (Jones, 1998). It is not dose related, and it is probably caused by the carbonic anhydrase inhibition properties of topiramate (Perucca, 1997; Shank et al., 2000); because of this, topiramate should not be combined with other carbonic anhydrase-inhibiting drugs, such as acetazolamide (Chengappa et al., 2001a). The occurence of renal stones can be minimized by advising patients to increase their fluid intake and avoid excessive antacid use or excessive milk or alcohol intake; also, topiramate should be avoided in patients with parathyroid disorders or gout (Chengappa et al., 2001a).

A few cases of topiramate overdose have been reported. In the study by Marcotte (1998), one patient overmedicated herself with 800 mg topiramate and 170 mg tranylcypromine sulfate along with alcohol, and subsequently experienced delirium; however, this side-effect, which resolved without complications, might have been due to the combined effect of the two drugs and alcohol. One other study (Smith et al., 2001) reported the case of patient who ingested 4000 mg of topiramate without any sequelae. In the clinical trials conducted by the pharmaceutical company, which distributes topiramate, five cases of topiramate overdose (1.8 to 100 gr) occurred. Three patients reported symptoms of confusion, ataxia, lethargy, sluggishness, hyperreflexia and memory lapses; one patient was found obtunded and unresponsive, while the patient who ingested 100 gr of topiramate was hospitalized in status epilepticus –although in the latter case, the cause of the status epilepticus is not known, as no information is provided on the patient's medical history or any concomitant medications (Smith et al., 2001).

Effects of Topiramate on Body Weight

Anorexia and weight-loss constitute well-documented effects of topiramate; mild weight loss (1-6 kg) has been reported in up to 20% of patients and it is more pronounced in those with highest weights at baseline (Jones, 2001). In the studies assessing topiramate in patients with bipolar disorder, this effect appears even more pronounced: in six studies (Chengappa et al., 1999; Ghaemi et al., 2001; Bozikas et al., 2002; Carpenter et al., 2002; Guille and Sachs, 2002; Vietta et al., 2002), a mean 48% of patients included experienced weight loss, while Chengappa et al. (1999) report that all patients in their study lost weight during treatment with topiramate. The mean amount of weight loss in these studies ranged between 1.5 and 13.5 kg. The mechanisms underlying weight loss are not known, although anorexia may be the explanation in some individuals; Chengappa et al. (2001b) have anecdotally noted that some female patients verbalized a lack of desire to eat carbohydrate rich foods, as well as a sooner appearance of the feeling of satiation. Topiramate-induced weight loss is often reported to depend on final topiramate dose and baseline weight, and women appear to lose more weight than men (Chengappa et al., 1999, 2001a), although some studies do not confirm these observations (McElroy et al., 2000; Ghaemi et al., 2001). The weight-reducing effect of topiramate appears to be sustained in the long term: Mc Elroy et al. (2000) and Chengappa et al. (1999) report that weight loss continued to increase over the total follow-up period in their studies (over a year and up to ten months, respectively); also, weight loss tended to correlate with duration of topiramate treatment in the retrospective chart-review of Carpenter et al. (2002).

Topiramate was found to be efficacious in the treatment of binge eating disorder associated with obesity in a randomized placebo controlled 14-week trial. Specifically, topiramate compared with placebo was associated with significantly greater rate of reduction in binge frequency, binge day frequency, global severity of illness, obsessive-compulsive features of binge eating symptoms, weight, and body mass index. Topiramate was also associated with a significantly higher level of at least moderate response, including rate of remission, among patients in the intent-to-treat group and those who completed the 14-week treatment period (McElroy et al., 2003).

The weight-reducing properties of topiramate are of great interest, since most other mood-stabilizers and antipsychotic agents used in the treatment of bipolar disorder are generally related with weight gain. Hospitalized patients with bipolar disorder presented a nearly threefold higher prevalence of diabetes mellitus than the national trends in USA (Cassidy et al., 1999). In a retrospective chart review conducted by Chengappa et al. (2002), psychiatric patients receiving either lithium or valproate gained a mean 6.3 kg and 6.4 kg respectively, whereas patients receiving topiramate lost a mean 1.2 kg; lithium- or valproate-treated patients gained >8% of their baseline body weight, whereas patients receiving topiramate lost 0.7±7.2% of their baseline weight. The weight loss associated with topiramate could bring about additional benefits, considering that overweight is known to be related to conditions such as hypertension, hyperlipidemia or type II diabetes mellitus. In the small case series of obese diabetic patients with bipolar disorder reported by Chengappa et al. (2001b), all patients demonstrated significant weight loss (20-33 kg) after the introduction of topiramate, as well as a considerably better glycemic control; they were all able to discontinue insulin and be managed with dietary measures or oral hypoglycemic agents. In addition, in one patient, who was being monitored for anti-hypertensive treatment prior to topiramate, blood pressure returned to normal levels. In concordance with these findings, adjunctive topiramate (Ketter, 2000) yielded appreciable weight loss in 8 out of 11 patients with bipolar disorder and weight problems and at least 50% decrease in binge eating episodes in 9 out of 13 patients with comorbid Axis I psychiatric disorders (mainly bipolar disorder) along with binge eating disorder (Shapira et al., 2000). It has been suggested (Chengappa et al., 2001a) that topiramate should be administered with great caution to anorexic or seriously underweight individuals; it is noted, however, that Guille and Sachs (2002) reported improvement of comorbid anorexia nervosa in one patient with bipolar disorder who received topiramate.

CONCLUSION

Open-label, non-randomized, studies of topiramate have shown promising results in the treatment of bipolar disorder; most of them focus on patients refractory to, or intolerant of, previous therapies. Based on these preliminary results it seems that topiramate is equally efficacious for the treatment of pure mania, dysphoric mania, bipolar depression, rapid cycling, as well as bipolar disorder associated with comorbid psychiatric conditions. On the other hand, evidence for the efficacy of topiramate in the treatment of continuation phase and prophylaxis is sparse and inconclusive. Larger, double blind controlled studies are warranted to establish a potential role of topiramate in the acute and prophylactic treatment of patients with bipolar disorder. Topiramate, also, presents a favorable side effect profile, while its weight-reducing properties might prove to be of great interest, since most other mood-stabilizers and antipsychotics used in the treatment of bipolar disorder are generally related with weight gain.

REFERENCES

American Psychiatric Association. Practice Guidelines for the treatment of patients with bipolar disorder. *American Journal of Psychiatry* 1994; 151(Suppl).

Bazil CW, Pedley TA. Clinical pharmacology of antiepileptic drugs. *Clinical Neuropharmacology* 2003;26:38-52.

Bazil CW. New antiepileptic drugs. *Neurologist* 2002; 8:71-81.

Bowden CL. Predictors of response to divalproex and lithium. *Journal of Clinical Psychiatry* 1995; 56 (Suppl 3):25-30.

Bozikas VP, Petrikis P, Kourtis A, Youlis P, Karavatos A. Treatment of acute mania with topiramate in hospitalized patients. *Progress in Neuro-Psychopharmacology and Biological Psychiatry* 2002; 26:1203-1206.

Calabrese JR, Keck PE, McElroy SL, Shelton MD. A pilot study of topiramate as monotherapy in the treatment of acute mania. *Journal of Clinical Psychopharmacology* 2001; 21:340-342.

Carpenter LL, Leon Z, Yasmin S, Price LH. Do obese patients respond to topiramate? A retrospective chart review. *Journal of Affective Disorders* 2002; 69:251-255.

Cassidy F, Ahearn E, Carroll BJ. Elevated frequency of diabetes mellitus in hospitalised manic-depressive patients. *American Journal of Psychiatry* 1999; 156:1417-1420.

Chengappa KNR, Chalasani L, Brar JS, Parepally H, Houck P, Levine J. Changes in body weight and body mass index among psychiatric patients receiving lithium, valproate, or topiramate: An open-label, nonrandomized chart review. *Clinical Therapeutics* 2002; 24:1576-1584.

Chengappa KNR, Gershon S, Levin J. The evolving role of topiramate among other mood stabilizers in the management of bipolar disorder. *Bipolar Disorders* 2001a; 3:215-232.

Chengappa KNR, Levine J, Rathore D, Parepally H, Atzert R. Long-term effects of topiramate on bipolar mood instability, weight change and glycemic control: a case series. *European Psychiatry* 2001b; 16:186-190.

Chengappa KNR, Rathore D, Levine J, Atzert R, Solai L, Parepally H, Levin H, Moffa N, Delaney J, Brar JS. Topiramate as add-on treatment for patients with bipolar mania. *Bipolar Disorders* 1999; 1:42-53.

Chong MS, Libretto SE. The rationale and use of topiramate fot treating neuropathic pain. *Clinical Journal of Pain* 2003; 19:59-68.

DelBello MP, Kowatch RA, Warner J, Schwiers ML, Rappaport KB, Daniels JP, Foster KD, Strakowski SM. Adjunctive topiramate treatment for pediatric bipolar disorder: A retrospective chart review. *Journal of Child and Adolescent Psychopharmacology* 2002; 12:323-330.

Doose DR, Kohl KA, Desai-Krieger J, Natarajan J, van Kammen DP. No clinically significant effect of topiramate on haloperidol plasma concentration. *European Neuropsychopharmacology* 1999; 9(Suppl 5):S357.

Doose DR, Kohl KA, Desai-Krieger D, Natarajan J, van Kammen DP. No significant effect of topiramate on lithium serum concentration. 152nd Annual Meeting of the American Psychiatric Association, Washington DC, USA, 15-20 May 1999.

Doose DR, Larson KL, Natarajan J, Neto W. Comparative single-dose pharmacokinetics of topiramate in elderly versus young men and women. *Epilepsia* 1998; 39(Suppl 6):56.

Doose DR, Walker SA, Venkataramanan R, Rabinovitz M, Lever J. Topiramate pharmacokinetics in subjects with liver impairments. *Pharmaceutical Research* 1994; 11(Suppl):S446.

Dubovsky SL, Buzan RD. Novel alternatives and supplements to lithium and anticonvulsants for bipolar affective disorder. *Journal of Clinical Psychiatry* 1997; 58:224-242.

Edwards KR, Potter DL, Wu SC, Kamin M, Hulihan J. Topiramate in the preventive treatment of episodic migraine: A combined analysis from pilot, double-blind, placebo-controlled trials. *CNS Spectrum* 2003; 8:428-432.

Elger CE, Bauer J. New antiepileptic drugs in epileptology. *Neuropsychobiology* 1998; 38:145-148.

Ghaemi SN, Manwani SG, Katzow JJ, Ko JY, Goodwin FK. Topiramate treatment of bipolar spectrum disorders: a retrospective chart review. *Annals of Clinical Psychiatry* 2001; 13:185-189.

Grunze HC, Normann C, Langosch J, Schaefer M, Amann B, Sterr A, Schloesser S, Kleindienst N, Walden J. Antimanic efficacy of topiramate in 11 patients in an open trial with an on-off-on design. *Journal of Clinical Psychiatry* 2001; 62:464-468.

Guille C, Sachs G. Clinical outcome of adjunctive topiramate treatment in a sample of refractory bipolar patients with comorbid conditions. *Progress in Neuro-Psychopharmacology and Biological Psychiatry* 2002; 26:1035-1039.

Hachad H, Ragueneau-Majlessi I, Levy RH. New antiepileptic drugs: Review on drug interactions. *Therapeutic and Drug Monitoring* 2002; 24:91-103.

Hilty DM, Brady KT, Hales RE. A review of bipolar disorder among adults. *Psychiatric Services* 1999; 50:201-213.

Hussain MZ, Chaudhry ZA, Zubaida A, Hussain S. Topiramate in treatment of refractory bipolar depression. *European Neuropsychopharmacology* 2001; 9(Suppl 3):S119-S120.

Jones MW. Topiramate-safety and tolerability. *Canadian Journal of Neurological Sciences* 1998; 25(Suppl 3):13-15.

Ketter TA, Frye MA, Corá-Locatelli G, Kimbrell TA, Post RM. Metabolism and excretion of mood stabilizers and new anticonvulsants. *Cellular and Molecular Neurobiology* 1999a; 19:511-532.

Ketter TA, Post RM, Theodore WH. Positive and negative psychiatric effects of antiepileptic drugs in patients with seizure disorders. *Neurology* 1999b; 53(Suppl 2):S53-S67.

Ketter TA. Low dose adjunctive topiramate attenuates weight gain in bipolar disorders patients. *International Journal of Neuropsychopharmacology* 2000; 3(Suppl 1):S244.

Kusumakar V, Yatham L, Kutcher S, O' Donovan C. Preliminary, open-label study of topiramate in rapid cycling bipolar women. *European Neuropsychopharmacology* 1999; 9(Suppl 5):S357.

Kwan P, Brodie MJ. Clinical trials of antiepileptic medications in newly diagnosed patients with epilepsy. *Neurology* 2003; 60(Suppl 4):S2-S12.

Li X, Ketter TA, Frye MA. Synaptic, intracellular, and neuroprotective mechanisms of anticonvulsants : Are they relevant for the treatment and course of bipolar disorders ? *Journal of Affective Disorders* 2002; 69:1-14.

Liao S, Palmer M. Digoxin and topiramate drug interaction study in male volunteers. *Pharmaceutical Research* 1993; 10(Suppl):S444.

Marcotte D. Use of topiramate, a new anti-epileptic as a mood stabilizer. *Journal of Affective Disorders* 1998; 50:245-251.

McElroy SL, Arnold LM, Shapira NA, Keck PE Jr, Rosenthal NR, Karim MR, Kamin M, Hudson JI. Topiramate in the treatment of binge eating disorder associated with obesity: A randomised, placebo-controlled trial. *American Journal of Psychiatry* 2003; 160:255-261.

McElroy SL, Suppes T, Keck PE, Frye MA, Denicoff KD, Altshuler LL, Sherwood Brown E, Nolen WA, Kupka RW, Rochussen J, Leverich GS, Post RM. Open-label adjunctive topiramate in the treatment of bipolar disorders. *Biological Psychiatry* 2000; 47:1025-1033.

McIntyre RS, Mancini DA, McCann S, Srinivasan J, Sagman D, Kennedy SH. Topiramate versus Bupropion SR when added to mood stabilizer therapy for the depressive phase of bipolar disorder: a preliminary single-blind study. *Bipolar Disorders* 2002; 4:207-213.

Mula M, Monaco F. Antiepileptic-antipsychotic drug interactions: A critical review of the evidence. *Clinical Neuropharmacology* 2002; 25:280-289.

Mula M, Trimble MR, Thompson P, Sander JW. Topiramate and word-finding difficulties in patients with epilepsy. *Neurology* 2003; 60:1104-1107.

Ojemann LM, Ojemann GA, Dodrill CB, Crawford CA, Holmes MD, Dudley DL. Language disturbances as side effects of topiramate and zonisamide therapy. *Epilepsy and Behavior* 2001; 2:579-584.

Patsalos PN, Perucca E. Clinically important drug interactions in epilepsy: General features and interactions between antiepileptic drugs. *Lancet Neurology* 2003; 2:347-356.

Patsalos PN. The pharmacokinetic profile of topiramate. *Reviews in Contemporary Pharmacotherapy* 1999; 10:155-162.

Perucca E. A pharmacological and clinical review on topiramate, a new antiepileptic drug. *Pharmacological Research* 1997; 35:241-256.

Perucca E. Pharmacokinetic profile of topiramate in comparison with other new antiepileptic drugs. *Epilepsia* 1996;37(Suppl 2):S8-S13.

Post RM, Denicoff KD, Frye MA, Dunn RT, Leverich GS, Osuch E, Speer A. A history of the use of anticonvulsants as mood stabilizers in the last two decades of the 20th century. *Neurobiology* 1998a; 38:152-166.

Post RM, Frye MA, Denicoff KD, Leverich GS, Kimbrell TA, Dunn RT. Beyond lithium in the treatment of bipolar illness. *Neuropsychopharmacology* 1998b; 19:206-219.

Post RM, Ketter TA, Denicoff K, Pazzaglia PJ, Leverich GS, Marangell LB, Callahan AM, George MS, Frye MA. The place of anticonvulsant therapy in bipolar illness. *Psychopharmacology* 1996;128:115-129.

Rosenfeld WE, Doose DR, Walker SA, Nayak RK. Effect of topiramate on the pharmacokinetics of an oral contraceptive containing norethidrone and ethinyl estradiol in patients with epilepsy. *Epilepsia* 1997a; 38:317-323.

Rosenfeld WE, Liao S, Kramer LD, Anderson G, Palmer M, Levy RH, Nayak RK. Comparison of the steady-state pharmacokinetics of topiramate and valproate in patients with epilepsy during monotherapy and concomitant therapy. *Epilepsia* 1997b; 38:324-333.

Sachdeo R, Sachdeo SK, Walker SA, Kramer LD, Nayak RK, Doose DR. Steady-state pharmacokinetics of topiramate and carbamazepine in patients with epilepsy during monotherapy and concomitant therapy. *Epilepsia* 1996; 37:774-780.

Schou M. Forty years of lithium treatment. *Archives of General Psychiatry* 1997; 54:9-13.

Shank RP, Gardocki JF, Streeter AJ, Mayanoff BE. An overview of the preclinical aspects of topiramate: pharmacology, pharmacokinetics, and mechanism of action. *Epilepsia* 2000; 41(Suppl 1):S3-S9.

Shapira NA, Goldsmith TD, McElroy SL. Treatment of binge-eating disorder with topiramate: A clinical case series. *Journal of Clinical Psychiatry* 2000; 61:368-372.

Smith AG, Brauer HR, Catalano G, Catalano MC. Topiramate overdose: A case report and literature review. *Epilepsy and Behavior* 2001; 2:603-607.

Suppes T. Review of the use of topiramate for treatment of bipolar disorders. *Journal of Clinical Psychopharmacology* 2002; 22:599-609.

Tatum WO 4th, French JA, Faught E, Morris GL 3rd , Liporace J, Kanner A, Goff SL, Winters L, Fix A, and the PADS Investigators. Postmarketing experience with topiramate and cognition. *Epilepsia* 2001; 42:1134-1140.

Vieta E, Torrent C, Garcia-Ribas G, Gilabert A, Garcia-Pares G, Rodriguez A, Cadevall J, Garcia-Castrillon J, Lusilla P, Arrufat F. Use of topiramate in treatment resistant bipolar spectrum disorders. *Journal of Clinical Psychopharmacology* 2002; 22:431-435.

In: Trends in Bipolar Disorder Research
Editor: Malcomb R. Brown, pp. 139-151
ISBN: 1-59454-060-8

Chapter 7

FURTHER RESEARCH WITH THE MANIC-DEPRESSIVENESS SCALE

Michael A. Thalbourne and James Houran
University of Adelaide

ABSTRACT

The 18-item Manic-Depressiveness Scale (MDS) has been Rasch-scaled as a result of top-down purification procedures, and now consists of 12 items (8, history of depression; 4, history of mania). This new scoring scheme (the R-MDS) was applied to the data of 250 undergraduates, and it was found that the correlations were mostly very close to the original scoring, but with only two-thirds of the MDS items and with no age or gender bias. Persons scoring high on the R-MDS tended also to subscribe to paranormal belief and experience, score high on magical ideation, high on schizotypal personality (and its three subscales), on mystical experience and on neuroticism, but were low on the lie scale. Not significantly correlated were extraversion, creative personality and Eysenckian psychoticism. Finally, there is some evidence that the R-MDS does not discriminate between bipolar disorder and schizophrenia, and may therefore be a general measure of psychoticism.

INTRODUCTION

Though there are a number of measuring instruments to gauge the severity of an individual's *current* manic or depressive state (Goodwin & Jamison, 1990), there seems to be dearth of questionnaires to measure *history* of manic-depressive symptoms. Therefore, in the early '90s, Thalbourne, Delin and Bassett (1994) produced an 18-item scale to perform this service: 9 items were intended to measure manic-like symptoms, and an equal number were proposed to measure depressive symptoms (for the wording of the items, see the Appendix, taken from Thalbourne & D. Bassett, 1998).

The most prolific user of these scales has been David Lester and his colleagues. His hypotheses and results prior to 1999 have been described elsewhere (Thalbourne, Keogh & Crawley, 1999) and will not be repeated here: see Lester & Kaplan, 1994; Kaplan & Lester,

1994; Andrews, Hass, & Lester, 1994; Lester & Moderski, 1995; Williams & Lester, 1996; Bergman, Carmel, & Lester, 1997; Rife & Lester, 1997; Andrews & Lester, 1998).

Using as their nonclinical sample a group of 241 Australian university students, Thalbourne and Delin (1994) found that Depressive Experience, Manic Experience, and the Manic-Depressiveness Scale (the sum of the two) were all significantly and positively related to belief in, and alleged experience of, the paranormal, mystical experience, creative personality, and magical ideation. Thalbourne and French (1995), working with 114 university students at Goldsmiths College, London, replicated the correlations with paranormal belief, although at a low level, and, at a moderate level, those with magical ideation.

A large-scale survey to replicate these results was conducted by Thalbourne, Keogh et al. (1999) in which the Mania scale, the Depression Scale, and the sum of the two scales (called Manic-Depressiveness) were correlated with 12 variables. The N of 250 consisted of undergraduate psychology students in Adelaide and in London. The results for the 18-item Manic-Depressiveness Scale are reproduced here in Table 2 (descriptive statistics are given in Table 1 of Thalbourne, Keogh et al., 1999, p. 49). It can be seen that, according to this analytic method, persons scoring high on the Manic-Depressiveness Scale were also more likely to claim belief in and experience of the paranormal, were higher on magical ideation, were *not* higher on Creative Personality, were higher on Mystical Experience, higher on Schizotypal Personality and all three of its subscales, and were higher on Neuroticism and Eysenckian Psychoticism, and lower on the Lie Scale.

Lester (1999) argued in favor of using the two subscales Manic and Depressive Experience (even though both scales have low Cronbach reliability) and that the Manic-Depressiveness Scale added no new information, and hence, results with it need not be given. We will revisit this claim later in the chapter.

Lester himself continued to be a prolific user of the Mania and Depression scales:

- Meelheim and Lester (1999) found that both manic and depressive tendencies were associated negatively with optimism ($r = -.34$, $p < .01$, and $r = -.45$, $p < .001$), respectively, as was the considering of suicide.
- Lester and Wittkowski (1999) found that religiosity scores did not appear to be associated with measures of psychological pathology, such as the Mania and Depression scales.
- Lester and Abdel-Khalek (1999) found significant but low correlations between the two scales and scores on the Arabic Obsessive Compulsive Scale ($r = .14$ for mania, .25 for depression) and the Maudsley Obsessional Compulsive Inventory ($r = .25$ for mania, .32 for depression).
- Street and Lester (2000) found moderate correlations between Depression scores and both perfectionism ($r = .38$, $p < .001$) and the Harvey Imposter Phenomenon Scale ($r = .40$, $p < .001$).
- D'Alessandro and Lester (2000) found that self-destructiveness scores were associated, in a sample of undergraduates, with scores for both Depression and Manic tendency (rs = .46 and .40, respectively) and with past suicidal ideation ($r = .26$, $p < .05$).

- Burge and Lester (2000) administered the Keirsey-Bates Temperament Sorter (Keirsey & Bates, 1984) and found judging scores to be negatively associated with depression and prior suicidal ideation (Partial *r*s = -.20 and -.25, p < .05).
- Finally in this series, Abdel-Khalek and Lester (2002) replicated the finding that scores on Mania, Depression and suicidal thoughts (translated into Arabic) were moderately associated with the Arabic Obsessive Compulsive Scale (*r* = .36 for mania, .49 for depression) and the Maudsley Obsessional Compulsive Inventory (*r* = .38 for mania, .31 for depression).

Symptom Structure and its Correlates

While Lester's findings with the Manic-Depressive Scale reviewed above seem to be consistent and make clinical sense, one of the pitfalls of Thalbourne et al.'s (1994) original scale (and indeed with most instruments) is that it was derived from statistical techniques associated with classical test theory. In particular, such scales can lead to artifacts related to: (1) the use of item-level factor analysis, a practice which has long been known to yield spurious results (Comrey, 1978); (2) the assumption that variables are adequately measured by raw scores or factor scores (Michell, 1990); and (3) the absence of testing to detect "differential item functioning" (item bias) due to scaling effects related to age and gender.

To avoid such psychometric pitfalls, Lange, Irwin, and Houran (2000) developed a "top-down purification" procedure involving Rasch scaling (a technique associated with Item Response Theory, see e.g., Rasch, 1960/1980; Wright & Stone, 1979), combined with tests for dimensionality (Nandakumar, 1991), and the removal of biased items (Shealy & Stout, 1993) in an iterative fashion. In other words, the top-down purification approach has the aim of creating reliable and unidimensional interval measures that have a known fit to the Rasch (1960/1980) model and clearly defined scaling properties.

In addition to developing psychometrically superior instruments, the purification approach also yields findings of theoretical or conceptual importance for the construct itself being investigated. For example, gender- or age-related response biases can cause "phantom factors" (i.e., actually non-existent) to appear in item-level factor analysis (see Lange et al., 2000, Appendix A). This is a crucial issue in light of recent efforts to model the symptom structure of thought and affective disorders. Since Crow (1980, 1985) and Andreasen (1982, 1985) proposed their respective two-factor theories of symptoms in schizophrenia (i.e., positive and negative), considerable debate has focused on evaluating these and other models of symptom structure (deLeon, Simpson, & Peralta, 1992). Although some studies have reported two-factor models (Gibbons, Lewine, & Davis, 1985; Lenzenweger, Dworkin, & Wethington, 1989), most research indicates that the dimensionality of symptoms is best captured by at least three factors (Arndt, Alliger, & Andreasen, 1991; A. Bassett, Bury, & Honer, 1994; Kay & Sevy, 1990). The three factors most commonly found correspond to negative, positive, and disorganization symptoms (Gur et al., 1991; Liddle, 1987; Liddle & Barnes, 1990), with other symptom factors related to depression (Van der Does et al., 1993) or relational impairment (Peralta, Cuesta, & deLeon, 1994).

Other approaches have examined the factor structure of symptom structure of mixed-diagnostic samples of psychiatric patients (e.g., Dingemans et al., 1983; Overall et al., 1967) via the popular, 18-item Brief Psychiatric Rating Scale (BPRS: Overall & Gorham, 1962).

The most widely cited structure of the BPRS is the five-factor solution as is described by Guy in the *ECDEU Assessment Manual for Psychopharmacology* (Guy, 1976). These factors are commonly referred to as Anxiety-Depression, Anergia, Thought Disturbance, Activation, and Hostile-Suspiciousness. However, more recent research (Mueser, McHugo, & Curran, 1997) based on more stringent confirmatory factor analysis suggested a four-factor solution consisting of Thought Disturbance, Anergia, Affect, and Disorganization dimensions. The respective BPRS test items that define these solutions are summarized in Table 1.

Table 1. ECDEU and Mueser et al. (1997) BPRS Factor Solutions

ECDEU solution	Mueser et al. (1997) solution
Thought Disturbance	**Thought Disturbance**
4. Conceptual disorganization	8. Grandiosity
8. Grandiosity	11. Suspiciousness
12. Hallucinatory behavior	12. Hallucinatory behavior
15. Unusual thought content	15. Unusual thought content
Anergia	**Anergia**
3. Emotional withdrawal	3. Emotional withdrawal
13. Motor retardation	13. Motor retardation
16. Blunted affect	14. Uncooperativeness
18. Disorientation	16. Blunted affect
Anxiety-Depression	**Affect**
1. Somatic concern	1. Somatic concern
2. Anxiety	2. Anxiety
5. Guilt feelings	5. Guilt feelings
9. Depressive mood	9. Depressive mood
	10. Hostility
Activation	**Disorganization**
6. Tension	4. Conceptual disorganization
7. Mannerisms and posturing	6. Tension
17. Excitement	7. Mannerisms and postering
Hostile-Suspiciousness	**Excluded Items**
10. Hostility	17. Excitement
11. Suspiciousness	18. Disorientation
14. Uncooperativeness	

To further complicate matters, there is debate as to whether depression (a common component throughout in Table 1) should be viewed as a distinct category or as a continuum including overlapping normal and clinical phenomena. Solomon, Haaga, and Arnow (2001) concluded that the epidemiological and taxonomic studies favor both a manifest and latent continuum of unipolar depression. By contrast, Santor and Coyne's (2001a, 2001b) recent applications of Item Response Theory yielded findings that contradict the view of depression as a simple continuum.

Lange, Thalbourne, Houran, and Lester (2002) applied top-down purification to the 18-item Manic-Depressiveness Scale and found that 6 items were biased with regard to gender or age. However, there was a *single* Rasch dimension underlying the twelve remaining items, which involved both depressive and manic/anxiety-related symptoms. This new version, which replaces the original (two subscale) scoring scheme, was termed the Rasch Manic-

Depressiveness Scale (R-MDS). Application of this scale to data previously collected by Thalbourne and Delin (1994) indicated that patients with manic-depression or schizophrenia received comparable mean scores, which are in fact significantly higher than those of a control group of students. Moreover, for a subgroup of patients with manic-depression, scores correlated .55 ($p \leq .001$) with number of manic-depression-relevant medications being taken. These findings tend to lend support to the validity of the Rasch Manic-Depressiveness Scale not as a measure solely of bipolar disorder but as a *general* measure of "psychoticism" and psychiatric status. Stated more conceptually, the finding of a unidimensional model of certain manic-like and depressive symptomatology suggests a continuum of thought and affective dysfunction, such as seen in the sharing of these respective symptom sets in atypical depression (e.g., major depressive episodes with hypomanic symptoms: see Benazzi, 2001). Thus, contrary to the multi-factor solutions for thought and mood disorders noted earlier and exemplified in Table 1, the R-MDS is consistent with the notion of a proposed continuum within the general population along which ordinary and pathological forms of cognition and perception may be mapped (Chapman & Chapman, 1980; Claridge, 1990, 1997; Hewitt & Claridge, 1989; Johns, Nazroo, Bebbington, & Kuipers, 2002; Peters, Day, McKenna, & Orbach, 1999; Posey & Losch, 1983-1984; Prentky, 1989). In addition, the fit of the Rasch model to the R-MDS items implies that such symptoms form a probabilistic hierarchy of severity (i.e., symptoms are cumulative rather than interchangeable). If this item hierarchy replicates with other psychometrically-sound inventories of depression (with associated psychoticism), then the practice of assigning equal weight to various *DSM-IV* (American Psychiatric Association, 1994) diagnostic categories concerning depressive and manic episodes may need to be reconsidered.

In light of these important methodological and conceptual issues, this chapter presents a re-analysis of Thalbourne, Keogh et al.'s (1999) data using the new R-MDS and subsequently comparisons of these previously unpublished findings to those using the original MDS.

METHOD

Participants

Two hundred fifty undergraduate psychology students participated, 27% of them male. Ages ranged from 17 to 66 years, with a M of 25 and an SD of 9. Of these participants, 139 were from Adelaide University, South Australia, and the remaining 111 were from Goldsmiths College in London.

Measures

Participants were administered two booklets. The first booklet contained (1) the visual analogue scale version of the 18-item Australian Sheep-Goat Scale, as a measure of belief in, and alleged experience of, the paranormal, viz., ESP, psychokinesis, and life after death (Thalbourne & Delin, 1993); (2) the 30-item Magical Ideation Scale (Eckblad & Chapman, 1983); (3) the 18-item Manic-Depressiveness Scale (Thalbourne, Delin et al., 1994; Thalbourne & Bassett, 1998) which is administered even when scored for the R-MDS to provide context; (4) a 9-item measure of creative personality, constructed by Thalbourne and Delin (1994) and partially validated by Thalbourne (1998, 2000); (5) a 22-item version of the Mystical Experience Scale devised by Thalbourne (1991); and (6) the 37-item STA scale devised by Claridge and Broks (1984) to measure schizotypal personality; factor analysis has led to the devising of three subscales (Hewitt & Claridge, 1989; Joseph & Peters, 1995), viz., magical ideation, unusual perceptual experience, and paranoid ideation and suspiciousness, and the STA was therefore scored for these three measures also. The second booklet contained the Eysenck Personality Questionnaire—Revised (Eysenck & Eysenck, 1991) as a measure of extraversion, neuroticism, psychoticism, and tendency to dissimulate. The means for all these variables are typical for students and for this age group; the range of dispersion of scores is adequate, and the measure of skewness is in each case acceptable.

RESULTS

Correlations between the 18-item MDS and the 12-item R-MDS with the 12 research variables are given in Table 2.

Table 2. Pearson Correlations (Two-tailed) between the 18-Item MDS and the 12-Item R-MDS with 12 Variables (Max N = 250)

Scale	18-item MDS	12-item R-MDS
Australian Sheep-Goat Scale (paranormal belief and experience)	.21‡	.21‡
Magical Ideation	.50‡	.45‡
Creative Personality	.06	-.00
Mystical Experience	.22‡	.23‡
STA (Schizotypal Personality)	.62‡	.59‡
Magical Ideation	.47‡	.44‡
Unusual Perceptual Experience	.48‡	.44‡
Paranoid Ideation	.53‡	.50‡
Eysenck Personality Questionnaire—Revised		
Extraversion	-.08	-.12
Neuroticism	.51‡	.54‡
Psychoticism	.13*	.09
Lie	-.22‡	-.18†

* $p \leq .05$.
† $p \leq .01$.
‡ $p \leq .001$.

It can be seen from this Table that despite the loss of 6 items, the R-MDS correlated with the 12 research variables to virtually the same degree, with increases or decreases of about .03 [tests of the significance of these differences in correlations (Hinkle, Wiersma, & Jurs, 1988, p. 279) were non-significant in every case]. For 9 of the research variables the correlations with the R-MDS are significant (10 in the case of the MDS), the highest being with Schizotypal Personality ($r = .59$, $p < .001$). High scorers on the R-MDS are significantly higher on paranormal belief/experience, magical ideation, mystical experience, schizotypal personality and its three subscales, neuroticism and negatively on the lie scale.

However, the fact that the findings in Table 2 remained consistent when based on the R-MDS should not be taken to mean that Lester's findings reviewed above will also remain robust if his data were to be scored with the new R-MDS scheme. Future research should therefore re-analyze Lester's findings to see how the corrected results with the R-MDS compare to his original findings as well as fit with the findings reported in this chapter.

DISCUSSION

Before we discuss the substantive results it is important to be clear as to exactly what the R-MDS is measuring. Is it manic-depressive tendencies and those tendencies alone? It seems clear from the work of Thalbourne and Houran (2002), where schizophrenics scored as highly on the scale as manic-depressives, that the scale is probably measuring general psychoticism, and thus we have failed to come up with a pure measure of history of bipolar disorder. Internal evidence agrees with this conclusion, inasmuch as the highest correlation with the R-MDS was with STA (schizotypal personality), which is more often thought to be related to schizophrenia. On the other hand, the new scale did not correlate significantly with Eysenckian psychoticism (impulsivity, egocentrism, and antisocial tendencies)—and this provides some evidence against the conclusion that we are measuring general psychoticism. Further research with a variety of patients is necessary before the issue can be decided. In the meantime, the unidimensionality of the symptom structure captured by the R-MDS suggests to us that key components of both thought and affective disorders are not mutually exclusive and that schizophrenic-like experience and manic-depression may not be distinct clinical entities. Rather, these two conditions may be different facets of a common underlying 'psychoticism' disorder. This view sides with the notion introduced earlier in this chapter of a proposed continuum along which ordinary and pathological forms of cognition and perception may be mapped.

Assuming for the moment that the R-MDS is measuring such a general psychoticism disorder, a number of conclusions follow. In those persons who obtain high scores on the scale it is the case that they are more likely to display magical ideation, unusual perceptual experiences and paranoid ideation, to believe in, and allege experience of, the paranormal, to score high on Eysenck's variable N (a general measure of psychopathology), to display mystical experience, and to score low on the Lie scale, i.e., they tend not to dissemble about themselves. Several of these results are consistent with the tendency for psychotics to claim preternatural experiences, including union with God.

On the other hand, those scoring high on the R-MDS were no more psychotic in the Eysenckian sense, as we have noted above; nor did they score higher on Creative Personality. Of course, it is an open question what Eysenck's variable P really measures. For example, some authors have argued that this variable merely taps 'unconventionality' as opposed to pathology. Moreover, high scorers on the R-MDS were no more likely to score higher on creative personality. The results from Thalbourne, Keogh et al. (1999: Table 2) suggest that the correlation is with Manic Experience rather than Depressive.

A further line of research suggests itself as to the conditions under which creativity occurs in psychotics. Our research suggests that creativity is somewhat more likely to occur in the manic phase of the bipolar patient. This is entirely consistent with other literature. For example, the tendency to find meaning and patterns in random events and coincidences is one of the most powerful driving forces underlying the experiences of psychosis and profound creativeness (for a detailed review: see Brugger, 2001). This observation is best expressed in the words of a schizophrenic nurse, who in retrospect, described her first psychotic episode:

Every single thing "means" something. This kind of symbolic thinking is exhaustive...I have a sense that everything is more vivid and important; the incoming stimuli are almost more than I can bear. There is a connection to everything that happens—no coincidences. I feel tremendously creative (Brundage, 1983, p. 584).

The propensity to see connections between seemingly unrelated objects or ideas most closely links psychosis to creativity. Indeed, with respect to the detection of subjectively meaningful patterns, apophenia (seeing patterns in random information) and creativity may even be conceived of as two sides of the same coin.

In closing, we feel it important to note that the concept of *transliminality* could be the metaphorical 'coin' that accounts for the frequent comorbidity of creativity, psychoticism, as well as depressive experience, paranormal belief-experience, and mystical experience. This construct, which was anticipated as early as William James (1902/1982), is defined as, "the hypothesised tendency for psychological material to cross (*trans*) thresholds (*limines*) into or out of consciousness" (Thalbourne & Houran, 2000, p. 861). Using the top-down purification methodology, Lange, Thalbourne, Houran, and Storm (2000) showed that there was a single Rasch dimension underlying seven psychological domains: Absorption, Fantasy-Proneness, Hyperesthesia (heightened sensitivity to environmental stimuli), (fleeting) Hypomanic or Manic Experience, Magical Ideation, Mystical Experience, as well as Positive (and perhaps obsessional) Attitude towards Dream Interpretation. Accordingly, the psychological material that is hypothesized to cross thresholds can encompass a wide range of imagery, ideation, affect, and perception.

The etiology of transliminality is thought to involve cognitive disinhibition (e.g., Houran & Thalbourne, 2003; Thalbourne, Crawley, & Houran, 2003; Thalbourne, Houran, Alias, & Brugger, 2001). In particular, the cognitive mechanisms responsible for active suppression (or gating) of irrelevant information from consciousness are hypothesized to be weak or erratic, which in turn promotes syncretic cognitions. Syncretic cognition entails a dedifferentiation (or fusion) of perceptual qualities in subjective experience. Examples include *physiognomic perception* (the fusion of perception and feeling), *synesthesia* (the fusion of sensory modalities), and *eidetic imagery* (the fusion of imagery and perception, i.e., structural eidetic imagery). Reviews of the conceptualization and correlates of transliminality can be found in Lange, Thalbourne et al. (2000) and Thalbourne (2000).

Applying the construct of transliminality to the wider issue of symptom perception in mental illnesses, future research might find that the symptom clusters identified in Table 1 above are on a continuum and that the demarcation between them is directly related to the degree of functional regulation of interaction among frontal cortical loops, temporal-limbic structures, and primary or secondary sensory areas and/or sensory association cortices. Manic-depression seems to embody aspects of both thought and affective disorders, so we speculate that bipolar disorder involves a significant degree of functional "hyperconnectivity" among the brain regions noted above.

APPENDIX

Manic Experience Items

2. On at least one occasion I thought that God had appointed me to an especially lofty or important mission of a religious or political nature.
4. I have gone for more than a day with much less sleep than I normally needed and yet still not been tired.
5. I have had times when I have been so touchy in a frustrating situation that I could (or did) "fly off the handle".
7. My thoughts have sometimes come so quickly that I couldn't write them all down fast enough.
10. I have been through times when it seemed almost unnecessary for me to eat.
11. My mind has sometimes been so full of different ideas that I couldn't keep my attention on one topic for very long.
14. I have never had an experience where I believed that I was, literally, a famous figure, such as Jesus Christ. (reverse scored)
15. I have sometimes behaved in a much more impulsive or uninhibited way than is usual for me.
16. I have never been so engrossed in my inner thoughts and emotions that I neglected to wash or change my clothes. (reverse scored)

Depressive Experience Items

1. I have on at least one occasion worried unduly that I did not have enough money or was going to become poor.
3. I have on at least one occasion felt that there was no purpose in life — that the universe was entirely meaningless.
6. I have experienced being so sad that I just sat (or lay in bed) doing nothing but feeling bad.
8. On at least one occasion I have felt so discouraged about life that I wanted to commit suicide.
9. I have on at least one occasion felt so unworthy and sinful that I despaired of ever being good enough for the Creator.
12. I have experienced being so unhappy that I was convinced that I had a fatal illness such as cancer or AIDS, though I later discovered that I was perfectly healthy after all.
13. I have had lengthy periods of time when my desire for sex seemed to be virtually or completely absent.
17. I tend to sleep more when life is going badly.
18. I have in the past made active attempts to die.

REFERENCES

Abdel-Khalek, A., & Lester, D. (2002). Manic-depressiveness, obsessive-compulsive tendencies, and suicidality in Kuwait College students. *Psychological Reports, 90,* 1007-1008.

Andreasen, N. C. (1982). Negative symptoms in schizophrenia: Definition and reliability. *Archives of General Psychiatry, 39*, 784-788.

_____ . (1985). Positive vs. negative schizophrenia: A critical evaluation. *Schizophrenia Bulletin, 11*, 380-389.

Arndt, S., Alliger, R. J., & Andreasen, N. C. (1991). The distinction of positive and negative symptoms: The failure of a two-dimensional model. *British Journal of Psychiatry, 158*, 317-322.

Bassett, A. S., Bury, A., & Honer, W. G. (1994). Testing Liddle's three-syndrome model in families with schizophrenia. *Schizophrenia Research, 12*, 213-221.

Benazzi, F. (2001). Atypical depression with hypomanic symptoms. *Journal of Affective Disorders, 65*, 179-183.

Brugger, P. (2001). From haunted brain to haunted science: A cognitive neuroscience view of paranormal and pseudoscientific thought. In J. Houran & R. Lange (Eds.), *Hauntings and poltergeists: Multidisciplinary perspectives* (pp. 195-213). Jefferson, NC: McFarland.

Brundage, B. E. (1983). First person account: What I wanted to know but was afraid to ask. *Schizophrenia Bulletin, 9*, 583-585.

Burge, M., & Lester, D. (2000). Manic-depressiveness and Jungian dimensions of personality. *Psychological Reports, 87,* 596.

Chapman, L. J., & Chapman, J. P. (1980). Scales for rating psychotic and psychotic-like experiences as continua. *Schizophrenia Bulletin, 6*, 476-489.

Claridge, G. (1990). Can a disease model of schizophrenia survive? In R. P. Bentall (Ed.), *Reconstructing schizophrenia* (pp. 157-183). London: Routledge.

Claridge, G. (1997) (Ed.). *Schizotypy: Implications for illness and health*. Oxford: Oxford University Press.

Comrey, A. L. (1978). Common methodological problems in factor analytic studies. *Journal of Consulting and Clinical Psychology, 46*, 648-659.

Crow, T. J. (1980). Molecular pathology of schizophrenia: More than one disease process? *British Medical Journal, 280*, 66-68.

_____ . (1985). The two-syndrome concept: Origins and current status. *Schizophrenia Bulletin, 11*, 471-486.

D'Alessandro, M., & Lester, D. (2000). Self-destructiveness and manic-depressive tendencies. *Psychological Reports, 87,* 466.

deLeon, J., Simpson, G. M., & Peralta, V. (1992). Positive and negative symptoms in schizophrenia: Where are the data? (editorial). *Biological Psychiatry, 31*, 431-434.

Dingemans, P. M., Frohn-de Winter, M. L., Bleeker, J. A. C., & Rathod, P. (1983). A cross-cultural study of the reliability and factorial dimensions of the Brief Psychiatric Rating Scale (BPRS). *Psychopharmacology, 80*, 190-191.

Gibbons, R. D., Lewine, R. R. J., & Davis, J. M. (1985). An empirical test of a Kraepelinian versus a Bleulerian view of negative symptoms. *Schizophrenia Bulletin, 11*, 390-396.

Goodwin, F. K., & Jamison, K. R. (1990). *Manic-depressive illness.* New York: Oxford University Press.

Gur, R. E., Mozley, P. D., Resnick, S. M., Levick, S., Erwin, R., Saykin, A. J., & Gur, R. C. (1991). Relations among clinical scales in schizophrenia. *American Journal of Psychiatry, 148*, 472-478.

Guy, W. (1976). *ECDEU assessment manual for psychopharmacology, revised* (DHEW Publication No. ADM 76-338). Rockville, MD: US Department of Health and Human Services.

Hinkle, D. E., Wiersma, W., & Jurs, S. G. (1988). *Applied statistics for the behavioral sciences* (2nd ed.). Boston, MA: Houghton Mifflin.

Houran, J., & Thalbourne, M. A. (2003). Transliminality correlates positively with aberrations in memory. *Perceptual and Motor Skills, 96*, 1300-1304.

Hewitt, J. K., & Claridge, G. S. (1989). The factor structure of schizotypy in a normal population. *Personality and Individual Differences, 10*, 323-329.

James, W. (1902/1982). *The varieties of religious experience.* Harmondsworth, England: Penguin.

Johns, L. C., Nazroo, J. Y., Bebbington, P., & Kuipers, E. (2002). Occurrence of hallucinatory experiences in a community sample and ethnic variations. *British Journal of Psychiatry, 180*, 174-178.

Kay, S. R., & Sevy, S. (1990). Pyramidical model of schizophrenia. *Schizophrenia Bulletin, 16*, 537-545.

Lange, R., Irwin, H. J., & Houran, J. (2000). Top-down purification of Tobacyk's Revised Paranormal Belief Scale. *Personality and Individual Differences, 29*, 131-156.

Lange, R., & Thalbourne, M. A. (2002). Rasch scaling paranormal belief and experience: The structure and semantics of Thalbourne's Australian Sheep-Goat Scale. *Psychological Reports, 91*, 1065-1073.

Lange, R., Thalbourne, M. A., Houran, J., & Lester, D. (2002). Depressive response sets due to gender and culture-based differential item functioning. *Personality and Individual Differences, 33*, 937-954.

Lange, R., Thalbourne, M. A., Houran, J., & Storm, L. (2000). The Revised Transliminality Scale: Reliability and validity data from a Rasch top-down purification procedure. *Consciousness and Cognition, 9*, 591-617.

Lenzenweger, M. F., Dworkin, R. H., & Wethington, E. (1989). Models of positive and negative symptoms in schizophrenia: An empirical evaluation of latent structures. *Journal of Abnormal Psychology, 98*, 62-70.

Lester, D. (1999). Comment on "Manic-Depressiveness and its correlates". *Psychological Reports, 85*, 1057-1058.

Lester, D., & Abdel-Khalek, A. M. (1999). Manic-depression, suicidality, and obsessive-compulsive tendencies. *Psychological Reports, 85,* 1100.

Lester, D., & Wittkowski, J. (1999). Religiosity and pathology. *Psychological Reports, 85,* 834.

Liddle, P. F. (1987). The symptoms of chronic schizophrenia: A reexamination of the positive–negative dichotomy. *British Journal of Psychiatry, 151*, 145-151.

Liddle, P. F., & Barnes, T. R. E. (1990). Syndromes of chronic schizophrenia. *British Journal of Psychiatry, 157*, 558-561.

Meelheim, L. G., & Lester, D. (1999). Optimism and manic-depressive tendencies. *Psychological Reports, 84,* 1122.

Michell, J. (1990). *An introduction to the logic of psychological measurement.* Hillsdale, NJ: Lawrence Erlbaum Associates.

Mueser, K. T., Curran, P. J., & Mchugo, G. J. (1997). Factor structure of the Brief Psychiatric Rating Scale in schizophrenia. *Psychological Assessment, 9,* 196-204.

Nandakumar, R. (1991). Traditional dimensionality versus essential dimensionality. *Journal of Educational Measurement, 28,* 99-117.

Overall, J. E., & Gorham, D. R. (1962). The Brief Psychiatric Rating Scale. *Psychological Reports, 10,* 799-812.

Overall, J. E., Hollister, L. E., & Pichot, P. (1967). Major psychiatric disorders: A four dimensional model. *Archives of General Psychiatry, 16,* 146-151.

Peralta, V., Cuesta, M. J., & deLeon, J. (1994). An empirical analysis of latent structures underlying schizophrenic symptoms: A four-syndrome model. *Biological Psychiatry, 36,* 726-736.

Peters, E. R., Day, S., McKenna, J., & Orbach, G. (1999). Delusional ideation in religious and psychotic populations. *British Journal of Clinical Psychology, 38,* 83-96.

Posey, T. B., & Losch, M. E. (1983-1984). Auditory hallucinations of hearing voices in 375 normal subjects. *Imagination, Cognition and Personality, 3,* 99-113.

Prentky, R. (1989). Creativity and psychopathology: Gambling at the seat of madness. In J. A. Glover, R. R. Ronning, & C. R. Reynolds (Eds.), *Handbook of creativity* (pp. 243-269). New York: Plenum.

Rasch, G. (1960/1980). *Probabilistic models for some intelligence and attainment tests.* Chicago, IL: MESA Press.

Santor, D. A., & Coyne, J. C. (2001a). Evaluating the continuity of symptomatology between depressed and non-depressed individuals. *Journal of Abnormal Psychology, 110,* 216-225.

Santor, D. A., & Coyne, J. C. (2001b). Examining symptom rating expression as a function of symptom severity: Item performance on the Hamilton Rating Scale for Depression. *Psychological Assessment, 13,* 127-139.

Shealy, R., & Stout, W. (1993). A model-based standardization approach that separates true bias/dif from group ability differences and detects test bias/dtf as well as item bias. *Psychometrika, 58,* 159-194.

Solomon, A., Haaga, D. A., & Arnow, B. A. (2001). Is clinical depression distinct from subthreshold depressive symptoms? A review of the continuity issue in depression research. *Journal of Nervous and Mental Disease, 189,* 498-506.

Street, M. E., & Lester, D. (2000). Manic-depressive tendencies, suicidality, and perfectionism. *Psychological Reports, 86,* 142.

Thalbourne, M. A. (2000). Transliminality: A review. *International Journal of Parapsychology, 11,* 1-34.

Thalbourne, M. A., & Bassett, D L. (1998). The Manic Depressiveness Scale: A preliminary effort at replication and extension. *Psychological Reports, 83,* 75-80.

Thalbourne, M. A., Crawley, S. E., & Houran, J. (2003). Temporal lobe liability in the highly transliminal mind. *Personality and Individual Differences, 34,* 1-10.

Thalbourne, M.A., & Delin, P.S. (1994). A common thread underlying belief in the paranormal, creative personality, mystical experience and psychopathology. *Journal of Parapsychology, 58*, 3-38.

Thalbourne, M. A., Delin, P. S., & Bassett, D. L. (1994). An attempt to construct short scales measuring manic-depressive-like experience and behaviour. *British Journal of Clinical Psychology, 33*, 205-207.

Thalbourne, M.A., & French, C.C. (1995). Paranormal belief, manic-depressiveness, and magical ideation: A replication. *Personality and Individual Differences, 18*, 291-292.

Thalbourne, M. A., & Houran, J. (2000). Transliminality, the Mental Experience Inventory, and tolerance of ambiguity. *Personality and Individual Differences, 28*, 853-863.

_____ . (2002). Preliminary validity data on the Rasch Manic-Depressiveness Scale. *Psychological Reports, 90,* 817-820.

Thalbourne, M. A., Houran, J., Alias, A. G., & Brugger, P. (2001). Transliminality, brain function, and synesthesia. *Journal of Nervous and Mental Disease, 189*, 190-192.

Thalbourne, M.A., Keogh, E., & Crawley, S.E. (1999). Manic-depressiveness and its correlates. *Psychological Reports, 85*, 45-53.

Van der Does, A. J. W., Linszen, D. H., Dingemans, P. M., Nugter, M. A., & Scholte, W. F. (1993). A dimensional and categorical approach to the symptomatology of recent-onset schizophrenia. *Journal of Nervous and Mental Disease, 181*, 744-749.

Wright, B. D., & Stone, M. H. (1979). *Best test design*. Chicago, IL: MESA Press.

In: Trends in Bipolar Disorder Research
Editor: Malcomb R. Brown, pp. 153-160

ISBN: 1-59454-060-8

Chapter 8

HIGH DOSE FLUOXETINE-INDUCED MANIA: BIBLIOGRAPHIC REVIEW AND CLINICAL CASE REPORT

María Carolina Vairo, Martín Ruiz, Daniel Matusevich and Carlos Finkelsztein
Hospital Italiano of Buenos Aires, Argentina

ABSTRACT

We report the case of a 53 year old woman who attempted suicide taking one high-dose of fluoxetine, developing a manic episode 19 days later. We also present a review about antidepressant-induced mania. In patients with mood disorders, the frequency of antidepressant-induced mania has been estimated to be 3.7 to 33%, varying across studies that included different diagnoses and different antidepressant treatments. Among the used data basis (Medline) there are papers reporting fluoxetine-induced mania. All of them include patients receiving adequate dose and time fluoxetine treatment. We found no reports of switch occurring after one high-dose of fluoxetine. As the impact on the clinical management of antidepressant-induced manic switches is quite high, several studies have focused on the possible clinical predictors of this phenomenon. By the time, is not possible to determine whether a manic episode is due to the natural course of bipolar disorder or to the medication. Thus, the phenomenon of antidepressant-induced mania should be defined and investigated with controlled prospective studies.

INTRODUCTION

We report in this paper the clinical case of a patient who suffered a manic episode after a self-inflicted intake of a high fluoxetine dose and we present a thorough review of antidepressant-induced maniac switch.

Although antidepressant-induced maniac switch is a wide known phenomenon, we were able to find just one definition for that term; we support our clinical case report under the definition of a research group from Charles-Perrens Medical Center in France16 who state the following:

1. Maniac or hypomaniac episodes must meet DSM-IV criteria
2. Patients follow-up must be at least six weeks after the antidepressant therapy begins
3. Switch must occur strait from the depression episode to mania or hypomania without remission in between.

Clinical Case Report

A 53-year-old female patient was referred to our department in December 2000 from the intensive care unit (ICU) where she was admitted due to a self-inflicting episode committed two days prior to admission.

She was admitted in the ICU in a coma state with diagnosis of medical intoxication with bromazepam 120 mg, alprazolam 70 mg, enalapril 100 mg and fluoxetine 200 mg. She underwent antimycrobial therapy for an aspirational pneumonia of the right lower lobe and spontaneous pneumotorax.

By the time of admission in our department (19 days after the self-inflicting episode) the patient showed the following symptoms: slightly unpleasant hyperthymia, marked ideoaffective dissociation, verbose speech, tachypsiquia, slight irritability and delirious guilt and ruin ideas. Even though she denied death or self-inflicting ideation, she asserted: "It was in my plans, I screw everything up, I'm useless, not even my husband loves me. This was a punishment because I made it all wrong, I'm a shame as a human being. I cannot longer cook, my family is starving, and they are getting sick".

Regarding the suicide attempt, the patient said she rented a hotel room that day, she disconnected her mobile soon after calling her daughter and then she ingested all the tablets (taken from her husband's medical box) with water. She left a welfare note. Her family told that she was found by the police two days later in coma surrounded by empty tablet blisters. According to the story, it seemed that she had been in a depressed mood during the last ten months (changing from mild to severe in the last month) and she showed the following symptoms: anhedony and diminished libido, irritability, anguish and anxiety, hypobulia, asthenia, inattention to her cleaning and personal care, hyporexia with 9kg loss of weight and what appeared as bizarre acts and delirious guilt ideas some days previous to the episode. Her husband declared: "She could remain seated in a corner for hours without talking and all of a sudden she would start going round saying she had not prayed enough to avoid her mother's death.

They referred she was distant to her husband without having had sexual relations in the last year; she gave up her job and stopped attending English courses. Her family described her like this: "She was always happy, she was well known in the neighborhood and everyone loved her. She was kind and sociable. She was always doing more than one thing at a time. She cares a lot about others". According to what they said it looked as a hyperthymic temperament.[1] Previous history of psychiatric disease was not found. Though the patient is a teacher, her jobs always dealt with administrative aspects. She has been living with her second husband for ten years. She has a 30-year-old daughter from her first marriage and both parents are dead. There is no family history of psychiatric disease.

By the second day of psychiatric admission she participated actively in all therapies referring to feel "very happy". Two days later, the medical history describes her as sometimes expansive, verbose, with persistent insomnia. The day after, she presents tangential speech, highly elevated mood, hyperactivity, feelings of grandiosity and paranoid delirious ideation. Psychological assessments results were as following: "...she has a verbose speech, she constantly loses the main topic and she stands up gesticulating and acting the answers of the Rorschach test. She has a reminder pad where she writes what she does in the interview... Organic affection parameters were not found...She has a state of excessive activity, she feels attracted by fully emotive situations or those that imply her affective nexus; unreal self-esteem highlighting her own skills; she appears very energetic with a wide variety of interests but she doesn't profit her energy cautiously. She excessively cares about people around with whom she establishes gratifying and harmonic relationships".

Organic affections were ruled out by means of complete blood tests, serology tests, endocrine axis assessment, EEG and imaging studies. She was treated with increasing doses of valproic acid up to 1000 mg/day and haloperidol 2,5 mg/day. The patient was discharged twenty days after her admission in the psychiatry ward. By that time, she was euthymic, at ease, without depressive ideas, without psychotic production and with normal sleeping pattern. She continued ambulatory psychiatric therapy and 8 months later she remains euthymic, treated with valproic acid 1000 mg/day (blood levels 70 μg/ml

According to the evolution of the patient's signs and symptoms, we concluded that she had been suffering a severe depressive syndrome for the last year, with psychotic symptoms by the time of the self-inflicting episode. 19 days from that episode the patient showed some maniac signs (explaining that way the presumptive diagnosis of mixed episode, according to DSM-IV[12]), presenting during admission a clear maniac episode.

MANIA SWITCH

Antidepressants

Maniac induction in patients undergoing antidepressant therapy is a complex situation that occurs with varying frequencies in patients with bipolar or unipolar disorders. In patients with affective disorders the rate of antidepressant-induced mania is thought to be between 3,7% and 33%. This wide gap can be justified by differences among studies with different diagnosis and different therapies included [30].

According to Henry et al.[16] the rates of maniac or hypomanic switch induced by antidepressants are about 27 % without a significant difference in the SSRI. Cohn et al.[11] have observed that 15% of patients treated with fluoxetine for bipolar depressions of type I

[1] According to Akiskal [4]: Happy and exuberant; talkative and joyful, hyperoptimist and unworried; over self-confident, self-assured and self-congratulating; friendly and sociable; energetic, versatile with a wide range of interests; over involved and interfering; uninhibited and stimuli seeking.

suffered a maniac switch. However, Peet33 states that less than 1% of patients with unipolar depressions develop such episode (without significant difference between drugs and placebo) , while in bipolar depressions, tricyclic antidepressants might trigger the switch in 11,2% of cases, 3,7% for SRII and 4,2% for placebo. Most papers agree that tricyclic antidepressants are related in a higher percentage to maniac switch. [5,9,15,18,23,33,34,37].

In the consulted database (Medline) there are papers that report fluoxetine-induced mania switch. In all cases, the patients were undergoing treatment with right time and dosing [6,8-11,13,16,19,20,22-25,28,31,33,35]. As an example, according to Henry et al.[16], the elapsed time between the antidepressant treatment starts and maniac switch occurs is 5,8 weeks (with a range of 3 to 10).

We found no reports of maniac switch triggered by a single dose of antidepressant.

Fluoxetine is an antidepressant of the SSRI group, which acts through inhibiting serotonin reuptake. Half-life is 4 to 6 days and up to 16 days for Norfluoxetine, its active metabolite[22]. The antidepressant effect would begin about the second week of an adequate dose intake with 75% of patients responding by the fourth week [32]. Most recent theories about antidepressants mechanism of action state that the immediate blockade of cathecolamines or indolamines reuptake triggers an adaptive response of pre and postsynaptic receptors, with further changes in protoncogenes and in brain derived neurotrophic factors. These final changes take place after a long period (weeks) of antidepressant exposure[9,30].

An aspect that should be kept in mind in maniac switch is the antidepressants blood level. On one hand, Megna and Devitt [28] assert that both fluoxetine and norfluoxetine plasma concentrations would help to keep balance between euthymia and mania in patients with bipolar disorder type I. On the other hand, Amsterdam et al. [6] jump up to the conclusion that no relation would exist between blood levels of the antidepressant (even norfluoxetine) and the clinical response.

The delay on the onset of the therapeutic response could not be explained just by plasma levels (and presumably brain levels); it is usually reached between days 7 and 10. [6,27,39].

Risk Factors

Bipolar disorders are many times overlooked in depressed patients [14]. The first pitfall that the internist faces is the onset of the first depressive episode in a patient without previous history of affective disorders. Since many of these patients later develop maniac episodes, several authors have focused their attention in looking for risk factors of bipolarity in depressed unipolar patients with the aim of setting clinical predictive aspects of this disease [1-3,7,9,15,16].

Henry et al. [16] and Akiskal et al. [1,2] agree that hyperthymic mood might be related to a high risk of antidepressant-induced maniac switch. Angst [7] gathered data from patients admitted for depression between 1920 and 1982. He found that 7% developed either maniac switch (1,7%) or hypomanic switch (5,3%). He also noted that bipolar patients had an eight times higher rate than unipolar ones, thus remarking the significance of distinguishing between bipolar and unipolar disorder as a predictor of antidepressant-induced maniac switch. However, as he did not found a significant increase in the switch rate either in unipolar or bipolar patients along decades, he estimates there would be no evidence for treatment-induced switch. For Boerlin et al. [9] the only clinical variable involved in maniac development during antidepressant therapy would be a high number of previous maniac or hypomanic episodes. Goldberg et al. [15] made a 15-years prospective study with patients who were firstly admitted for major unipolar depression. 27% of the studied group spontaneously developed a clear period of hypomania and 19% did show a maniac episode. While family history of bipolarity was not associated to major risk, they concluded that the existence of a depressive episode with psychotic symptoms in youth increases the risk for bipolar disorder. However, according to Akiskal et al. [3] family history of bipolarity imply an important risk factor for developing this disorder. The serotonin carrier (5HTT) is the specific site of action of most proserotoninergic agents used to treat bipolar depression. The 5-HTT (SLC6A4) gene has two polimorphisms. The most important genetic study on this field is the one made by Mundo et al. [30]who focused on the role of SLC6A4 variations in the pathogenesis of antidepressants-induced mania in bipolar patients. They found that, in patients who developed mania or hypomania with proserotoninergic agents, the promoting zone (5-HTTLPR) had a short allele excess compared to those who did not develop the switch (37% at 7% respectively). They suggest the hypothesis that bipolar patients who are homozygotes for the short variation of the 5-HTTLPR allele might be more sensitive to serotonin reuptake blockade or to serotonin bioavailability increase since they have less gene expression and thus less 5-HTT sites. A reduced number of 5-HTT sites would imply high serotonin levels in the synaptic gap as a consequence of a lesser reuptake rate leading to a better response to agents that block the serotonin reuptake. They finally declare that if maniac induction is just an exaggerated response to antidepressants, this would explain the risk of switch in these patients and 5-HTTLPR polymorphism might become an important predictive factor of antidepressant-induced maniac switch

Clinic Presentation and Diagnosis

Stoll et al. [37] run a retrospective study at McLean Hospital in Massachusetts comparing admissions of patients with antidepressants-induced mania with patients suffering spontaneous mania. They come up to the conclusion that antidepressants-induced maniac episodes would have the following features:

- Lower intensity
- Greater time limits
- Less severe delusions and hallucinations
- Less severe psychomotor irritability and bizarre actions.

According to DSM-IV [12] the antidepressants-induced maniac episode would be included in substance-induced mood disorders and it is deliberately excluded from bipolar disorders: "The mania or hypomania-like episodes that are clearly induced by a somatic antidepressant therapy (i.e. drugs, electro convulsive therapy, light therapy), must not be diagnosed as bipolar disorder type I (or type II)". Akiskal, in the 2000 edition of the Kaplan and Saddock´s Psychiatry Text Book as well as Hiltry et al in a 1999 review of bipolar disorder, classify this syndrome as a secondary mania [4,17]. However, Akiskal et al. [3] in subsequent studies state that the appearance of a maniac episode induced by antidepressant therapy is diagnostic of bipolar disorder and they name it as type III. They include in this type the substance abuse related mania or hypomania and other somatic treatments.

Discussion

A major depressive episode may naturally precede a switch, and lead at the same time to an antidepressant therapy, thus resembling a false connection between the two episodes. It is not possible to differentiate whether a maniac episode is due to the natural course of the bipolar disorder or it is induced by medication. Therefore, we believe that the antidepressant-induced mania should be described and further studied in prospective controlled trials.

As they do not exist, we can just observe in our case report the temporal and causal relation between the intake of a fluoxetine high single dose and the triggering of a maniac episode. The patient suffers this episode 19 days after the fluoxetine intake and that can be explained by the norfluoxetine blood level. Considering that the patient had a hyperthymic mood and she presented a depressive episode with psychotic symptoms, which are both risk factors for bipolar disorder, it can be thought that the antidepressant triggered a manic episode in a presumably vulnerable patient with mild symptoms and a rapid response to the appropriate treatment. Though various authors do not agree with the inclusion of antidepressant-induced mania in the bipolar disorder category, it would share several features with spontaneous mania. This fact leads us to think that our patient should be included in the broad field of bipolar disorders

Bibliography

[1] Akiskal HS, Maser JD, Zeller PJ et al. Switching from "unipolar" to bipolar II: an 11-year prospective study of clinical and temperamental predictors in 559 patients. *Arch Gen Psychiatry 1995; 52:* 114-123.

[2] Akiskal HS. Delineating irritable-choleric and hyperthymic temperaments as variants of cyclothymia. *J Pers Disord 1992; 6:* 326-342.

[3] Akiskal HS, Pinto O. The evolving bipolar spectrum. *Psychiatr Clin North Am 1999; 2 (3):* 518-533.

[4] Akiskal HS. Mood disorders: clinical features. In *Comprehensive textbook of psychiatry / VII.* Kaplan HI, Sadock BJ, eds. Baltimore, MD: Lippincott, Williams & Wilkins 2000; vol I, cap 14.6: 1338-1377.

[5] Altshuler LL, Post RM, Leverich GS et al. Antidepressant-induced mania and cycle acceleration: a controversy revisited. *Am J Psychiatry 1995; 152:* 1130-1138.

[6] Amsterdam JD, Fawcett J, Quitkin FM et al. Fluoxetine and norfluoxetine plasma concentrations in major depression: a multicenter study. *Am J Psychiatry 1997; 154:* 963-969.

[7] Angst J. Switch from depression to mania. A record study over decades between 1920 and 1982. *Psychopathology 1985; 18:* 140-154.

[8] Baldessarini RJ. Fármacos y tratamiento de los trastornos psiquiátricos: depresión y manía. En Las bases farmacológicas de la terapéutica / IX. Goodman & Gilman. México: McGraw-Hill Interamericana 1996; vol I, cap 19: 459-489.

[9] Boerlin HL, Gitlin MJ, Zoellner LA, Hammen CL. Bipolar depression and antidepressant-induced mania: a naturalistic study. *J Clin Psychiatry 1998; 59 (7):* 374-379.

[10] Chouinard G, Steiner W. A case of mania induced by high dose fluoxetine treatment. *Am J Psychiatry 1986; 143 (5):* 686.

[11] Cohn JB, Collins G, Ashbrook E et al. A comparison of fluoxetine, imipramine and placebo in patients with bipolar depressive disorder. *Int Clin Psychopharmacol 1989; 4:* 313-322.

[12] DSM-IV. Manual Diagnóstico y Estadístico de los Trastornos Mentales. Cuarta Edición. España: Masson 2000; 323-399.

[13] Feder R. Fluoxetine induced mania. *J Clin Psychiatry 1990; 51 (12):* 524-525.

[14] Ghaemi SN, Sachs GS, Chiou Am et al. Is bipolar disorder still under-diagnosed? Are antidepressants overutilized*? J Affect Disord 1999; 52:* 135-144.

[15] Goldberg JF, Harrow M, Whiteside JE. Risk for bipolar illness in patients initially hospitalized for unipolar depression. *Am J Psychiatry 2001; 158 (8):* 1265-1270.

[16] Henry C, Sorbara F, Lacoste J et al. Antidepressant-induced mania in bipolar patients: identification of risk factors. *J Clin Psychiatry 2001; 62 (4):* 249-255.

[17] Hilty DM, Brady KT, Hales RE. A review of bipolar disorder among adults. *Psychiatric Services 1999; 50 (2):* 201-213.

[18] Himmelhoch JM, Thase ME, Mallinger AG et al. Tranylcypromine versus imipramine in anergic bipolar depression. *Am J Psychiatry 1991; 148:* 910-916.

[19] Hon D, Preskorn SH. Mania during fluoxetine treatment for recurrent depression. *Am J Psychiatry 1989; 146 (12):* 1638-1639.

[20] Howland RH. Induction of mania with serotonin reuptake inhibitors. *J Clin Psychopharmacol 1996; 16*: 425-427.

[21] Hyman SE, Nestler EJ. Initiation and adaptation: a paradigm for understanding psychotropic drug action. *Am J psychiatry 1996; 153:* 151-162.

[22] Kelsey JE, Nemeroff CB. Selective serotonin re-uptake inhibitors. En Comprehensive textbook of psychiatry / VII. Kaplan HI, Sadock BJ, eds. Baltimore, MD: Lippincott, Williams & Wilkins 2000; vol II, cap 31.25: 2432-2455.

[23] Kupfer DJ, Carpenter LL, Frank E. Possible role of antidepressants in precipitating mania and hypomania in recurrent depression. *Am J Psychiatry 1988; 145:* 804-808.

[24] Lebegue B. Mania precipitated by fluoxetine. Am J Psychiatry 1987; 144 (12): 1620.

[25] Lensgraf SJ, Favazza AR. Antidepressant induced mania. *Am J Psychiatry 1990; 147* (11): 1569.

[26] Leonard B. Clinical implications of mechanisms of action of antidepressants. *APT 2000; 6:* 178-186.

[27] Leonard B. Effect of antidepressants on specific neurotransmitters: are such effects relevant their therapeutic action? In: *Handbook of depression and anxiety. A biological approach*. Den Boer JA, Sitzen JM, eds. New York, 1994, 379-404.

[28] Megna JL, Devitt PJ. Treatment of bipolar depression with twice-weekly fluoxetine: management of antidepressant-induced mania. *Ann Pharmacotherapy 2001; 35:* 45-47.

[29] Mischoulon D. Why do antidepressants take so long to work? *Am Soc Clin Psychopharmacolgy Progress Notes 1997; 8:* 9-11.

[30] Mundo E, Walker M, Cate T et al. The role of serotonin transporter protein gene in antidepressant-induced mania in bipolar disorder: preliminary findings. *Arch Gen Psychiatry 2001; 58 (6):* 539-544.

[31] Nakra BR, Szwabo P, Grossberg GT. Mania induced by fluoxetine. *Am J Psychiatry 1989; 146 (11):* 1515-1516.

[32] Nierenberg AA, Farabaugh AH, Alpert JE et al. Timing of onset of antidepressant response with fluoxetine treatment. *Am J Psychiatry 2000; 157 (9):* 1423-1428.

[33] Peet M. Induction of mania with selective serotonin re-uptake inhibitors and tricyclic antidepressants. *Br J Psychiatry 1994; 164:* 549-550.

[34] Sachs GS, Lafer B, Stoll A et al. A double-blind trial of bupropion versus desipramine for bipolar depression. *J Clin Psychiatry 1994; 55:* 391-393.

[35] Settle EC, Settle GP. A case of mania associated with fluoxetine. *Am J Psychiatry 1984; 141 (2):* 280-281.

[36] Solomon R, Rich CL, Darko DF. Antidepressant treatment and occurence of mania in bipolar patients admitted for depression. *J Affect Disord 1990; 18:* 253-257.

[37] Stoll AL, Mayer PV, Kolbrener M et al. Antidepressant-associated mania: a controlled comparison with spontaneous mania. *Am J Psychiatry 1994; 151:* 1642-1645.

[38] Wehr TA, Goodwin FK. Can antidepressants cause mania and worsen de course of affective illness? *Am J Psychiatry 1987; 144:* 1403-1411.

[39] World Health Organization Mental Health Collaborating Centres. Pharmacotherapy of depressive disorders: a consensus statements. *J Affect Disord 1989; 17:* 197-198.

In: Trends in Bipolar Disorder Research
Editor: Malcomb R. Brown, pp. 161-193
ISBN: 1-59454-060-8

Chapter 9

Quality of Life and Economics of Bipolar Disorder

Lizheng Shi
Lilly Research Laboratories, Indianapolis, Indiana
Mauricio Tohen
Lilly Research Laboratories, Indianapolis, Indiana
Mclean Hospital, Harvard Medical School, Belmont, Massachusetts

Introduction

Bipolar disorder, also referred to as manic-depressive illness, may be one of the most complex psychiatric disorders. It can negatively affect patients' quality of life (QoL) and is associated with substantial costs in health care systems. Bipolar disorder is characterized by distinct episodes (manic, depressive, and mixed) and a varied course and clinical features (eg, rapid cycling course and psychotic feature). Patients with bipolar disorder exhibit a periodic exacerbation of discrete symptomatic episodes, ranging from the characteristic manic mood to the dysphoric mood (American Psychiatric Association, 1994). Rapid cycling occurs in 13% to 20% of patients with bipolar disorder (American Psychiatric Association, 1994). Psychotic symptoms, including delusion and hallucinations, may be present during different stages of bipolar disorder. Depending on their symptom manifestations, patients may have a diagnosis of bipolar I disorder (depression and mania) or bipolar II disorder (depression and hypomania) (American Psychiatric Association, 1994). The lifetime prevalence of bipolar I disorder in the US population is estimated to range from 1.2% to 1.6% (Goodwin and Jamison, 1990; Kessler et al, 1994). A more recent study estimated the prevalence of bipolar disorder at as high as 8% (Hirschfield, 2001). Patient's quality of life—an individual's subjective assessment of his or her functioning and well-being in multiple dimensions (eg, physical, psychological, social, or occupational)—is seriously compromised by bipolar disorder. In 1990, the World Health Organization identified bipolar disorder as the sixth leading cause of disability-adjusted life years in the world among people aged 15 to 44 years (Murray and Lopez, 1996). In the last decade, the QoL impairment among patients with bipolar disorder has been increasingly recognized, and new interventions have been evaluated to improve QoL in bipolar disorder (Namjoshi and Buesching, 2001).

The assessment of QoL among patients with bipolar disorder may be valuable for several reasons. Firstly, QoL instruments put patient at the center, rather than the periphery, of assessing the effectiveness of pharmacological treatment interventions. Traditional outcome measures in bipolar disorder focus on the reduction of symptoms (manic, depressive, etc), which may be the primary goal of a clinician. In addition to clinical outcomes of treatment efficacy and tolerability, it is important to understand patients' perceived functioning and well-being (Van Putten and May, 1978). Patient-centered QoL instruments place more emphasis on attaining sufficient productivity, restoring family relationships, or being able to engage in leisure activities (Thunedborg et al, 1995). Secondly, generic QoL assessments can apply to all (or no) health conditions or general population and thus allow comparisons of QoL between patients with different health conditions and general population. Thirdly, it makes sense to measure quality of life among patients with bipolar disorder rather than attempt to cure them because there is no cure for bipolar disorder.

The literature on the economic burden of bipolar disorder documents its substantial costs of care (Wyatt and Henter, 1995). The cost of this disorder to the society includes not only the heavy use of health care services by patients with bipolar disorder (direct cost), but the lost productivity of both the ill and those whom they directly affect (indirect cost). Furthermore, patients with misdiagnosed or unrecognized bipolar disorder incur more costs than patients with a diagnosis of bipolar disorder (Birnbaum et al, 2003).

This chapter reviews QoL and economics research in bipolar disorder with a focus on the following areas:

1. Psychometric evaluation of QoL instruments in patients with bipolar disorder
2. QoL and its correlates among patients with bipolar disorder at different stages of the disease
3. Comparisons of QoL among patients with bipolar disorder with that among other patient populations
4. Medication treatment effects on QoL among patients with bipolar disorder
5. Economic consequences associated with bipolar disorder
6. Medication treatment effects on economic outcomes among patients with bipolar disorder.

Areas of Research in Quality of Life and Economics of Bipolar Disorder

Table 1 presents a summary of the studies related to QoL scales used in the research of bipolar disorder. The information in this table covers areas 1 through 4 (see above). Studies that used clinician-rated scales are not included in this table.

Table 2 summarizes the results of the studies that assessed health-related quality of life (HRQoL), using the domains of the Medical Outcomes Study (MOS) 36-Item Short-Form Health Survey (SF-36; Ware et al, 1993), among patients with bipolar disorder compared with a US general population sample (McHorney, 1994; Ware et al, 2001).

Table 3 provides an overview of medication treatments of bipolar disorder and their effects on patients' quality of life.

Table 4 presents economical evaluation of medication treatments in bipolar disorder.

1. Psychometric Evaluation of QoL Instruments in Patients With Bipolar Disorder

Different QoL instruments have been evaluated psychometrically to assess the QoL among patients with bipolar disorder and ultimately examine the relationship between changes in the patient-perceived functioning and well-being. There exists a speculation about the validity of using patient-reported QoL instruments among populations with affective disorders. On one hand, a good correlation exists between patient-reported QoL and clinician-rated functionality (such as the Global Assessment of Functioning [GAF] scores [MacQueen et al, 2000]). In addition, there is a good correlation between in-person– and telephone interview–derived data on affective symptoms, QoL, disability days, and medication compliance among patients with bipolar disorder (Revicki et al, 1997). Therefore, patients with bipolar disorder may be capable of providing accurate descriptions of their QoL, particularly regarding the mental health and social functioning domains. On the other hand, Atkinson et al (1997) (Table 1) found that scores on the subjectively reported QoL instrument, the Quality of Life Inventory (Frisch et al, 1992), were lower among patients with bipolar disorder or major depressive disorder (MDD) than among those with schizophrenia. Interestingly, this trend was reversed for objectively assessed QoL, which included measures such as medical history, health risk behaviors, educational and financial levels, and social functioning (Atkinson et al, 1997). Some other studies that compared the QoL among patients with bipolar disorder with that among patients with schizophrenia also had mixed results; a variety of QoL instruments were used in these studies, including the Lehman Quality of Life Interview (QOLI) (Russo et al, 1997; Dickerson et al 2001), the Quality of Life Scale (Bellack et al, 1989), the Social Functioning Scale (Dickerson et al, 2001), and the Levenstein–Klein–Pollack (LKP) scale (Levenstein et al; 1966, Grossman et al, 1991).

Russo et al (1997) performed a rigorous psychometric evaluation of the QOLI in a large sample (N = 981) of acutely ill inpatients with different psychiatric diagnoses (n = 138, bipolar depression; n = 103, acute mania; other patients had a diagnosis of unipolar depression, schizophrenia, or other psychiatric disorders) (Table 1). The QOLI contains 44 items and 7 satisfaction subscales, a global satisfaction item, and 14 functional items, with all satisfaction scores ranging from 1 (terrible) to 7 (delighted). Patients were administered the instrument using a structured interview procedure within 48 hours of hospital admission and discharge. Whereas the QOLI was successfully completed by 90% of patients overall, completion rates did vary according to patients' diagnoses, with noncompletion rates being lowest among patients with bipolar depression (12%) and highest in patients with acute mania (31%). Reasons given for noncompletion of the instrument varied, the most common being "inadequate staff time" (39%); "patient too psychotic, demented, or confused" (13%); or "[patient] too agitated or sleepy" (12%). In this study, the QOLI showed good psychometric properties overall, although there was some concern about an apparent lack of construct consistency (low correlations between patient satisfaction and functional measures) in patients with acute mania.

Table 1. Summary of Quality of Life of Patients With Bipolar Disorder*

Author	Study Design and Location	Population(s)	QoL Instrument(s)	Main Findings
Arnold et al (2000)	Cross-sectional; USA	44 patients with BD (38, type I; 5, type II; 1, NOS) 30 chronic (>6 month) patients with low back pain 2474 US general population	SF-36	Patients with BD had substantial HRQoL impairment compared with the US general population. Compared with patients with BD, patients with chronic back pain showed more impairment in all SF-36 domains except general health, role limitation (emotional), and mental health.
Atkinson et al (1997)	Cross-sectional; Canada	37 patients with BD 35 patients with MDD 69 patients with schizophrenia	Quality of Life Inventory	Patients with BD or MDD subjectively reported lower QoL than patients with schizophrenia. In contrast, patients with schizophrenia had poorer objectively measured functional outcomes.
Bellack et al (1989)	Cross-sectional; USA	29, BD 21, negative schizophrenia 37, nonnegative schizophrenia 16, schizoaffective	SAS II QLS	Patients with schizophrenia showed more impairment than those with bipolar disorder on all subscales.
Cooke et al (1996)	Cross-sectional; Canada	68 euthymic patients with BD (55, type I; 13, type II)	SF-20	SF-20 scores among patients with BD were comparable with those reported for patients with MDD in the RAND Corporation MOS study (Wells et al, 1989). Patients with BD II reported considerably poorer QoL in the SF-20 domains of social functioning and mental health than patients with BD I.
Dickerson et al (2001)	Cross-sectional; USA	26, BD type I 74, schizophrenia	SFS QOLI	Patients with BD and patients with schizophrenia had comparable scores on both instruments, except for the QOLI satisfaction with finances subscale, on which patients with BD scored significantly lower.
Kusznir et al (2000)	Cross-sectional; Canada	61 euthymic patients with BD (47, type I; 14, type II)	OPQ, SF-20, IIRS	One-third of the sample did not meet the criteria for adequate community functioning according to the OPQ.

Table 1. Summary of Quality of Life of Patients With Bipolar Disorder* (Continued)

Author	Study Design and Location	Population(s)	QoL Instrument(s)	Main Findings
Leidy et al (1998)	Prospective cohort; North America	62 patients with type I BD (34, euthymia; 28, bipolar depression)	MOS SF-36, QLDS, MHI-17, and MOS CFS	Marked impairment in SF-36 scores was apparent, and QLDS scores were lower than reported elsewhere for patients with unipolar depression.
MacQueen et al (1997)	Cross-sectional; Canada	62 euthymic outpatients with BD I, index episode of mania (16, with psychosis; 46, without psychosis)	SF-20	No significant differences in SF-20 scores between patients with or without psychosis.
MacQueen et al (2000)	Cross-sectional; Canada	64 euthymic patients with BD I	SF-20	The number of previous depressive episodes was a stronger determinant of QoL than the number of previous manic episodes.
Namjoshi et al (2002)	3-week RCT + 49-week open-label olanzapine study; USA	122 acutely manic type I 65, olanzapine 57, placebo	SF-36	Acute treatment with olanzapine resulted in improved SF-36 physical functioning scores; improvement in vitality, pain, general health and social functioning domains were apparent in the open-label phase.
Namjoshi et al (in press)	6-week RCT; USA/Canada	239, acutely manic type I 161, olanzapine plus lithium or valproate 78, lithium or valproate alone	QOLI	Olanzapine combination with lithium or valproate therapy was associated with better outcome in several QOLI domains compared with monotherapy with lithium or valproate. Improvement in QOLI subjective satisfaction scores was highly associated with improvement in the HAMD total score.
Ozer et al (2002)	Cross-sectional; Turkey	100 euthymic patients with BD (subdivided into 3 groups [low, moderate, and high] according to severity of their depressive symptoms)	Q-LES-Q	Depression scores significantly predicted lower Q-LES-Q scores. None of the historical variables were predictive of mean Q-LES-Q scores.
Patelis-Siotis et al (2001)	Open-label trial; Canada	49 mildly depressed or euthymic patients with BD	SF-36	SF-36 vitality and role (emotional) scores significantly improved after CBT.
Revicki et al (2003)	12-week RCT; USA	120 acutely manic type I 63, divalproex 57, olanzapine	Q-LES-Q	Comparable improvement in Q-LES-Q between divalproex and olanzapine in the 12-week treatment in patients hospitalized for a DSM-IV acute manic episode.

Table 1. Summary of Quality of Life of Patients With Bipolar Disorder* (Continued)

Author	Study Design and Location	Population(s)	QoL Instrument(s)	Main Findings
Ritsner et al (2002)	Cross-sectional; Israel	199 patients with severe mental illness 17 patients with BD (9, mania; 4, depression; 4, mixed symptoms)	Q-LES-Q and LQOLP	Q-LES-Q scores were lowest among patients with bipolar depression, highest among patients with mania.
Robb et al (1997)	Cross-sectional; Canada	68 euthymic BD patients (55, type I; 13, type II)	IIRS	Greater illness intrusiveness was associated with higher HAMD scores, recent depression, and type II BD.
Robb et al (1998)	Cross-sectional; Canada	69 euthymic patients with BD (54, type I; 15, type II or male, 27; female, 42)	SF-20	Women demonstrated significantly lower SF-20 scores in the domains of bodily pain and physical health.
Russo et al (1997)	Cross-sectional; USA	981 patients with different psychiatric diagnoses, of whom 241 inpatients with BD (138, bipolar depression; 103, acute mania)	QOLI	Patients with mania reported the highest levels of satisfaction and functioning, whereas patients with bipolar or unipolar depression reported the lowest QoL levels. Patients with concurrent substance abuse reported less satisfaction and lower QoL than patients without concurrent substance abuse.
Salyers et al (2000)	Cross-sectional; USA	946 patients with severe mental illness, of whom 164 patients with BD	SF-12†	SF-12 mental health scores were considerably lower in patients with unipolar depression.
Shi et al (2002)	France, Spain, Bulgaria, Brazil, USA, Peru, Mexico, Venezuela, South Africa	453 acutely manic, type I 234, olanzapine 219, haloperidol	SF-36	Compared with patients treated with haloperidol, olanzapine-treated patients showed superior improvement in QoL during acute and continuation treatment in most SF-36 domains.
Shi et al (May 2002)	47-week RCT; USA	167 acutely manic, type I 77, olanzapine 70, divalproex	PGWB	Improvement in PGWB was highly associated with improvement in the HAMD total score.

Table 1. Summary of Quality of Life of Patients With Bipolar Disorder* (Continued)

Author	Study Design and Location	Population(s)	QoL Instrument(s)	Main Findings
Shi et al (September 2003)	6-month open-label study; USA	423 patients with bipolar depression 101, olanzapine 194, olanzapine/fluoxetine (OFC) 128, exposure to olanzapine and OFC	SF-36	Long-term olanzapine or OFC treatment improved the scores on the SF-36 scales in bipolar-depressed patients over a 6-month open-label period.
Shi et al (2004)	8-week RCT; USA, Colombia, Spain, Mexico, Australia, Portugal, Greece	573 patients with bipolar depression, type I BD 250, olanzapine 58, OFC 265, placebo	SF-36, QLDS	Bipolar-depressed patients on olanzapine and OFC had greater improvement in QoL than patients on placebo. Additionally, OFC-treated patients achieved greater improvement in QoL than patients on olanzapine. Patients with bipolar depression had markedly lower baseline SF-36 scores in multiple dimensions than those of the US general population.
ten Have et al (2002)	Prospective cohort; Netherlands	2718 patients with psychiatric disorders (other than BD) 136 patients with BD (93, type I; 43, BD NOS)	SF-36	Patients with BD generally showed greater impairment in most of SF-36 domains than patients with other psychiatric diagnoses.
Tsevat et al (2000)	Cross-sectional; USA	53 outpatients with BD	SF-36, TTO, and SG	TTO (0.61) and SG (0.70) scores for mental health were comparable with those reported for other psychiatric conditions.
Vojta et al (2001)	Cross-sectional; USA	86 patients with BD (16, mania/hypomania; 26, MDD; 14, mixed mania/hypomania and depression; 30, euthymia)	SF-12 and EuroQoL	There were significant intergroup differences in both the SF-12 mental health score and the EuroQoL scores. Post-hoc comparisons demonstrated that SF-12 mental health scores were significantly lower among patients with mania than those among patients with euthymia. SF-12 mental health scores among patients with MDD or mixed symptoms were significantly lower than those among patients with mania or euthymia. EuroQoL scores showed similar results.

Table 1. Summary of Quality of Life of Patients With Bipolar Disorder* (Continued)

Author	Study Design and Location	Population(s)	QoL Instrument(s)	Main Findings
Wells and Sherbourne (1999)	Cross-sectional; USA	331 patients with lifetime BD 944, 12-month double depression 3479, 12-month major depression 151, 12-month dysthymia 987, 1-month depressive symptoms	SF-12, TTO, and SG	Patients with BD showed levels of QoL impairment (SF-12 scores) secondary only to patients with double depression. In addition, patients with BD had lower health utility (TTO and SG) than patients with major depression, dysthymia, and depressive symptoms.

BD, bipolar disorder; CBT, cognitive behavior therapy; EuroQoL, European Quality of Life Scale; HAMD, Hamilton Depression Rating Scale; HRQoL, health-related quality of life; IIRS, Illness Intrusiveness Rating Scale; LQOLP, Lancashire Quality of Life Profile; MDD, major depressive disorder; MHI-17, Mental Health Index 17; MOS, Medical Outcomes Study; MOS CFS, MOS Cognitive Function Scale; MOS SF-12, MOS 12-item Short-Form Health Survey; MOS SF-20, MOS 20-item Short-Form Health Survey; MOS SF-36, MOS 36-item Short-Form Health Survey; NOS, nonspecified; OFC, olanzapine/fluoxetine combination; OPQ, Occupational Performance Questionnaire; PGWB, Psychological Global Well-Being; Q-LES-Q, Quality of Life Enjoyment and Satisfaction Questionnaire; QLDS, Quality of Life in Depression Scale; QoL, quality of life; QOLI, Quality of Life Interview; QLS, Quality of Life Sale; RCT, randomized clinical trial; SAS II, Social Adjustment Scale II; SFS, Social Functioning Scale; SG, standard gamble; SMI, severe mental illness; TTO, time tradeoff.

* Studies using other scales such as GAF and LKP are not listed in the table. † The instrument was administered by trained interviewers.

Table 2. Summary of the SF-36 Scores in Patients With Bipolar Disorder*

Author	Patient Population	Physical Functioning	Social Function	Role-Physical	Role-Emotional	Bodily Pain	Mental Health	General Health	Vitality
Arnold et al (2000)	44 BD outpatients (38, type I; 5, type II; 1, NOS)	78.8±22.4	57.9±27.7	63.1±41.6	38.6±43.1	64.9±25.7	55.3±23.8	61.9±25.4	43.6±24.3
Leidy et al (1998)	34, euthymic	84.4±20.2	73.2±18.2	86.2±28.0	76.2±31.2	59.6±29.0	69.2±17.9	70.9±20.7	52.0±16.2
	28, depressed	72.2±28.3	29.3±20.0	32.3±38.6	8.3± 20.3	54.7±25.3	33.4±16.5	58.0±21.2	20.4±17.5
Namjoshi et al (2002)	122, BD I (manic/mixed)	86.8±16.8	47.1±28.3	70.4±40.2	37.4±42.3	68.4±26.4	59.9±22.6	69.0±22.7	63.3±24.0
	65, olanzapine	84.5±21.9	46.0±31.8	65.4±40.3	36.3±43.3	61.7±25.0	58.5±19.8	65.2±24.3	66.6±20.0
	57, placebo								
Patelis-Siotis et al (2001)	34, BD CBT completers	80.4±19.3	58.1±25.0	41.2±39.8	17.6±33.1	68.5±23.7	52.4±18.0	66.6±21.7	39.4±19.3
	8, BD CBT noncompleters	63.8±30.6	46.9±28.1	40.6±44.2	29.2±41.5	63.4±27.0	44.0±22.0	46.4±29.6	28.1±21.4
Shi et al (2002)	453, BD I (manic/mixed)	85.2±23.2	61.1±31.8	66.1±39.6	53.3±43.2	79.8±26.2	71.0±20.4	73.6±21.8	75.8±19.1
	234, olanzapine	90.5±15.7	61.2±29.1	72.8±36.3	50.1±43.7	81.2±26.1	72.8±16.5	75.1±19.2	80.0±14.9
	219, haloperidol								
Shi et al (2004)†	573, BD I (depressive)	66.6±26.2	32.5±21.4	46.4±42.3	14.6±28.7	57.8±26.1	31.3±15.7	48.6±22.6	25.6±17.6
	265, placebo	65.8±27.6	29.1±20.9	47.8±44.0	12.2±25.4	60.6±27.1	30.0±16.1	51.1±22.3	25.5±17.5
	250, olanzapine	68.8±25.0	30.6±20.8	44.8±41.8	9.8±23.4	60.8±25.6	31.0±17.3	52.3±20.7	25.3±19.0
	58, olanzapine/fluoxetine								
ten Have et al (2002)‡	93, BD I	89.6	73.6	77.6	69.5	74.1	62.3	62.6	58.0
	43, BD NOS	91.2	80.8	81.7	80.6	82.5	68.7	68.2	62.0
Tsevat et al (2000)	53, BD	78.7±23.4	58.7±27.9	63.2±40.9	38.9±42.3	65.3±26.0	56.2±23.7	62.1±24.3	45.4±24.4
Ware et al (2001)	US general population (n=2474)	84.2±23.3	83.3±22.7	80.9±34.0	81.3±33.0	75.2±23.7	74.7±18.1	71.9±20.3	60.9±20.9

BD, bipolar disorder; CBT, cognitive behavior therapy; NOS, nonspecified.

* Data presented for baseline SF-36 scores in longitudinal studies or SF-36 scores in cross-sectional studies (mean±SD).

† Shi et al (September 2003) presented the open-label–phase QoL results of the Shi et al (2004) study.

‡ SDs not available.

Table 3. Treatments of Bipolar Disorder and Their Effects on Patients' Quality of Life and Functioning

Author	Study Type and Duration of Each Treatment Period	Patient Diagnosis	Compared Treatments	Treatment Effect on QoL
Banov et al (1994)	Prospective naturalistic study (mean follow-up time of 18.7 months)	Bipolar disorder (mania, depression, and mixed)	Single-arm clozapine (manic, n = 28; depressed, n = 9; mixed, n = 15)	Patients with mania had more favorable GAS or other outcomes than patients with bipolar depression.
Bowden et al (1999)	48-week open label study	Rapid-cycling (n = 41) and nonrapid-cycling (n = 34) BD	Add-on lamotrigine (n = 60) monotherapy (n = 15)	Patients treated with the add-on lamotrigine showed significant improvement in mean GAF scores.
Bowden et al (2000)	52-week RCT	BD with an index manic episode	Lithium (n = 91) divalproex (n = 187) placebo (n = 94)	Divalproex was more beneficial in stopping the progressive deterioration of functioning (measured by GAF) among patients in the mania subgroup.
Calabrese et al (2000)	26-week RCT	Stable rapid-cycling BD I and II	Lamotrigine (n = 93) placebo (n = 89)	No significant differences in GAF scores were observed between treatment groups.
Clark et al (1997)	4-week RCT	Acute mania (nonpsychotic)	Clonazepam (n = 15) lithium (n = 15)	The effects of clonazepam on patients' GAF scores were similar to those of lithium.
Fatemi et al (1997)	Open, naturalistic, and prospective study (mean duration of lamotrigine treatment of 225.8 days)	Rapid-cycling BD I and II	add-on lamotrigine (n = 4) lamotrigine monotherapy (n = 1)	Results were similar to the Bowden et al (1999) study.
Ghaemi et al (1997)	Chart review (open series)	BD I	Risperidone (n = 14)	Risperidone was beneficial in the treatment of outpatients with bipolar disorder.
Ghaemi and Goodwin (2001)	Chart review	BD I (n = 9), BD II (n = 5), BD NOS (n = 5), or cyclothymic disorder (n = 2).	Gabapentin monotherapy (n = 8) gabapentin combination therapy (n = 13)	Patients treated with gabapentin monotherapy demonstrated improvement in GAF scores.
Goldberg et al (1996)	Naturalistic study with standardized interviews at 2 and 4.5 years	Bipolar disorder; hospitalized for mania	Lithium monotherapy (n = 8) lithium + another antipsychotic (n = 21) no medication (n = 8)	Patients treated with lithium monotherapy demonstrated the lowest functionality impairment (LKP scale) compared with patients treated with lithium combination therapy.

Table 3. Treatments of Bipolar Disorder and Their Effects on Patients' Quality of Life and Functioning (Continued)

Author	Study Type and Duration of Each Treatment Period	Patient Diagnosis	Compared Treatments	Treatment Effect on QoL
Hayes (1989)	≥1-year follow-up study	Mixed bipolar disorder	Valproate monotherapy (n = 6) valproate + lithium (n = 6)	Valproate administration produced significant affective response. Patients in either treatment group demonstrated similar and substantially improved functionality (measured by GAS).
Ichim et al (2000)	4-week RCT	Mania	Lithium (n = 15) lamotrigine (n = 15)	Both groups increased their mean GAF scores.
Muller-Oerlinghausen et al (2000)	3-week RCT	Acute mania	Valproate (n = 69) placebo (n = 67)	Compared with patients on placebo, valproate-treated patients demonstrated significant improvements in GAF scores.
Namjoshi et al (2002)	RCT: 3-week + 49-week open-label olanzapine phase	Acute mania, BD I	Olanzapine (n = 65) placebo (n = 57)	Acute treatment with olanzapine resulted in improved SF-36 physical functioning scores; improvement in vitality, pain, general health and social functioning domains were apparent in open-label phase.
Namjoshi et al (in press)	RCT: 6-week double-blind period	Acute mania, BD I	Olanzapine + lithium or valproic acid (n = 161) placebo + lithium or valproic acid (n = 78)	Olanzapine combination with lithium or valproic acid was associated with better outcome in several QOLI domains compared with lithium or valproic-acid monotherapy.
Revicki et al (2003)	12-week RCT	Acute mania, BD I	Divalproex sodium (n = 63) olanzapine (n = 57)	Comparable improvement was observed in Q-LES-Q scores of divalproex sodium– and olanzapine-treated patients who were hospitalized with an acute mania episode.
Sanderson (1998)	Chart review	Geriatric inpatients with BD	Lithium (n =41) valproic acid (n = 20) carbamazepam (n = 11)	No significant differences were observed in GAF scores across treatment groups.
Segal et al (1998)	4-week RCT	Mania	Risperidone (n = 15) lithium (n = 15) haloperidol (n = 15)	Risperidone-treated patients had GAF scores equivalent to those of patients on lithium or haloperidol.

Table 3. Treatments of Bipolar Disorder and Their Effects on Patients' Quality of Life and Functioning (Continued)

Author	Study Type and Duration of Each Treatment Period	Patient Diagnosis	Compared Treatments	Treatment Effect on QoL
Shi et al (2002)	12-week RCT (6 weeks of the acute period and 6 weeks of continuation period)	Acute mania, BD I	Olanzapine (n = 234) haloperidol (n = 219)	Compared with haloperidol-treated patients, olanzapine-treated patients demonstrated a superior improvement in QoL during acute and continuation treatment in most SF-36 domains.
Shi et al (May 2003)*	8-week double-blind RCT	Rapid-cycling or nonrapid-cycling bipolar depression	Olanzapine (n = 250) OFC (n = 58) placebo (n = 265)	Compared with olanzapine- or placebo-treated patients, patients on OFC experienced greater improvement in the SF-36 scores on multiple domains, as well as QLDS total scores in both rapid- and nonrapid-cycling bipolar depression.
Shi et al (September 2003)[†]	RCT: 6-month open-label period	Bipolar depression	Olanzapine (n = 101) OFC (n = 194) switch between olanzapine and OFC (n = 128)	Long-term treatment with olanzapine or OFC improved patients' SF-36 scores.
Shi et al (2004)	8-week RCT	Bipolar depression, BD I	Olanzapine (n = 250) OFC (n = 58) placebo (n = 265)	Olanzapine- or OFC-treated patients had greater improvement in QoL (as measured by SF-36 and QLDS) than patients on placebo. Additionally, OFC-treated patients achieved greater improvement in QoL than olanzapine-treated patients.
Small et al (1995)	8-week RCT	Bipolar mania	Lithium-carbamazepine combination (n = 17) lithium-haloperidol combination (n = 16)	Patients demonstrated significant improvement of GAF scores, but no differences were observed between the 2 treatment groups.

BD, bipolar disorder; GAF, Global Assessment of Functioning scale; GAS, Global Assessment Scale (same as GAF); LKP, Levenstein–Klein–Pollack scale; NOS, nonspecified; OFC, olanzapine/fluoxetine combination; Q-LES-Q, Quality of Life Enjoyment and Satisfaction Questionnaire; QLDS, Quality of Life in Depression scale; QoL, quality of life; QOLI, Quality of Life Interview; RCT, randomized clinical trial; SF-36, 36-item Short-Form Health Survey.

* Shi et al (May 2003) was a preliminary analysis, by rapid-cycling, of the results reported by Shi et al (2004).

† The Shi et al (September 2003) presentation described the open-label period of the trial reported by Shi et al (2004).

Leidy et al (1998) (Table 1) examined the psychometric properties of 4 QoL instruments among 62 patients with bipolar I disorder. Patients completed the MOS SF-36, the Quality of Life in Depression Scale (QLDS), the Mental Health Index-17 (MHI-17), and the MOS Cognitive Function Scale (CFS). The SF-36 is currently the most widely used measure of QoL (Garratt et al, 2002). This self-report questionnaire contains 8 domains that assess physical functioning, social functioning, role limitations (physical) (also referred to as "role-physical"), role limitations (emotional) (also referred to as "role-emotional"), bodily pain, mental health, general health, and vitality. These domain scores yield an overall domain score on a 0 to 100 scale, where 0 represents worst possible health and 100, best possible health.[1] (More results on SF-36 scores at the baseline of reviewed studies were summarized in Table 2.) The QLDS was designed to assess the ability of patients with depression to satisfy their needs as a result of treatment (Hunt and McKenna, 1992; McKenna et al, 2001). This scale is self-administered and consists of 34 dichotomous items, which describe specific needs of patients with depression. The QLDS scores range from 0 (good quality of life) to 34 (very poor quality of life). The MHI-17 is a measure of psychological distress and well-being. It includes the 5 questions from the mental health domain of the SF-36 and 12 additional items measuring psychological well-being (Stewart et al, 1992). The CFS has 6 items that address memory, attention, reasoning, and judgment. Both the MHI-17 and CFS scores range from 0 (worst quality of life) to 100 (best quality of life). The Leidy et al study provided further evidence that both euthymic and depressed patients with bipolar disorder are capable of providing accurate self-reports of their QoL. The psychometric properties of the QoL instruments varied in degrees of reliability, validity, and responsiveness, but generally fell within acceptable ranges.[2] According to the results of this study, the MHI-17 and CFS demonstrated reliability and validity in assessing QoL among patients with bipolar disorder.

Salyers et al (2000) conducted a psychometric evaluation of another MOS instrument, the 12-Item Short-Form Health Survey (SF-12) (Ware et al, 1996), in a sample of 946 patients with severe mental illness, 164 of whom had a diagnosis of bipolar disorder (Table 1). The instrument showed acceptable levels of reliability and validity in the entire sample, although it is worth noting that is was administered by trained interviewers rather than as a self-report measure.

Ritsner et al (2002) compared responses on the Quality of Life Enjoyment and Satisfaction Questionnaire (Q-LES-Q) (Endicott et al, 1993) and the Lancashire Quality of Life Profile (Oliver et al, 1997) in a sample of 199 Israeli patients with severe mental illness, 17 of whom had a diagnosis of bipolar disorder (Table 1). Both instruments showed generally acceptable levels of internal consistency, test-retest reliability, and criterion validity in the entire patient sample, but notably low levels of convergent validity between the instruments' domains, particularly in the control group.

Whereas few psychometric studies have been performed in patients with bipolar disorder, even fewer have examined the health state utilities among patients with bipolar depression.

---

[1] An alternative method exists for scoring SF-36, which derives the physical component score (PCS) and mental component score (MCS) based on a principal components analysis. A linear T-score transformation method is used so that both the PCS and MCS have a mean of 50 and a standard deviation of 10 in the 1998 general US population (Ware et al, 2001).

[2] In addition, Shi et al (2004) found that changes in the SF-36 scores of mental health, social functioning, role-emotional, and vitality were highly correlated to changes in the QLDS total score. The results of the Shi et al (2004) analysis support the construct validity of the QLDS.

The concept of health state utility refers to an individual's preferences for different states of health under conditions of uncertainty. Health preferences are values that reflect an individual's level of subjective satisfaction, distress, or desirability associated with various health conditions. Health state utility and health preferences are frequently assessed by the "time tradeoff" (TTO) and "standard gamble" (SG) approaches (Torrance, 1986). TTO refers to the years of life a person is willing to exchange for perfect health. For example, patients may be asked to imagine that a treatment exists that would allow them to live in health, but with reduced life expectancy. They may then be asked to indicate how much time they would give up for a treatment that would permit them to live in perfect health, if they had 10 years to live. SG refers to the required chance for successful outcome to accept a treatment that could result in either immediate death or perfect health. For example, patients may be asked to imagine that they had 10 years to live in their current state of health, and that a treatment existed that could either give them perfect health, or kill them immediately. Patients may then be asked to indicate what chance of success the treatment would have to have before they would trade their current state of health for it. Health state utility and health preference values are frequently expressed as a score of 0 to 1, with higher values representing better health. In a health utility study of 53 outpatients with bipolar disorder recruited from 1 arm of the multicenter Stanley Foundation Bipolar Network study, Tsevat et al (2000) found the TTO scores for current overall health were 0.71, but were higher than scores for current mental health, which averaged 0.61. One advantage of the health utility/health preference approach to QoL assessment is that it allows the calculation of quality-adjusted life years (QALYs). QALYs are a commonly used outcome measure in cost-effectiveness studies, but they are complicated to calculate, and our literature search did not find any studies that had calculated QALYs for populations with bipolar disorder.

2. QoL and Its Correlates among Patients with Bipolar Disorder at Different Stages of the Disease

The majority of QoL assessments in bipolar disorder has been conducted in outpatients with euthymia. Euthymic patients with bipolar disorder are likely to be less prone to the effects of cognitive distortion than symptomatic patients (ie, patients manifesting manic, depressive, or mixed symptoms). However, patients with euthymia are not necessarily asymptomatic because many of them have mild subsyndromal symptoms, which are strongly associated with impaired QoL. Psychosocial deficits have been sustained for as long as 4 years following recovery, and may be the results of residual symptoms during the euthymic period (Tohen et al, 2000).

Cooke et al (1996) used MOS 20-Item Short-Form Health Survey (SF-20) to examine QoL by type of bipolar disorder in a sample of outpatients (N = 68) with bipolar disorder type I or II, who had been clinically euthymic for at least 1 month (Table 1). SF-20 (Stewart et al, 1988) is a self-report questionnaire designed to assess patient-perceived well-being in 6 domains (physical, social, and role functioning; mental health status; health perceptions; and bodily pain). Patients with bipolar II disorder reported significantly poorer QoL than patients with bipolar I disorder in the areas of social functioning and mental health.

In a sample of 68 euthymic outpatients with bipolar disorder attending a university hospital–based clinic, Robb et al (1997) reported patients' functioning by using the Illness

Intrusiveness Rating Scale (Flanagan, 1978; Devins et al, 1993) (Table 1). This scale addresses the impact that a disorder and/or its treatment have upon an individual's activities across 13 life domains: health, diet, active recreation, passive recreation, work, financial status, self-expression/self-improvement, family relationships, relations with spouse, sex life, other social relationships, religious expression, and community involvement. In the Robb et al (1997) study, individuals with bipolar disorder experienced considerable illness intrusiveness across all life domains, of which the most highly disrupted domains were self-expression/self-improvement, family relationships, other social relationships, and work. Patients with bipolar II disorder reported greater intrusiveness than patients with bipolar I disorder on all life domains except religious expression.

Kusznir et al (2000) found that one-third of euthymic patients with bipolar disorder did not meet the criteria for adequate functioning according to the Community Functioning Scale, a component of the Occupational Performance Questionnaire (Kusznir et al, 1996) (Table 1).

Compared with euthymic symptoms of bipolar disorder, the relationship between QoL and manic symptoms is less well understood. Both mania and hypomania can be associated with substantial depressive symptoms, either in the form of dysphoric mania/hypomania or mixed-episode symptoms. This understanding led Vojta et al (2001) to hypothesize that patients with manic symptoms would report significantly lower QoL than would patients with euthymia. To test this theory, Vojta et al administered the SF-12 in patients with mania/hypomania, MDD, mixed mania/hypomania and depression, or euthymia (Table 1). Patients with mania/hypomania did show significantly lower SF-12 mental health scores than patients with euthymia.

Depressive symptoms in bipolar disorder can seriously affect patients' QoL. The Vojta et al (2001) study also found that patients with depressive or mixed symptoms had significantly poorer QoL scores than patients with manic/hypomanic symptoms. Some studies (Cooke et al 1996; Arnold et al 2000; Shi et al, 2004) have shown that individuals with bipolar disorder have poor quality of life during the bipolar depressive phase. The mean baseline QLDS total score in the Shi et al (2004) study is also comparable with that reported previously in a sample of patients with bipolar depression (mean = 17.1) (Leidy et al, 1998).

Among patients with bipolar disorder, depression usually causes more distress than does mania (Shi et al, May 2002). A recent study by Ozer et al (2002) assessed euthymic patients with bipolar disorder (Table 1) to examine the correlation between the "present symptomatology" factor and the Q-LES-Q scores. Of the symptoms assessed in the Ozer et al study, only depressive symptoms predicted lower Q-LES-Q scores, accounting for 13% of the observed variance. Robb et al (1997) (Table 1) reported that greater illness intrusiveness was associated with higher Hamilton Depression Rating Scale scores, a recent episode of depression, and type II bipolar disorder. Patients with acute mania in the Namjoshi et al (in press) study (Table 1) demonstrated improvement in the QOLI subjective satisfaction scores, which was highly associated with improvement in Hamilton Depression Rating Scale total scores in the same sample of patients.

The influence of patients' demographic and illness characteristics on their quality of life has been reported with mixed results. Robb et al (1998) specifically focused on differences in SF-20 scores among male and female patients (Table 1), finding that women possessed numerically lower SF-20 scores in all of the questionnaire's domains except for mental health, with significant differences in the domains of bodily pain and physical health. Using multivariate analysis, Ozer et al (2002) (Table 1) found that none of the historical variables (including age at first episode, number of previous depressive or manic episodes, duration of illness, number of hospitalizations, age at first hospitalization, or number of symptoms during the first episode) were predictive of mean Q-LES-Q scores. MacQueen et al (2000) (Table 1) found that the number of past depressions was a stronger determinant of QoL than was the number of previous manic episodes.

Research indicates that psychosis can impact patients with bipolar disorder differentially, depending on the disease stage; however, results across different studies are not consistent. The presence of psychosis or a psychotic episode may not predict the QoL level after recovery. MacQueen et al (1997) examined SF-20 scores in euthymic outpatients with bipolar I disorder with or without psychotic symptoms during an index episode of mania (Table 1). No significant differences in SF-20 scores were apparent between patients with or without psychosis, although the number of patients with psychosis may have been too small to detect significant differences between the subgroups. In the MacQueen et al (1997) study, QoL and functioning scores did not differ when patients returned to a euthymic state, even in those who experienced psychotic episodes.[3]

The course of illness among rapid-cycling patients may fundamentally differ, which can affect treatment strategy and be associated with functional impairment. In an open-label study of lamotrigine efficacy, both rapid-cycling and nonrapid-cycling patients were able to improve their functional scores (measured with GAF), with nonrapid-cycling patients demonstrating greater improvements (Bowden et al, 1999). Increases in GAF scores greater than or equal to 10 points occurred among a larger proportion of nonrapid-cycling (69%) than rapid-cycling (49%) patients.[4]

3. Comparisons of QoL among Patients with Bipolar Disorder with that of Other Patient Populations

A number of studies assessed quality of life among patients with bipolar disorder or other affective disorders. Comparison of the results of such studies may provide partial evidence on burden of prevalent bipolar disorder to society.

Both Cooke et al (1996) (Table 1) and Wells et al (1989) (the latter was a large RAND Corporation MOS study) examined patients' levels of QoL using the SF-20. Mean SF-20 scores among patients with bipolar disorder in the Cooke et al (1996) study were comparable with those reported for patients with MDD in the Wells et al (1989) study.

According to the Ozer et al (2002) study (Table 1), mean Q-LES-Q scores among euthymic patients with bipolar disorder varied according to the severity of their depressive symptoms and were 39% (low severity), 38% (medium severity), and 35% (high severity). In comparison, Miller et al (1998) reported mean Q-LES-Q scores of patients with chronic MDD to be 53%.

---

[3] However, in a study evaluating 89 psychotic inpatients with bipolar I disorder (Rosen et al, 1983), the investigators found lower scores for best level of social functioning and, to a lesser extent, overall functioning during the 5-year prehospitalization period.

[4] Some researchers note that patients with bipolar disorder, or indeed any psychiatric diagnoses and concurrent substance abuse, have a lower QoL than patients without such diagnoses (Russo et al, 1997; O'Connell et al, 1991).

Salyers et al (2000) evaluated quality of life measured by SF-12 (Ware et al, 1996) in a large sample of patients with severe mental illness, 164 of whom had a diagnosis of bipolar disorder (Table 1). Mean (±SD) SF-12 scores among patients with bipolar disorder were 46.1±11.5 (physical functioning) and 39.6±12.7 (mental health), whereas SF-12 mental health scores were significantly lower (31.8±13.4) among patients with unipolar MDD. A comparison of 2 studies (Leidy et al, 1998; Hunt and McKenna, 1992) that used QLDS as a measure of patients' quality of life found similar results: In the Leidy et al (1998) study (Table 1), QoL among patients with bipolar depression was poorer than that reported for patients with unipolar depression in the Hunt and McKenna (1992) study.

In the Dutch Mental Health Survey and Incidence Study (NEMESIS) (ten Have et al, 2002), 136 patients with a lifetime diagnosis of bipolar disorder (Table 1) showed significantly greater impairment in most of the SF-36 domains compared with NEMESIS participants with diagnoses of other psychiatric disorders (n = 2718). Patients with bipolar I disorder also experienced significantly lower SF-36 scores that patients with nonspecified bipolar disorder in the SF-36 domains of mental health, role limitations (emotional), social functioning, and bodily pain.

Wells and Sherbourne (1999) compared QoL (assessed with SF-12 global physical and mental subscales) and health utility (assessed by TTO and SG) among patients with bipolar disorder with those among patients with other depressive disorders within 7 managed care organizations in the United States (Table 1). In terms of QoL, patients with bipolar disorder showed levels of impairment secondary only to patients with double depression. Health utility was also lower in patients with bipolar disorder compared with patients with major depression, dysthymia, or brief depressive symptoms; however, there were no considerable health utility differences between patients with bipolar disorder and those with double depression.

Additionally, some studies compared QoL among patients with bipolar disorder with that among patients with certain physical conditions and general public. Arnold et al 2000 compared HRQoL (as assessed by the SF-36) among patients with bipolar disorder with that among patients with chronic (>6 months) low back pain (Table 1). In addition, SF-36 scores for these patients were compared with those previously generated for the US general population (n = 2474) (McHorney et al, 1994). Patients with bipolar disorder had substantial HRQoL impairment compared with the general population. Interestingly, patients with bipolar disorder were less compromised in areas of physical and social functioning than patients with chronic back pain, but both patient groups had similar impairment in mental health scores such as role limitation (emotional) and mental health.

Shi et al (2004) (Table 1) compared QLDS scores of patients with bipolar depression with the corresponding SF-36 domain scores in the US general population (Ware et al, 1993). These researchers reported markedly lower baseline SF-36 scores in multiple domains. The mean baseline MCS among patients in the Shi et al (2004) study was nearly 3 standard deviations below the mean MCS (50) for the US 1998 general population (Ware et al, 2001).

4. Medication Treatment Effects on QoL in Patients With Bipolar Disorder

Lithium, anticonvulsants, and novel antipsychotics are all monotherapy options in current pharmacological treatment algorithms for bipolar disorder (Suppes et al, 2002). In addition, combinations of 2, 3, or more drugs (which may include any of the former in addition to conventional antipsychotics) are commonly required to treat this patient population. The current literature regarding medication effects on QoL reflects the range of complex therapeutic options used in treatment of patients with bipolar disorder.

Until the 1980s, lithium was the standard treatment for bipolar disorder. The Solomon et al (1996) study showed that the attainment of standard lithium serum levels could increase patients' psychosocial functioning. According to the Lepkifker et al (1988) study, life satisfaction and adjustment scores did not significantly differ between lithium-treated patients with affective disorders (unipolar or bipolar depression) and healthy controls. Harrow et al (1990) found no difference in overall outcomes (LKP scale) in a follow-up study of lithium-treated patients with bipolar disorder compared with patients not taking lithium.

Anticonvulsants such as valproate (also referred to as valproic acid, divalproex sodium, or divalproex), carbamazepine, gabapentin, and lamotrigine have become important medication treatments of bipolar disorder. In general, anticonvulsants improve patients' functioning; such improvements are similar to those seen with other treatment regimes (such as lithium). The Muller-Oerlinghausen et al (2000) study compared valproate with placebo and found significant improvement in GAF scores among valproate-treated patients compared with the placebo group. Across treatment options (lithium, valproic acid, or carbamazepine), the Sanderson (1998) study found no significant differences in clinical outcomes, as well as similar increases in mean GAF scores, among acutely ill geriatric inpatients with bipolar disorder. A randomized, double-blind, placebo-controlled, parallel-group, multicenter study by Bowden et al (2000) found no difference in efficacy between lithium and divalproex, but did find the latter more beneficial in stopping the progressive deterioration of functioning (assessed by GAF) among patients in the mania subgroup. A small study by Hayes (1989), which followed up for at least a year patients receiving valproate in monotherapy or valproate in combination with lithium, found similar and substantially improved functionality (measured by the Global Assessment Scale [GAS])[5] in both treatment groups. The Small et al (1995) study found significant improvements in GAF scores among patients with bipolar mania over time, but no differences between the 2 treatment groups (lithium-carbamazepine combination or lithium-haloperidol combination). Revicki et al (2003) found comparable improvement in Q-LES-Q between divalproex sodium– and olanzapine-treated inpatients with acute mania during the 12-week study. In a chart review of patients before and after treatment with gabapentin, Ghaemi and Goodwin (2001) found that mean GAF scores increased among patients treated with gabapentin in monotherapy and as an adjunct (Ghaemi and Goodwin, 2001). In the Bowden et al (1999) study, rapid-cycling and nonrapid-cycling patients who received the add-on lamotrigine therapy for 48 weeks showed significant improvement in mean GAF scores. Similar results were observed among rapid-cycling patients treated with lamotrigine as both an add-on agent and as monotherapy (Fatemi et al, 1997). A randomized, double-blind, controlled, head-to-head trial by Ichim et al (2000) compared lamotrigine-treated patients with mania with lithium-treated patients; lamotrigine patients increased their mean GAF scores by almost 25%. However, Calabrese et al (2000) observed no significant differences in GAF scores between patients with rapid-cycling bipolar disorder randomly assigned to lamotrigine or placebo. Clark et al (1997), in their report on the use of clonazepam (a high-potency anticonvulsant), suggested this agent may be effective as a

[5] Note that Global Assessment Scale (GAS) is another term used for GAF.

monotherapy or adjunctive treatment for acute mania (nonpsychotic); the effect of this agent on patients' GAF scores was similar to that of lithium.

Antipsychotics are frequently used in treatment of bipolar disorder, both as a combination with mood stabilizers and as monotherapy. A naturalistic study reported by Goldberg et al (1996) showed significant differences in overall functioning (as measured by the LKP) among patients with bipolar disorder who received lithium monotherapy, lithium in combination with other antipsychotics, or no medication. The lowest QoL impairment was found among patients on lithium monotherapy compared with lithium in combination with other antipsychotics.

Banov et al (1994) reported the results of a long-term study of clozapine (the first atypical antipsychotic) that measured patients' social, residential, and vocational functioning. The study found that patients with bipolar mania and mixed mania had more favorable outcomes than patients with bipolar depression. In the Segal et al (1998) study, risperidone-treated patients with mania appeared to have GAF scores equivalent to those among lithium- and haloperidol-treated patients. However, according to Ghaemi et al (1997), risperidone-treated patients tended to discontinue the study early due to extrapyramidal symptoms.

Several studies compared the impact of olanzapine treatment on QoL of patients with bipolar mania with that of placebo, haloperidol, or valproate. Namjoshi et al (2002) evaluated QoL outcomes of acute (3-week, olanzapine or placebo) and long-term (49-week, open-label olanzapine) treatment of patients with acute mania. During the acute-phase treatment, a significant improvement was observed in the SF-36 physical functioning domain in the olanzapine group. During the open-label treatment period, however, olanzapine-treated patients showed significant improvements over time in the following SF-36 domains: bodily pain, vitality, general health, and social functioning. Shi et al (2002) also compared the treatment effects of olanzapine and haloperidol in patients with acute mania (N = 453) (Table 3). Following the 6 weeks of acute-phase treatment, olanzapine-treated patients demonstrated greater improvement in 5 of the SF-36 domains (general health, physical functioning, role-physical, social functioning, and vitality). Compared with haloperidol-treated patients, olanzapine-treated patients maintained higher SF-36 scores on these domains during the study's 6-week continuation phase; in addition, patients on olanzapine demonstrated concomitant improvements in work and household functioning. Namjoshi et al (in press) reported on the effects of combination therapy (olanzapine added to lithium orolanzapine added to valproic acid) on quality of life among patients with acute mania. Olanzapine cotherapy with lithium or valproic acid was associated with better outcomes in several QOLI domains, compared with lithium or valproic acid monotherapy.

Improving QoL among patients with bipolar depression could be an important treatment goal because of the effect depressive symptoms may have on patients' lives. Shi et al (2004) compared the impact of treatment with olanzapine or olanzapine/fluoxetine combination (OFC) on QoL of patients with bipolar depression with that of placebo in an 8-week double-blind clinical trial. Patients treated with olanzapine or OFC demonstrated greater improvement in QoL (measured by the SF-36 and QLDS) than patients on placebo. Additionally, OFC-treated patients achieved greater improvement in QoL than olanzapine-treated patients. In a different study of patients with bipolar depression, Shi et al (September 2003) found that long-term (6-month) open-label treatment with olanzapine or OFC improved patients' SF-36 scores over a 6-month open-label period. In a secondary analysis of the 8-week, double-blind, randomized controlled trial in patients with rapid-cycling or nonrapid-cycling bipolar depression, Shi et al (May 2003) found that OFC-treated patients (both rapid cyclers and nonrapid cyclers) experienced greater improvement in the multiple SF-36 domain scores and QLDS total score than olanzapine- or placebo-treated patients. According to this analysis, olanzapine monotherapy effectively improved QoL in nonrapid cyclers.

Whereas a host of studies examined QoL in patients with major depressive disorder, until recently comparatively few had specifically focused upon the relationship between perceived QoL and bipolar disorder. This may have occurred for several reasons. Bipolar disorder is one of the most complex psychiatric disorders as the condition is characterized by distinct episodes (manic, depressive, and mixed) and a varied course (ie, rapid cycling, ultra rapid cycling). There are difficulties inherent in developing a tool that works well for patients in both depressed and manic episodes and, as of yet, no measure has been designed to specifically assess QoL in bipolar disorder. In the absence of a disease-targeted measure, a variety of generic and health-related QoL measures have been used in the field, most commonly the MOS range of instruments, in particular the SF-36 (Ware et al, 1993) and the SF-20 (Stewart et al, 1988). The slow uptake of QoL research in bipolar disorder may have also occurred because of reservations about the ability of bipolar patients to reliably and accurately complete self-report measures of health status, particularly when in a manic phase.

5. Economic Consequences Associated With Bipolar Disorder

The literature on the economic burden of bipolar disorder documents its substantial costs. For example, research by Greenberg et al (1993) suggests the annual cost of bipolar disorder in 1990 in the United States was approximately $10 billion. One widely cited report estimates that in 1991, the total economic burden of bipolar disorder in the United States was $45 billion, of which only $7 billion was due to actual treatment costs (Wyatt and Henter, 1995). While these estimated costs may be substantial, bipolar disorder undoubtedly represents a significant economic burden. Research by Greenberg et al (1993) suggests the annual cost of bipolar disorder in 1990 in the USA was approximately $10 billion. Another study found that the lifetime costs for all US persons with the onset of bipolar disorder in 1998 was $24 billion (Begley et al, 2001). Bipolar disorder places a huge burden on society's resources in Europe as well (Lowin et al, 2002). De Zelicourt et al (2003) conducted a cost-of-illness study in France to assess the frequency of hospitalization and the inpatient care costs associated with manic episodes in patients with bipolar I disorder, based on data from a hospital payer perspective. The annual number of manic episodes among patients with bipolar I disorder was estimated to be around 265,000 in France. Based on data from hospitals in Paris, the proportion of manic episodes that required hospitalization was estimated to be around 63%. The average length of hospital stay was 32.4 days, and the hospitalization-related costs were estimated to be around 8.8 billion French francs (€1.3 billion [1999 values]).

At the patient level, a study using 1996 claims data found that the average annual treatment costs of patients with at least 1 hospitalization for mania was approximately US $17,000 (Stender et al, 2002). Another study of patients with 1987–1989 MEDSTAT claims for depression found that more severe depression was associated with greater per-episode inpatient treatment costs, with 1989 payments of US $1233 (depression NOS), US $2501 (major depression), and US $2971 (bipolar disorder) (Hu and Rush, 1995). A fairly recent 1-year study found that patients with a primary diagnosis of bipolar disorder used nearly 3 to 4 times the health care resources and incurred more than 4 times greater costs per patient compared with the randomly selected age- and sex-matched nonbipolar group during the 1-year period (1997: US $7663 versus US $1962), and that patients with bipolar depression (among the single bipolar diagnostic categories of mixed, manic, or depressed) incurred the highest health care costs (Bryant-Comstock et al, 2002).

Bipolar disorder affects patients in many aspects of their lives, leading to an increase in indirect costs of this disease. Moreover, bipolar disorder is associated with high rates of family discord (eg, divorce or adjustment problems among children of divorced parents), legal complications, and other problems (Lish et al, 1994). One study found that less than half of bipolar patients discharged from a psychiatric hospital were employed 6 months after the discharge (Dion et al, 1988). It is not surprising that among physical and psychiatric disorders, bipolar disorder is the sixth highest cause of disability (Murray and Lopez, 1996).

Few studies have quantitatively assessed the indirect costs of bipolar disorder. Some of such studies focused on work impairment, which was expressed as long-term unemployment, absenteeism due to emotional problems and somatic complaints, and poor work performance. Each of these factors was observed consistently more often among patients with bipolar than other patient populations, even when compared with people with other types of mental illness (ten Have et al, 2002; Tsai et al, 1997).

Haglund and colleagues (1998) found that patients with bipolar disorder had lower scores than patients with major depression and similar scores compared with patients with schizophrenia (as measured by most components of the Occupational Case Analysis Interview and Rating Scale). Although the groups of bipolar patients with either manic, melancholic, or mixed symptoms were small in the Haglund et al study, the means of each component score relating to occupational performance were similar for both patients with bipolar disorder and those with schizophrenia. Rosen et al (1983) found the presence of psychotic features in bipolar episodes did not negatively affect occupational functioning; however, patient age and duration of illness had a significant negative effect.

Dion et al (1988) prospectively studied patients with bipolar disorder for 6 months following hospitalization. Although almost 80% of patients were symptom free or only mildly symptomatic, only 43% of them were employed and only 21% were working at their expected level of employment. Some studies have shown that recovery of role performance and occupational function following treatment may deteriorate as the number and duration of episodes increase (Strakowski et al, 2000; Jiang, 1999). Close to 33% of patients were unable to work at any level of employment, and only 12% achieved their expected level of occupational function (Strakowski et al, 2000). Additionally, some data indicate that the symptomatic development of bipolar disorder among adolescents is associated with measurable impairment in school performance (Lewinsohn et al, 1995).

Unrecognized bipolar disorder (frequently misdiagnosed as unipolar depression) is also associated with certain economic consequences. One study using the paid claims data (1993–1999) from the California Medicaid program found that patients with unrecognized bipolar disorder have higher rates of hospital use and attempted suicide compared with patients with recognized bipolar disorder (McCombs et al, 2003). Birnbaum et al (2003) found that, of the 9009 patients treated for depression with antidepressants (1998 to mid-2001 data), 8383 (93.1%) were patients with nonbipolar depression; 293 (3.3%), recognized bipolar disorder; and 333 (3.7%), unrecognized bipolar disorder. Patients with unrecognized bipolar disorder incurred significantly more monthly medical costs (US $1179) in the 12 months following initiation of antidepressant treatment compared with patients with recognized (US $801) or no bipolar disorder (US $585). Monthly indirect costs were significantly greater for employees with unrecognized (US $570) and recognized bipolar disorder (US $514) compared with employees with nonbipolar depression (US $335) in the 12 months following antidepressant initiation.

6. Medication Treatment Effects on Economic Outcomes Among Patients With Bipolar Disorder

Inpatient care may represent 60% to 70% of direct costs of bipolar disorder (Wyatt and Henter, 1993; Simon and Unutzer, 1999). Strategies that address the need for rehospitalization of patients with bipolar disorder are paramount in terms of adequate use of health care resources. In this light, appropriate drug regimens for such patients are extremely important. The Li et al (2002) study on the cost of treating bipolar disorder in the California Medicaid program found that the use of mood stabilizers after hospitalization was inconsistent with treatment guidelines: Only 42.4% of the study participants received any mood stabilizer (lithium, valproate, carbamazepine, etc) during the first year, and only 5.5% used a mood stabilizer consistently for 1 year. The lack of medication use was associated with increased use of outpatient and inpatient services and subsequent higher direct health care costs. Birnbaum et al (2003) (based on managed-care claims) and McCombs et al (2003) (based on California Medicaid claims) reported similar rates of mood stabilizer (lithium and valproate) use in patients with a diagnosis of bipolar disorder.

Table 4 presents major studies of medication treatments on economic outcomes in bipolar disorder. Among the treatments studied for their impact on health care utilization and cost, Dardennes et al (1999) found that lithium had both clinical and economic advantages compared with carbamazepine in prophylactic treatment of recurrent mood disorders in France. In a before-and-after study of clozapine treatment, Banov et al (1994) showed that clozapine reduced the hospitalization rate among patients with bipolar mania but not necessarily among patients with bipolar depression. Namjoshi et al (2002) found that olanzapine-treated patients with bipolar mania experienced savings of almost $900 per month during the 49 weeks of the open-label period compared with costs incurred in the 12 months prior to the open-label treatment. These cost savings were largely driven by reductions in inpatient costs during the open-label extension. Namjoshi et al (May 2003) compared hospitalization rates among patients who received maintenance treatment of olanzapine or lithium during 52 weeks. Fourteen percent (n = 31) of the olanzapine patients were admitted to the hospital during the 12 months of treatment, whereas 23% (n = 49) of the lithium patients were hospitalized during the same period. Olanzapine patients had a total of 31 hospital admissions during the study with a mean of 0.14 admissions compared with a total of 51 hospital admissions with a mean of 0.24 admissions for lithium patients.

According to some studies, the use of anticonvulsants for treatment of bipolar disorder may reduce some health care costs. Tohen et al (1996) (Table 4) found that in first-episode patients with manic or mixed episodes, divalproex reduced the length of hospital stay compared with lithium, whereas Dalkilic et al (2000) (Table 4) found no statistically significant difference in length of hospital stay for patients on divalproex (11.5±6.9 days) and lithium (10.3±5.2 days). Frye et al (1996) (Table 4) found that patients treated with divalproex sodium and patients treated with lithium-carbamazepine combination had shorter length of hospital stay compared with patients treated with lithium or carbamazepine.

Two studies compared direct costs of olanzapine versus divalproex. Zhu et al (2002) focused on direct costs associated with olanzapine and divalproex in the treatment of acute mania (Table 4). Hospitalization was required for the first week of the double-blind treatment (total of 47 weeks), with subsequent hospital discharge if clinically appropriate. Inpatient and outpatient health care resource utilization data were collected at the end of the acute phase of the trial (3 weeks) and during the maintenance phase (weeks 7, 15, 23, 31, 39, and 47). Costs were analyzed for all patients who entered the maintenance phase (olanzapine, n = 77; divalproex, n = 70). Acute and maintenance phase costs were estimated by assigning prices (in year 2000 US dollars) from a standard list to units of applicable medical services. Olanzapine treatment was associated with significantly higher medication costs, but significantly lower outpatient and overall inpatient costs over the course of treatment. Outpatient costs were higher among divalproex-treated patients due to higher rate of emergency department and other outpatient visits. These findings suggest that during olanzapine treatment, differences in medication cost may be offset by lower costs for other clinical services. Further research is needed to determine the extent to which these findings can be generalized to practice settings outside the clinical trial context.

In addition, Revicki et al (2003) (Table 4) compared economic outcomes of divalproex sodium and olanzapine in the treatment of acute mania associated with bipolar disorder. These researchers collected data on medical resource use and costs from a 12-week, double-blind, double-dummy, randomized clinical trial, which included 120 subjects with DSM-IV bipolar disorder, type I, hospitalized for an acute manic episode. The subjects were recruited from 21 US clinical centers. No significant differences in total medical costs were found between the 2 treatment groups (divalproex, US $13,703; olanzapine, US $15,180), despite the fact that divalproex was associated with lower outpatient costs during the 12 weeks compared with olanzapine.

In the Solomon et al (1996) study, patients who attained standard lithium serum levels achieved better work performance compared with patients who had low lithium serum levels, suggesting that undertreatment can have a significantly negative effect on work productivity. A study that compared bipolar patients treated with lithium monotherapy with those treated with lithium in combination with other medications show better work functioning in the former group, potentially indicating that the patients treated with lithium monotherapy may differ clinically from those requiring multiple psychotropic medications (Goldberg et al, 1996).

Table 4. Effects of Medication Treatments on the Economics (Direct Health Care Utilization or Cost) of Bipolar Disorder

Author	Population(s)	Study Design	Main Findings
Banov et al (1994)	Bipolar disorder 28, manic 9, depressed 15, mixed	Hospital chart review; before vs after clozapine treatment	Clozapine was effective in reducing the hospitalization rate among patients with bipolar mania but not necessarily among patients with bipolar depression.
Dardennes et al (1999)	Index-episode patients treated with lithium or carbamazepine	Pharmacoeconomic model	Lithium led to an economic benefit of 4280 French francs per year of treatment for a single patient compared with carbamazepine. Inpatient costs were the most important part of annual medical costs for mood disorders (70% of the total costs). Prophylactic medication costs accounted for only 6.9% of total costs.
Dalkilic et al (2000)	All inpatients with bipolar disorder at the Connecticut Mental Health Center in 1997	Retrospective medical records	No statistically significant difference was found in length of hospital stay for patients on divalproex and lithium.
Frye et al (1996)	Antimanic treatment groups 52, lithium 15, carbamazepine 5, divalproex sodium 6, lithium + carbamazepine	Retrospective chart review	Shorter length of hospital stay was observed for patients treated with divalproex sodium and lithium + carbamazepine combination groups, as compared with the lithium or carbamazepine monotherapy groups.
Namjoshi et al (2001)	Acutely manic, type I 76, olanzapine	Open-label period (49 weeks); before vs after olanzapine treatment	Olanzapine-treated patients experienced cost savings during the 49 weeks of olanzapine therapy compared with costs incurred in the previous 12 months of therapy. These cost savings were largely driven by reductions in inpatient costs during the open-label extension.
Namjoshi et al (May 2003)	Maintenance therapy (431 patients randomized to olanzapine and lithium)	Randomized clinical trial (52 weeks); olanzapine vs lithium	Olanzapine-treated patients had fewer hospitalizations.
Revicki et al (2003)	Acutely manic, type I 63, divalproex 57, olanzapine	Randomized clinical trial (12 weeks); divalproex vs olanzapine	No significant difference in total medical costs were observed between the 2 groups despite the fact that divalproex was associated with lower 12-week outpatient costs compared with olanzapine.
Tohen et al (1996)	First-episode patients with manic or mixed symptoms	Prospective observational study	Length of hospital stay was shorter among divalproex-treated patients compared with those treated with lithium.
Zhu et al (2002)	Acutely manic, type I acute + maintenance therapy 77, olanzapine 70, divalproex	Randomized clinical trial (47 weeks); olanzapine vs divalproex	No significant difference in total medical costs was observed between the 2 groups. Olanzapine treatment was associated with significantly higher medication costs, but significantly lower outpatient and overall inpatient costs over the course of treatment.

Shi et al (2002) found that at the end of week 12, patients with acute mania treated with olanzapine showed significantly greater improvement than haloperidol-treated patients in the work activities impairment scores and household activities impairment scores (as measured by the Streamlined Longitudinal Interview Clinical Evaluation from the Longitudinal Interval Follow-up Evaluation; Keller et al, 1987). Further subgroup analyses revealed that olanzapine treatment significantly increased a proportion of employed patients and their weekly paid working hours. Shi et al (October 2002) found that OFC was associated with improved work functioning in patients with bipolar depression compared with placebo.

Discussion and Summary

According to our review, patients with bipolar disorder consistently had lower QoL and functionality scores than comparator populations regardless of the instrument used to assess patients' QoL or the stage of bipolar disorder. These results indicate that the reduced HRQoL and impairment of functionality among patients with bipolar disorder may be perniciously affected even in the absence of active symptoms.

The studies with regard to the measurement of QoL in patients with bipolar disorder were quite heterogeneous in nature. Firstly, the psychometric properties of a variety of generic and health-related QoL instruments among populations with bipolar disorder have been evaluated in very few studies. Generic instruments such as SF-36 or QOLI hold good psychometric properties in assessment of both patients with bipolar disorder and other patient populations. Although generic QoL instruments have been successfully administered in bipolar populations (Arnold et al, 2000; Shi et al, 2002; Namjoshi et al, 2002; Namjoshi et al, in press; Shi et al, 2004), and were as responsive as a disease-specific QoL measure to changes in clinical status (Leidy et al, 1998; Shi et al, 2004), there is a concern about generic instruments not adequately reflecting the key concerns of patients with bipolar disorder.

Whereas some of the reviewed QoL instruments are disease-specific in the sense that they have been developed in and for populations with depression (ie, the Q-LES-Q and QLDS), there is at present no QoL measure specifically designed for use in populations with bipolar mania. One of the most rigorous studies to date was performed by Russo et al (1997), in which nurses administered the QOLI via a structured interview procedure to 103 patients with acute mania. Bipolar disorder presents a unique challenge to researchers because the condition can be characterized by distinctly alternating mood states (mania, depression, and mixed). This disorder is further complicated by the fact that mania can also be associated with depressive symptoms, and that patients with euthymia may experience residual symptoms. Although previous research (Altman, 1998) indicated that patients with mild-to-moderate manic symptoms could provide reliable descriptions of their symptoms, more research is needed to ascertain how feasible it is to administer self-report QoL instruments in populations with mania.

Furthermore, an important and aggressive step forward in this field of research would be the development of a bipolar disorder–specific QoL instrument. It would be useful if such instrument were available in self-report, interviewer-administered, and proxy-respondent formats to provide alternative methods of administration in bipolar populations. Finally, the psychometric properties of this disease-specific instrument would need to be carefully evaluated in terms of reliability, validity, and other standard psychometric assessments.

Secondly, the studies were also heterogeneous in terms of the QoL instruments they used. By far the most frequently used were the SF-12, SF-20, or the SF-36, all of which originated from the MOS studies. A number of other QoL instruments were used in the reviewed studies, including the Illness Intrusiveness Rating Scale (IIRS) (Robb et al, 1997), the Q-LES-Q (Ozer et al, 2002; Revicki et al, 2003; Ritsner et al, 2002), the QOLI (Namjoshi et al, in press; Russo et al, 1997), as well as the TTO and SG approaches (Tsevat et al, 2000; Wells et al, 1999). Additionally, we reviewed a number of cross-sectional studies that used generic instruments to compare patients' QoL during different stages of bipolar disorder (Tsevat et al, 2000; Vojta 2001; Wells et al, 1999). Other reviewed studies (Arnold, 2000; Salyers et al, 2000; ten Have et al, 2002; Leidy et al, 1998; Wells et al, 1999) compared QoL among patients with bipolar disorder with that of other patient populations, both with other psychiatric disorders and with chronic physical conditions. Therefore, it remains difficult to make any generalizations on the basis of existing data owing to differences in the type of instrument used and sample sizes. Additional research is needed to determine the longitudinal course of QoL in patients with bipolar disorder because the majority of the studies we identified were cross-sectional in nature.

Of the reviewed studies that assessed the effects of treatment on either GAF or other QoL measures, most of existing pharmacological interventions have been evaluated with mixed results in different research settings. Additionally, these results of outcome measures were impacted by such factors as the type of diagnosis (eg, rapid cycling).

Although current American Psychiatric Association recommendations favor the use of lithium and mood stabilizers in the initial treatment and symptom management of bipolar disorder, there is an increasing recognition of the role of psychotherapy in the management of the disorder. QoL measures are commonly used to assess outcome following psychotherapeutic interventions for bipolar disorder. For example, Patelis-Siotis et al (2001) found that the SF-36 vitality and role-emotional scores were significantly improved following group cognitive behavior therapy in patients with bipolar disorder.

Bipolar disorder is a chronic illness associated with enormous health care costs, both for the individual and for society, and more information is still needed about health care use and work impairment among patients with bipolar disorder. However, the literature on direct and indirect costs of this disorder is quite sparse. Furthermore, the literature that evaluates the medication treatment effects on costs of the disorder and patients' work productivity is even more limited. According to the Haglund et al (1998) study, work productivity among patients with bipolar disorder was worse than that among patients with depression and similar to that among patients with schizophrenia. High rates of unemployment, absenteeism from or failure to return to work following an acute episode, and work impairment frequently occur among patients with bipolar disorder. Measures of unemployment, absenteeism from work, and work impairment appear to deteriorate with increased numbers of bipolar episodes that occur during a patient's lifetime. Some studies have shown that bipolar patients had high occupational impairment with low role performance recovery following recovery from a bipolar episode. Regier et al (1993) and Narrow et al (1993) indicated that a little more than half of patients with bipolar disorder receive some medication treatment and approximately one-third are seen by a mental health professional each year. Even so, with high rates of inpatient services use, the costs of care in bipolar disorder can be enormous. However, once a diagnosis of bipolar disorder is established, appropriate medication treatments can effectively reduce direct costs associated with this condition because inpatient treatment may account for up to 70% of direct costs of bipolar disorder (Dardennes et al, 1999). In addition, medications such as lithium, divalproex, and olanzapine have been shown to reduce rehospitalization rates, length of hospital stay, and other factors impacting direct costs. Limited research has shown that medication treatments may have beneficial effects on occupational functioning of patients with bipolar disorder as well. Additional research is needed to establish the effects of medication treatments on the QoL and functioning of patients with bipolar disorder, as well as the effect of such treatments on direct and indirect costs of this disease.

Conclusion

It is noteworthy that a growing interest exists in characterizing QoL in populations with bipolar disorder. A number of bipolar studies with large sample sizes, particularly some of the large clinical trials of treatment interventions for bipolar disorder, used QoL instruments to assess clinical and economic outcomes. QoL impairment appears to be greater among patients with bipolar disorder than the general population, and especially those with other chronic nonmental health–related disorders. These decrements are evident in bipolar patients even when they are symptom free and euthymic. Several researchers have found a higher incidence of depressive, rather than manic, symptoms to have the greatest negative impact on patients' QoL. We have highlighted several important avenues for future research of QoL in bipolar disorder, including more assessments of QoL in patients with acute mania, the development of a bipolar disorder–specific measure of QoL, and more longitudinal research of treatment effects on costs of bipolar disorder.

References

Altman E. Rating scales for mania: is self-rating reliable? *J Affect Disord.* 1998;50:283-286.

American Psychiatric Association. *Diagnostic and Statistical Manual of Mental Disorders, Fourth Edition.* Washington, DC: American Psychiatric Association; 1994.

Arnold LM, Witzeman KA, Swank ML, McElroy SL, Keck PE. Health-related quality of life using the SF-36 in patients with bipolar disorder compared with patients with chronic back pain and the general population. *J Affect Disord.* 2000;57:235-239.

Atkinson M, Zibin S, Chuang H. Characterizing quality of life among patients with chronic mental illness: a critical examination of the self-report methodology *Am J Psychiatry.* 1997;154:99-105.

Banov MD, Zarate CA Jr, Tohen M, et al. Clozapine therapy in refractory affective disorders: polarity predicts response in long-term follow-up. *J Clin Psychiatry.* 1994;55:295-300.

Begley CE, Annegers JF, Swann AC, et al. The lifetime cost of bipolar disorder in the US: an estimate of new cases in 1998. *Pharmacoeconomics.* 2001;19(5Pt1):483-495.

Bellack AS, Morrison RL, Mueser KT, Wade J. Social competence in schizoaffective disorder, bipolar disorder, and negative and non-negative schizophrenia. *Schizophr Res.* 1989;2:391-401.

Birnbaum HG, Shi L, Dial E, Oster E, Greenberg PE, Mallet D. Economic consequences of not recognizing bipolar disorder patients. *J Clin Psychiatry.* 2003;64:1201-1209.

Bowden CL, Calabrese JR, McElroy SL, Gyulai L, Wassef A, Petty F. A randomized, placebo-controlled 12-month trial of divalproex and lithium in treatment of outpatients with bipolar I disorder. Divalproex Maintenance Study Group. *Arch Gen Psychiatry.* 2000;57:481-489.

Bowden CL, Calabrese JR, McElroy SL, Rhodes LJ, Keck PE Jr, Cookson J. The efficacy of lamotrigine in rapid cycling and non-rapid cycling patients with bipolar disorder. *Biol Psychiatry.* 1999;45:953-958.

Bryant-Comstock L, Stender M, Devercelli G. Health care utilization and costs among privately insured patients with bipolar I disorder. *Bipolar Disord.* 2002;4:398-405.

Calabrese JR, Suppes T, Bowden CL, Sachs GS, Swann AC, McElroy SL. A double-blind, placebo-controlled, prophylaxis study of lamotrigine in rapid-cycling bipolar disorder. Lamictal 614 Study Group. *J Clin Psychiatry.* 2000;61:841-850.

Clark HM, Berk M, Brook S. A randomized controlled single blind study of the efficacy of clonazepam and lithium in the treatment of acute mania. *Hum Psychopharmacol* 1997;12:325-328.

Cooke RG, Robb JC, Young LT, Joffe RT. Well-being and functioning in patients with bipolar disorder assessed using the MOS 20-item Short Form (SF-20). *J Affect Disord.* 1996;39:93-97.

Dalkilic A, Diaz E, Baker CB, Pearsall HR, Woods SW. Effects of divalproex versus lithium on length of hospital stay among patients with bipolar disorder. *Psychiatr Serv.* 2000;51:1184-1186.

Dardennes R, Lafuma A, Watkins S. [Prophylactic treatment of mood disorders: cost effectiveness analysis comparing lithium and carbamazepine]. [French] *Encephale.* 1999;25:391-400.

Devins GM, Edworthy SM, Seland TP, Klein GM, Paul LC, Mandin H. Differences in illness intrusiveness across rheumatoid arthritis, end-stage renal disease, and multiple sclerosis. *J Nerv Ment Dis.* 1993;181:377-381.

de Zelicourt M, Dardennes R, Verdoux H, et al. Frequency of hospitalisations and inpatient care costs of manic episodes: in patients with bipolar I disorder in France. *Pharmacoeconomics.* 2003;21:1081-1090.

Dickerson FB, Sommerville J, Origoni AE, Ringel NB, Parente F. Outpatients with schizophrenia and bipolar I disorder: do they differ in their cognitive and social functioning? *Psychiatry Res.* 2001;102:21-27.

Dion GL, Tohen M, Anthony WA, Waternaux CS. Symptoms and functioning of patients with polar disorder six months after hospitalization. *Hosp Community Psychiatry.* 1988;39:652-657.

Endicott J, Nee J, Harrison W, Blumenthal R. Quality of Life Enjoyment and Satisfaction Questionnaire: a new measure. *Psychopharmacol Bull.* 1993;29:321-326.

Fatemi SH, Rapport DJ, Calabrese JR, Thuras P. Lamotrigine in rapid-cycling bipolar disorder. *J Clin Psychiatry.* 1997;58:522-527.

Flanagan JC. A research approach to improving our quality of life. *American Psychology.* 1978;33:138-147.

Frisch MB, Cornell J, Villanueva M, Retzlaff PJ. Clinical validation of the Quality of Life Inventory. A measure of life satisfaction for use in treatment planning and outcome assessment. *Psychol Assess.* 1992;4:92-101.

Frye MA, Altshuler LL, Szuba MP, Finch NN, Mintz J. The relationship between antimanic agent for treatment of classic or dysphoric mania and length of hospital stay. *J Clin Psychiatry.* 1996;57:17-21.

Garratt A, Schmidt L, Mackintosh A, Fitzpatrick R. Quality of life measurement: bibliographic study of patient assessed health outcome measures. *BMJ.* 2002;324:1417.

Ghaemi SN, Goodwin FK. Gabapentin treatment of the non-refractory bipolar spectrum: an open case series. *J Affect Disord.* 2001;65:167-171.

Ghaemi SN, Sachs GS, Baldassano CF, Truman CJ. Acute treatment of bipolar disorder with adjunctive risperidone in outpatients. *Can J Psychiatry.* 1997;42:196-199.

Goldberg JF, Harrow M, Leon AC. Lithium treatment of bipolar affective disorders under naturalistic followup conditions. *Psychopharmacol Bull.* 1996;32:47-54.

Goodwin F, Jamison K. *Manic Depressive Illness.* New York: Oxford University Press; 1990.

Greenberg PE, Stiglin LE, Finkelstein SN, Berndt ER. The economic burden of depression in 1990. *J Clin Psychiatry.* 1993;54:405-418.

Grossman LS, Harrow M, Goldberg JF, Fichtner CG. Outcome of schizoaffective disorder at two long-term follow-ups: comparisons with outcome of schizophrenia and affective disorders. *Am J Psychiatry.* 1991;148:1359-1365.

Haglund L, Thorell LH, Walinder J. Occupational functioning in relation to psychiatric diagnoses: schizophrenia and mood disorders. *Nord J Psychiatry.* 1998;52:223-229.

Harrow M, Goldberg JF, Grossman LS, Meltzer HY. Outcome in manic disorders: a naturalistic follow-up study. *Arch Gen Psychiatry.* 1990;47:665-671.

Hayes SG. Long-term use of valproate in primary psychiatric disorders. *J Clin Psychiatry.* 1989;50(suppl):35-39.

Hirschfeld RM. A test for bipolar disorder: the mood disorder questionnaire. *The Economics of Neuroscience.* 2001;3:45-48.

Hu TW, Rush AJ. Depressive disorders: treatment patterns and costs of treatment in the private sector of the United States. *Soc Psychiatry Psychiatr Epidemiol.* 1995;30:224-230.

Hunt SM, McKenna SP. The QLDS: a scale for the measurement of quality of life in depression. *Health Policy.* 1992;22:307-319.

Ichim L, Berk M, Brook S. Lamotrigine compared with lithium in mania: a double-blind randomized controlled trial. *Ann Clin Psychiatry.* 2000;12:5-10.

Jiang HK. A prospective one-year follow-up study of patients with bipolar affective disorder. *Zhonghua Yi Xue Za Zhi* (Taipei). 1999;62:477-486.

Keller MB, Lavori PW, Friedman B, et al. The Longitudinal Interval Follow-up Evaluation. A comprehensive method for assessing outcome in prospective longitudinal studies. *Arch Gen Psychiatry.* 1987;44:540-548.

Kessler RC, McGonagle KA, Zhao S, et al. Lifetime and 12-month prevalence of DSM-III-R psychiatric disorders in the United States. *Arch Gen Psychiatry* 1994;51:8-19.

Kusznir A, Cooke RG, Young LT. The correlates of community functioning in patients with bipolar disorder. *J Affect Disord.* 2000;61:81-85.

Kusznir A, Scott E, Cooke RG, Young LT. Functional consequences of bipolar affective disorder: an occupational therapy perspective. *Can J Occup Ther.* 1996;63:313-322.

Lehman AF. A Quality of Life Interview for the chronically mentally ill. *Evaluation and Program Planning.* 1988;11:51-62.

Leidy NK, Palmer C, Murray M, Robb J, Revicki DA. Health-related quality of life assessment in euthymic and depressed patients with bipolar disorder. Psychometric performance of four self-report measures. *J Affect Disord.* 1998;48:207-214.

Lepkifker E, Horesh N, Floru S. Life satisfaction and adjustment in lithium-treated affective patients in remission. *Acta Psychiatr Scand.* 1988;78:391-395.

Levenstein S, Klein DF, Pollack M. Follow-up study of formerly hospitalized voluntary psychiatric patients: the first two years. *Am J Psychiatry.* 1966;122:1102-1109.

Lewinsohn PM, Klein DN, Seeley JR. Bipolar disorders in a community sample of older adolescents: prevalence, phenomenology, comorbidity, and course. *J Am Acad Child Adolesc Psychiatry.* 1995;34:454-463.

Li J, McCombs JS, Stimmel GL. Cost of treating bipolar disorder in the California Medicaid (Medi-Cal) program. *J Affect Disord.* 2002;71:131-139.

Lish JD, Dime-Meenan S, Whybrow PC, Price RA, Hirschfeld RM. The National Depressive and Manic-Depressive Association (DMDA) survey of bipolar members. *J Affect Disord.* 1994;31:281-294.

Lowin A, Knapp M, Grant D, Gandhi G, Edgell ET. Economic aspects of bipolar disorder in Europe. *European Psychiatry.* 2002;17(suppl 1):151.

MacQueen GM, Young LT, Robb JC, Cooke RG, Joffe RT. Levels of functioning and well-being in recovered psychotic versus nonpsychotic mania. *J Affect Disord.* 1997;46:69-72.

MacQueen GM, Young, LT, Robb JC, Marriott M, Cooke RG, Joffe RT. Effect of number of episodes on well-being and functioning of patients with bipolar disorder. *Acta Psychiatr Scand.* 2000;101:374-381.

McCombs JS, Thiebaud P, Shi L. Impact of unrecognized bipolar disorders in patients treated with antidepressant medications. *Value in Health.* 2003;6:352.

McHorney CA, Kosinski M, Ware JE Jr. Comparisons of the costs and quality of norms for the SF-36 health survey collected by mail versus telephone interview: results from a national survey. *Med Care.* 1994;32:551-567.

McKenna SP, Doward LC, Kohlmann T, et al. International development of the Quality of Life in Depression Scale (QLDS). *J Affect Disord.* 2001;63:189-199.

Miller IW, Keitner GI, Schatzberg AF, et al. The treatment of chronic depression, part 3: psychosocial functioning before and after treatment with sertraline or imipramine. *J Clin Psychiatry.* 1998;59:608-619.

Muller-Oerlinghausen B, Retzow A, Henn FA, Giedke H, Walden J. Valproate as an adjunct to neuroleptic medication for the treatment of acute episodes of mania: a prospective, randomized, double-blind, placebo-controlled, multicenter study. European Valproate Mania Study Group. *J Clin Psychopharmacol.* 2000;20:195-203.

Murray CJL, Lopez AD. *The Global Burden of Disease.* World Health Organization, Cambridge, Mass: Harvard University Press; 1996.

Namjoshi MA, Buesching DP. A review of the health-related quality of life literature in bipolar disorder. *Qual Life Res.* 2001;10:105-115.

Namjoshi M, Jacobs T, Shi L, Tohen M. Hospitalization rates associated with olanzapine and lithium in patients with bipolar disorder: results from an international randomized controlled trial [abstract]. In: New Research Abstracts of the156th American Psychiatric Association Annual Meeting; May 2003; San Francisco, Calif. Abstract NR206.

Namjoshi MA, Rajamannar G, Jacobs T, et al. Economic, clinical, and quality-of-life outcomes associated with olanzapine treatment in mania. Results from a randomized controlled trial. *J Affect Disord.* 2002;69:109-118.

Namjoshi MA, Risser R, Shi L, Tohen M, Breier A. Quality of life assessment in patients with bipolar disorder treated with olanzapine added to lithium or valproic acid. *J Affect Disord.* In press.

Narrow WE, Regier DA, Rae DS, Manderscheid RW, Locke BZ. Use of services by persons with mental and addictive disorders. Findings from the National Institute of Mental Health Epidemiologic Catchment Area Program. *Arch Gen Psychiatry.* 1993;50:95-107.

O'Connell RA, Mayo JA, Flatow L, Cuthbertson B, O'Brien BE. Outcome of bipolar disorder on long-term treatment with lithium. *Br J Psychiatry.* 1991;159:123-129.

Oliver JPJ, Huxley J, Priebe S, Kaiser W. Measuring the quality of life of severely mentally ill people using the Lancashire Quality of Life Profile. *Soc Psychiatry Psychiatr Epidemiol.* 1997;32:76-83.

Ozer S, Ulusahin A, Batur S, Kabakci E, Saka MC. Outcome measures of interepisode bipolar patients in a Turkish sample. *Soc Psychiatry Psychiatr Epidemiol.* 2002;37:31-37.

Patelis-Siotis I, Young, LT, Robb JC, et al. Group cognitive behavioral therapy for bipolar disorder: a feasibility and effectiveness study. *J Affect Disord.* 2001;65:145-153.

Regier DA, Narrow WE, Rae DS, Manderscheid RW, Locke BZ, Goodwin FK. The de facto US mental and addictive disorders service system. Epidemiologic catchment area prospective 1-year prevalence rates of disorders and services. *Arch Gen Psychiatry.* 1993;50:85-94.

Revicki DA, Paramore LC, Sommerville KW. Swann AC, Zajecka JM. Depakote Comparator Study Group. Divalproex sodium versus olanzapine in the treatment of acute mania in bipolar disorder: health-related quality of life and medical cost outcomes. *J Clin Psychiatry.* 2003;64:288-294.

Revicki DA, Tohen M, Gyulai L, et al. Telephone versus in-person clinical and health status assessment interviews in patients with bipolar disorder. *Harvard Rev Psychiatry.* 1997;5:75-81.

Ritsner M, Kurs R, Kostizky H, Ponizovsky A, Modai I. Subjective quality of life in severely mentally ill patients: a comparison of two instruments. *Qual Life Res.* 2002;11:553-561.

Robb JC, Cooke RG, Devins GM, Young LT, Joffe RT. Quality of life and lifestyle disruption in euthymic bipolar disorder. *J Psychiatr Res.* 1997;31:509-517.

Robb JC, Young LT, Cooke RG, Joffe RT. Gender differences in patients with bipolar disorder influence outcome in the Medical Outcomes Survey (SF-20) subscale scores. *J Affect Disord.* 1998;49:189-193.

Rosen LN, Rosenthal NE, Dunner DL, Fieve RR. Social outcome compared in psychotic and nonpsychotic bipolar I patients. *J Nerv Ment Dis.* 1983;171:272-275.

Russo J, Roy-Byrne P, Reeder D, et al. Longitudinal assessment of quality of life in acute psychiatric inpatients: reliability and validity. *J Nerv Ment Dis.* 1997;185:166-175.

Salyers MP, Bosworth HB, Swanson JW, Lamb-Pagone J, Osher FC. Reliability and validity of the SF-12 health survey among people with severe mental illness. *Med Care.* 2000;38:1141-1150.

Sanderson DR. Use of mood stabilizers by hospitalized geriatric patients with bipolar disorder. *Psychiatr Serv.* 1998;49:1145-1147.

Segal J, Berk M, Brook S. Risperidone compared with both lithium and haloperidol in mania: a double-blind randomized controlled trial. *Clin Neuropharmacol.* 1998;21:176-180.

Shi L, Namjoshi M, Swindle R, et al. Effects of olanzapine alone and olanzapine/fluoxetine combination (OFC) on health-related quality of life in patients with bipolar depression: secondary analysis of a double-blind, placebo-controlled trial. *Clin Ther.* 2004;26:125-134.

Shi L, Namjoshi MA, Yu X, et al. Effects of olanzapine monotherapy and olanzapine in combination with fluoxetine on work functioning in patients with bipolar depression [abstract]. Poster presented at the 54th Meeting of the Institute for Psychiatric Services; October 2002; Chicago. Ill.

Shi L, Namjoshi MA, Zhang F, et al. Olanzapine versus haloperidol in the treatment of acute mania: clinical outcomes, health-related quality of life and work status. *Int Clin. Psychopharmacol.* 2002;17:227-237.

Shi L, Vallarino C, Namjoshi M, Tohen MF. Olanzapine/fluoxetine combination and quality of life in rapid-cycling bipolar depression [abstract]. In: New Research Abstracts of the156th American Psychiatric Association Annual Meeting; May 2003; San Francisco, Calif. Abstract NR235.

Shi L, Vallarino C, Prabhakar V, Juarez R, Namjoshi M, Tohen M. Olanzapine/fluoxetine combination improves long-term HRQoL in patients with bipolar depression [abstract]. Poster presented at the 16th European College of Neuropsychopharmacology Annual Meeting, September 2003; Prague, Czech Republic.

Shi L, Zhu B, Namjoshi M, et al. Improvement in health-related quality of life was associated with antidepressive property: evidence from an acute mania clinical trial of olanzapine versus divalproex [abstract]. Poster presented at the 155th American Psychiatric Association Annual Meeting; May 2002; Philadelphia, Pa. Abstract NR302.

Simon GE, Unutzer J. Health care utilization and costs among patients treated for bipolar disorder in an insured population. *Psychiatr Serv.* 1999;50:1303-1308.

Small JG, Klapper MH, Marhenke JD, Milstein V, Woodham GC, Kellams JJ. Lithium combined with carbamazepine or haloperidol in the treatment of mania. *Psychopharmacol Bull.* 1995;31:265-272.

Solomon DA, Ristow WR, Keller MB, et al. Serum lithium levels and psychosocial function in patients with bipolar I disorder. *Am J Psychiatry.* 1996;153:1301-1307.

Stender M, Bryant-Comstock L, Phillips S. Medical resource use among patients treated for bipolar disorder: a retrospective, cross-sectional, descriptive analysis. *Clin Ther.* 2002;24:1668-1676.

Stewart AL, Hays RD, Ware JE Jr. The MOS Short-Form General Health Survey. Reliability and validity in a patient population. *Med.Care.* 1988;26:724-735.

Stewart AL, Ware JE, Sherbourne CD, Wells K. Psychological distress/well-being and cognitive function measures. In: Stewart AL, Ware JE (eds). *Measuring Functioning and Well-being: The Medical Outcomes Study Approach.* Duke University Press; Durham, NC; 1992.

Strakowski SM, Williams JR, Fleck DE, DelBello MP. Eight-month functional outcome from mania following a first psychiatric hospitalization. *J Psychiatr Res.* 2000;34:193-200.

Suppes T, Dennehy EB, Swann AC, et al. Report of the Texas Consensus Conference Panel on medication treatment of bipolar disorder 2000. *J Clin Psychiatry.* 2002;63:288-299.

ten Have M, Vollebergh W, Bijl R, Nolen WA. Bipolar disorder in the general population in The Netherlands (prevalence, consequences and care utilisation): results from The Netherlands Mental Health Survey and Incidence Study (NEMESIS). *J Affect Disord.* 2002;68:203-213.

Thunedborg K, Black CH, Bech P. Beyond the Hamilton depression scores in long-term treatment of manic-melancholic patients: prediction of recurrence of depression by quality of life measurements. *Psychother Psychosom.* 1995;64:131-140.

Tohen M, Hennen J, Zarate CM Jr, et al. Two-year syndromal and functional recovery in 219 cases of first-episode major affective disorder with psychotic features. *Am J Psychiatry.* 2000;157:220-228.

Tohen M, Zarate CAJ, Zarate SB, Gebre-Medhin P, Pike S. The McLean/Harvard first-episode mania project: Pharmacologic treatment and outcome. *Psychiatr Ann.* 1996;26:S444-S448.

Torrance GW. Measurement of health state utilities for economic appraisal. *J Health Econ.* 1986;5:1-30.

Tsai SY, Chen CC, Yeh EK. Alcohol problems and long-term psychosocial outcome in Chinese patients with bipolar disorder. *J Affect Disord.* 1997;46:143-150.

Tsevat J, Keck PE, Hornung RW, McElroy SL. Health values of patients with bipolar disorder. *Qual Life Res.* 2000;9:579-586.

Van Putten T, May PR. Subjective response as a predictor of outcome in pharmacotherapy: the consumer has a point. *Arch Gen Psychiatry.* 1978;35:477-480.

Vojta C, Kinosian B, Glick H, Altshuler L, Bauer MS. Self-reported quality of life across mood states in bipolar disorder. *Compr Psychiatry* 2001;42:190-195.

Ware JE, Kosinski M. *The SF-36 Physical and Mental Health Summary Scales: A Manual for Users of Version 1.* 2nd edition. QualityMetric Inc; Lincoln, RI; 2001.

Ware J Jr, Kosinski M, Keller SD. A 12-Item Short-Form Health Survey: construction of scales and preliminary tests of reliability and validity. *Med Care.* 1996;34:220-233.

Ware JE, Snow KK, Kosinski, M, Gandek B. *SF-36 Health Survey: Manual and interpretation guide.* Boston, Mass; The Health Institute; 1993.

Wells KB, Sherbourne CD. Functioning and utility for current health of patients with depression or chronic medical conditions in managed, primary care practices. *Arch Gen Psychiatry.* 1999;56:897-904.

Wells KB, Stewart A, Hays RD, et al. The functioning and well-being of depressed patients. Results from the Medical Outcomes Study. *JAMA.* 1989;262:914-919.

Wyatt RJ, Henter I. An economic evaluation of manic-depressive illness-1991. *Soc Psychiatry Psychiatr Epidemiol.* 1995;30:213-219.

Zhu B, Baker RW, Altshuler L, et al. Economic outcomes associated with olanzapine versus divalproex treatment for acute mania: results from a randomized clinical trial. Poster presented at the 7th Meeting of the International Society for Pharmacoeconomics and Outcomes Research; May April 2002; Arlington, Va.

ACKNOWLEDGEMENTS

The authors gratefully acknowledge the editing assistance of Svetlana Dominguez.

INDEX

#

5-HIAA, 70
5-HT, 65, 69-72, 74, 79
5-HT_2 receptor, 69, 75

A

abnormalities, 1, 70, 79
acute-phase proteins, 101, 103, 104, 106, 107, 110, 112
affect, 3, 87, 119, 120, 142, 146, 161, 162, 175, 176, 181
affective disorders, 20, 21, 24, 25, 27, 29, 30, 65, 67, 73, 75-78, 81, 141, 145, 146, 155, 156, 163, 176, 178, 187, 189
affective symptoms, 3, 163
aggression, 6
animism, 43
antipsychotics, 85, 93, 102, 127, 135, 177, 179
anxiety, 5, 7, 8, 10, 19, 22-24, 35, 52, 58, 66, 94, 124, 125, 129, 154, 159
appetite, 3, 5, 7, 123, 124, 126
α_1-acid glycoprotein (AGP), 103

B

behavior therapy, 53, 168, 169, 186
binding protein, 97
bipolar I disorder, 86, 99, 108, 127, 161, 173-177, 180, 188, 192
bipolar II disorder, 25, 26, 31, 61, 128, 161, 174, 175
body mass index, 84, 99, 100, 125, 134, 135
brain imaging, 70

C

carbamazepine, 85, 117, 118, 120, 123, 125, 127, 138, 178, 182-184, 188, 192
carbohydrate metabolism, 81, 113
chlorpromazine, 85
chromosome regions, 1
circadian rhythms, 1
clozapine, 84-86, 88-90, 126, 170, 179, 182, 184
cognitive disinhibition, 146
cognitive-behavior (CBT), 37, 51-56, 165, 168, 169
cognitive-behavior interventions, 34, 45
comorbidity, 13, 15, 17, 23, 81, 84, 89, 93, 146, 190
corticotrophin-releasing factor, 71
C-reactive protein, 103, 104, 108, 112, 114, 115
CSF analysis, 70
cycling moods, 33
cytokines, 97, 98, 105-107, 111-113, 116

D

delusion, 3, 4, 8, 11, 18, 24, 44, 52, 99, 161
delusional disorder, 4, 21, 23
dementia, 82, 84, 86, 89, 94, 121, 123
depression, vii, 2-6, 8-12, 16-31, 34, 35, 42, 47, 50, 51, 55, 58, 60, 61, 64-67, 69-72, 76-79, 82, 83, 91-93, 95-101, 103, 106, 108, 112, 114-118, 121, 125, 128, 130, 135, 136, 139-143, 148, 150, 154, 156, 158-161, 163, 165-168, 170, 172, 173, 175, 177-182, 184-186, 189, 190, 192, 193
desensitization, 53
diabetes mellitus, 81-85, 90, 92, 94-96, 130, 134, 135
disorganization, 3, 11, 18, 19, 24, 141, 142
divalproex sodium, 171, 178, 183, 184
dopaminergic systems, 1
driven thoughts, 33
drug dependency, 34
drug interactions, 117, 136, 137
DSM, 6, 30, 68, 75, 86, 100
dysphoric mania, 118, 135, 175, 189

dysphoric mood, 161
dysthymia, 7, 8, 23, 24, 168, 177

E

eating disorders, 34, 50, 125
eidetic imagery, 146
emergent networks, 33, 34, 36, 37, 43, 47, 48, 51, 52, 53, 54
energy level, 35, 44, 49, 53
energy metabolism, 81, 92, 94
environmental stressors, 15
excitement, 3, 6, 11, 18
extended family, 15
extreme religiosity, 34

F

family history, 13, 26, 27, 155, 157
fatigue, 7, 8, 10, 119, 123, 126, 132
fenfluramine, 69, 71, 72, 79
finance, 15
fluoxetine, 28, 71, 93, 153-156, 158-160, 167-169, 172, 179, 192

G

gabapentin, 117, 118, 119, 170, 178
gender bias, 139
gene variants, 1
genetic studies, 8, 29, 70, 78
glucose, 44, 81, 82, 84, 85, 90-96, 107
grandiosity, 34, 155
growth hormone, 71-73, 75, 79

H

hallucinations, 4, 5, 7, 11, 17, 131, 150, 157, 161
haptoglobin, 103
homeostasis, 103, 104, 107
hopelessness, 7
hyperglycemia, 82, 85, 91, 94
hypnotic states, 34, 50
hypochondria, 34, 50
hypothalamic-pituitary axis, 71

I

ideas of influence, 34
ideas, 34, 38, 44, 46, 49, 52-55, 57, 63, 131, 146, 147, 154, 155
ideation, 3, 5, 10, 139-141, 144-146, 150, 151, 154, 155
imagery, 34, 146
immunologic malfunctions, 1
indecisiveness, 7
infection, 33, 46, 48, 55, 98, 101, 103, 104, 111, 112
insomnia, 5, 7, 8, 129, 155
irritability, 4, 6, 12, 35, 154, 157
irritable, 4, 6, 11, 45

L

lamotrigine, 117-119, 170, 171, 176, 178, 188
leisure activities, 15, 162
lithium, 16, 17, 19, 29-31, 33, 45, 54, 63, 71, 72, 75, 78, 85, 95, 101, 102, 111, 114, 117, 118, 120, 123, 125, 129, 134-136, 138, 165, 170, 171, 178, 179, 182-184, 186-192
liver, 57, 97, 103-105, 110, 113, 114, 118-120, 136

M

major depression, 7, 15, 20, 21, 23-25, 27-30, 67, 70, 72, 75-77, 79, 83, 84, 94, 95, 97-100, 103, 105, 106, 108, 112-114, 158, 168, 177, 180, 181
major depressives, single episode (MDSE), 10, 12
mania, vii, 3, 8, 9, 17-19, 23, 29, 31, 34, 59, 70-72, 77, 79, 82, 92, 97, 99, 101, 103, 108, 112, 113, 115, 117, 118, 123, 125, 126, 135, 136, 139-141, 153-161, 163, 165-167, 170-172, 175, 176, 178-180, 182-185, 187-193
manic depressive illness, 67
manic relapses, 53
manic switches, 18, 153
manic symptoms, 9, 10, 25, 123, 124, 129, 175, 185
manic syndrome, 6
Manic-Depressiveness Scale (MDS) 139, 140, 142-144, 151
marital difficulties, 34
marital status, 11
m-chlorophenylpiperazine, 69, 72, 75, 77
medications, 30, 45, 53, 84-86, 88-90, 93, 94, 125, 126, 128, 133, 137, 143, 183, 187, 190
migraine, 65-70, 72-79, 118, 125, 131, 136
minor depression, 9
monoamine oxidase inhibitors, 85, 102
mood changes, 33, 34, 45, 65
mood disorders, 2, 8, 9, 13-15, 17, 20, 23, 24, 27-31, 50, 63, 65, 70, 74, 77, 97, 98, 99, 111, 143, 153, 157, 182, 184, 188, 189

moods, 37, 45, 46, 48, 52, 53, 55
mood-stabilizing agents, 117, 118
myeloma, 98

N

network theory, 34, 35, 38, 42, 55
networks, 33, 35-37, 39, 40, 42, 43, 47-49, 51-56, 58-61, 64
neuroanatomic defects, 1
neuroticism, 139, 144, 145
norfluoxetine, 156, 158
nosography, 1, 2, 7

O

obsessive compulsive disorder, 34
olanzapine, 84-86, 88-90, 96, 165, 166, 167-169, 171, 172, 179, 182-185, 187, 190-193
operational criteria checklist for psychotic illness (OPCRIT), 3-7, 10, 17, 22

P

panic, 23, 34, 35, 47, 50, 131
paranoia, 34
perception, 3, 11, 12, 19, 41, 143, 145, 146
personality disorders, 1, 10, 13, 15, 21, 34, 50, 58, 76
pessimistic thoughts, 7
pharmacological therapy, 18
physical violence, 97, 99, 101
pituitary hormones, 71
platelet function, 70
post partum period, 13
psychiatric disorder, 24, 73, 75, 77, 82-85, 89, 134, 150, 161, 163, 167, 177, 180, 181, 186, 189
psychiatric illness, 13, 28, 81, 82, 84, 94, 101
psychometric evaluation, 163, 173
psychomotor acceleration, 6
psychomotor disturbance, 7
psychosis, 2, 3, 6, 11, 18, 25, 29, 114, 121, 123, 124, 127, 129, 146, 165, 176
psychosocial functioning, 178, 190
psychotropic medications, 83, 85, 86, 90, 93, 183
pure mania, 135

Q

quality of life (Q_oL), 161-180, 185-193

R

rapid cycling, 10-12, 18, 19, 27, 114, 123, 125, 129, 135, 137, 161, 180, 186, 188
reasoning, 50, 53, 173
relapses, 13, 14, 19, 21, 31, 53, 125
remission, 15, 59, 106, 134, 154, 190
Research Diagnostic Criteria (RDC), 6, 66, 68, 79
reserpine, 69
retardation, 5, 10, 12, 16, 17, 100, 142

S

sadness, 7, 8
schizophrenia, 2, 3, 6, 20-22, 24, 25, 52, 56, 76, 83, 84, 86, 89, 95-100, 110, 111-113, 116, 139, 141, 143, 145, 148-151, 163, 164, 181, 186-189
scientific insights, 34
self-esteem, 7, 12, 15, 28, 29, 155
self-management, 53, 56
self-monitoring, 53
serotonin, 16, 19, 29, 69-71, 73-79, 93, 96, 156, 157, 159, 160
social adjustment, 13, 15, 17, 19, 29
spare time, 15
suicidality, 7, 148, 149, 150
sumatriptan, 69, 72-77, 79
symptomatology, 2-13, 17, 22-24, 130, 143, 150, 151, 175
synesthesia, 146, 151

T

thyroid, 1, 20, 118
tissue damage, 103, 104
topiramate, 117-120, 122-138
trait marker, 71
transliminality, 146
tricyclic antidepressants, 85, 93, 102, 156, 160
type-2 diabetes mellitus (T2DM), 81, 83-94

V

valproate, 71, 77, 117-120, 123, 125-127, 129, 134, 135, 138, 165, 171, 178, 179, 182, 189
valproic acid, 85, 120, 155, 171, 178, 179, 191

W

weight gain, 85, 95, 118, 119, 129, 134, 135, 137